Warning!

Violence and the Supernatural

The fictional worlds of Palladium Books® are violent, deadly and filled with supernatural monsters. Other-dimensional beings, often referred to as "demons," torment, stalk and prey on humans. Other alien life forms, monsters, gods and demigods, as well as magic, insanity, and war are all elements in these books.

Some parents may find the violence, magic and supernatural elements of the games inappropriate for young readers/players. We suggest parental discretion.

Please note that none of us at Palladium Books® condone or encourage the occult, the practice of magic, the use of drugs, or violence.

The Rifter® Number 60

Your guide to the Palladium Megaverse®!

D1224329

First Printing – October 2012

Robotech® and Robotech® The Shadow Chronicles® are Registered Trademarks of Harmony Gold USA, Inc.

Palladium Books®, Rifts®, The Rifter®, Coalition Wars®, After the Bomb®, The Mechanoids®, The Mechanoid Invasion®, Megaverse®, Nightbane®, Palladium Fantasy Role-Playing Game®, Phase World®, RECON®, and Splicers® are registered trademarks owned and licensed by Kevin Siembieda and Palladium Books Inc.

The slogan "A Megaverse of adventure – limited only by your imagination," and titles and names such as Armageddon Unlimited, Aliens Unlimited, Arzno, Atorian Empire, ARCHIE-3, Beyond Arcanum, Beyond the Supernatural, BTS-2, Brodkil, Biomancy, Biomancer, Bio-Wizardry, 'Burbs, 'Borg, 'Bot, Chaos Earth, Dead Reign, Dimensional Outbreak, Dinosaur Swamp, Dyval, Elf-Dwarf War, Heroes Unlimited, I.S.P., Land of the Damned, Lazlo, Victor Lazlo, Lazlo Agency, Lazlo Society, Palladium of Desires, Chi-Town, CS, Coalition States, Cosmo-Knight, Crazy, Cyber-Knight, D-Bee, Dark Day, Dead Boy, Doc Reid, Dog Boy, Dog Pack, Dweomer, Emperor Prosek, Erin Tarn, Fadetown, Free Quebec, Gadgets Unlimited, Gargoyle Empire, Glitter Boy, Gramercy Island, Hardware Unlimited, Heroes of the Megaverse, Heroes Unlimited, HU2, Juicer, Ley Line Walker, M.D.C., Mechanoid Space, Mega-Damage, Mega-Hero, Megaversal, MercTown, Minion War, Morphus, Mutant Underground, Mysteries of Magic, Merc Ops, Naruni, Naruni Enterprises, NEMA, Ninjas & Superspies, NGR, Northern Gun, The Nursery, P.P.E., Powers Unlimited, Psi-Stalker, Psyscape, SAMAS, S.D.C., Shifter, Siege on Tolkeen, Skelebot, Skraypers, Sorcerer's Forge, Splugorth, Splynncryth, Splynn, Techno-Wizard, Temporal Magic, Temporal Wizard, Three Galaxies, Tome Grotesque, Triax, Vampire Kingdoms, Warpath: Urban Jungle, Void Runners, Wilk's, Wolfen, Wolfen Wars, Wormwood, Wulfen, Xiticix, and other names, titles, slogans, and the likenesses of characters are trademarks owned by Kevin Siembieda and Palladium Books Inc.

Palladium Online **www.palladiumbooks.com**
Also visit us at facebook.com/PalladiumBooks

The Rifter® #60 RPG sourcebook series is published by Palladium Books Inc., 39074 Webb Court, Westland, MI 48185. Printed in the USA.

Palladium Books® Presents:

BRANDT -97

Sourcebook and Guide to the Palladium Megaverse®

Coordinator & Editor in Chief: **Wayne Smith**

Editor: **Alex Marciniszyn**

Contributing Writers:
    J.V. Adams
    Timothy Dorman
    Liam Gray
    Hendrik Härterich
    Thomas Morrison
    Kevin Siembieda
    Kristen Tipping

Interior Artists:
    Kent Burles
    Mark Dudley
    Joseph Lawn
    Allen Manning
    Brian Manning
    Michael Mumah
    Benjamin Rodriguez
    Charles Walton

Proofreader: **Julius Rosenstein**

Cover Illustration: **John Zeleznik**

Cover Logo Design: **Steve Edwards**

Credits Page Logo: **Niklas Brandt**
Typesetting & Layout: **Wayne Smith**

Art Direction: **Kevin Siembieda**

Based on the RPG rules, characters,
concepts and Megaverse® created by **Kevin Siembieda**.

   Special Thanks to all our contributors, writers and artists – and a special welcome on board to the artists and writers making their debut this issue. Our apologies to anybody who may have gotten accidentally left out or their name misspelled.

– Kevin Siembieda, 2012

Contents – The Rifter® #60 – October, 2012

Page 6 – From the Desk of Kevin Siembieda

The holidays are here. At least they are for Palladium Books. You see, our annual *Palladium Christmas Surprise Package* starts in October. For us, that means X-Mas is already here. If you've never gotten a *Christmas Surprise Package* from Palladium, you need to give it a try. Kevin talks about it a bit here, but see the full description on page 18.

Halloween is another favorite holiday around the Palladium office, especially for *Kathy Simmons* and *Kevin Siembieda*. Those two are crazy about Halloween. In fact, Kathy and Kevin make a giant yard display in a huge front yard, with 100+ life-sized halloween figures. 99% of which are all homemade and placed in thematic scenes. It is impressive, and people come from miles around to see the display. This year, there are new zombies, a lab on the front porch, caged werewolves, and more mad scientists and their creations.

Read all about it in this issue's *From the Desk of . . .*

Page 8 – News

Here's the latest news, including the scoop on the Robotech® game pieces, but this issue starts out with a photograph of Kevin's adorable granddaughter Chloe. Don't worry, there's a bunch of gamer news too.

Page 10 – Coming Attractions

Yeah, we're behind deadline with everything, so the stuff that was coming last issue is still coming. Though there are some new details, a hardcover collector's edition of Rifts® Black Market, more books back in print, and new books actually coming out over the next several months. No, really. You're holding the Rifter® #60 in your hand, **Rifts® Black Market** is out and a smash hit, **Robotech® Genesis Pits™ Sourcebook** is in final production and so is **Rifts® Vampires Sourcebook, Rifts® Northern Gun 1 & 2,** and **Rifts® Megaverse® in Flames™** will follow quickly. Get the low-down on everything that is out and coming out soon.

Page 18 – 2012 Christmas Surprise Package

Here are all the details on Palladium Books' annual Christmas Surprise Package made with autographs and love. Read all about it and place your order today! Oh, and tell your friends. Game on and happy holidays from all of us at Palladium Books.

Page 20 – Kids Game: Something Wonderful!
– *Tips for gaming with youngsters*

Experienced Game Master *Hendrik Härterich* presents a wonderful "how to" for introducing young gamers (including girls) to the world of role-playing games. Hendrik is an outstanding Game Master who has run games at the Palladium Open House. Here, he draws on his personal experience with introducing role-playing to his three daughters. It is a fun, tip-filled instruction that really works. Kevin Siembieda said he has had very similar experiences with kids, and that he found this article to be an accurate, excellent guide to bringing young gamers into RPGs.

Photo by Hendrik Härterich depicting his children Calliope (the youngest), Charlotte and Paula.

Page 25 – House Pandorum
– *Optional* source material for the Splicers® RPG

Kris Tipping offers up a dynamic trip to the world of **Splicers®** where he introduces House Pandorum and its history, goals, notable people, spliced creations, mutants, monsters and more. And they should all help to generate adventure ideas for your Splicers campaign.

Artwork by *Mark Dudley, Chuck Walton and Mike Mumah.*

Page 45 – Trust and Intimidation: A Way of Life
– *Optional* source material for Rifts® & any Palladium setting

Liam Gray makes his Rifter® debut with an article about the M.A. (Mental Affinity) attribute and the use of trust and intimidation in role-playing.

Artwork by *Kent Burles.*

Page 49 – Sorcerer's Forge
– *Optional* source material for Rifts®

Timothy Dorman present a comprehensive Rifts® city-state, set in North America. It's a little known corner of the world where a hidden society of Techno-Wizards live in secret and security. The history, characters, and TW creations can make a fun addition to any game. Additional text and ideas by Kevin Siembieda.

Artwork by *Allen Manning, Brian Manning* and D-Bees by *Ben Rodriguez.*

Page 77 – CSV New Hope – *Optional* source material and adventure for Heroes Unlimited™

Thomas Morrison gives us an epic adventure setting and outline that starts in outer space with a group of alien superheroes, and boldly goes where adventure abounds. Best of all, we get floor plans for the starship, CSV Hope. Enjoy.

Artwork by *Joseph Lawn.*

Page 94 – Strange Things in the Bootheel – A Short Story suitable for Nightbane®, Beyond the Supernatural™ or Heroes Unlimited™

J.V. Adams presents a strange little tale of coincidence and things that go bump in the night.
Artwork by *Mike Mumah.*

The Theme for Issue 60

The October issue of **The Rifter®** is what we think of as our "horror" issue. While there may not be **Beyond the Supernatural™, Nightbane®** or **Dead Reign™** articles this time, there are plenty of strange, monstrous and dangerous characters, creatures, and machines of war to make everyone happy. We hope you find this issue filled with bold, fun ideas that bring you compelling source material to fill your own campaigns with adventure, unique settings, menaces, monsters, and gadgets. We hope you enjoy these contributions from fans like you, and that they inspire new avenues of adventure.

The Rifter® Needs You

We need new writers and artists to fill the next few decades of **The Rifter®**. You do not need to be a professional writer to contribute to **The Rifter®**. This publication is like a "fanzine" written by fans for fans. A forum in which gamers just like *you* can submit articles, G.M. advice, player tips, house rules, adventures, new magic, new psionics, new super abilities, monsters, villains, high-tech weapons, vehicles, power armor, short works of fiction and more. So think about writing up something short (even something as small as 4-6 pages). Newcomers and regular contributors are always welcomed.

The **Rifter®** needs new material, especially when it comes to adventures and source material, for *all* of our game lines, especially *Rifts®, Chaos Earth™, Palladium Fantasy RPG®, Heroes Unlimited™, Ninjas and Superspies™, Beyond the Supernatural™, Dead Reign™, Splicers®* and *Nightbane®.*

Pay is lousy, fame is dubious, but you get to share your ideas and adventures with fellow gamers and get four free copies to show to your friends and family.

The Cover

The cover is by **John Zeleznik** who whipped up this devilish treat special for **The Rifter® #60**. We thought it reflected the horror/Halloween theme, the ongoing Minion War series that comes to a head in **Rifts® Megaverse® in Flames** (coming soon), as well as fantasy.

Optional and Unofficial Rules & Source Material

Please note that most of the material presented in **The Rifter®** is "unofficial" or "optional" rules and source material.

They are alternative ideas, homespun adventures and material mostly created by fellow gamers and fans like you, the reader. Things one can *elect* to include in one's own campaign or simply enjoy reading about. They are not "official" to the main games or world settings.

As for optional tables and adventures, if they sound cool or fun, use them. If they sound funky, too high-powered or inappropriate for your game, modify them or ignore them completely.

All the material in **The Rifter®** has been included for two reasons: One, because we thought it was imaginative and fun, and two, we thought it would stimulate your imagination with fun ideas and concepts that you can use (if you want to), or which might inspire you to create your own wonders.

www.palladiumbooks.com – Palladium Online

The Rifter® #61

The Rifter® #61, our January issue, is sure to contain more thrills and adventure to help you ring in the New Year.

- **Cover by Amy L. Ashbaugh (and a hint of things to come)**
- **Source material for Rifts®.**
- **Source material for Palladium Fantasy®.**
- **Source material for numerous settings.**
- **News, coming attractions and much more.**
- **And maybe YOUR submission. Send us something and see if you get published.**

Palladium Books® – world building for 31 years. And bringing you infinite possibilities limited only by your imagination™

From Halloween to Christmas and New Year's Eve – happy holidays from all of us at Palladium Books.

From the Desk of Kevin Siembieda

The holiday seasons are already upon us at Palladium Books. Not just the rapid approach of *Christmas, Hanukkah* and *Thanksgiving Day*, but *Halloween.*

Christmas at Palladium starts in October

Palladium is abuzz with constant activity from October thru December. In addition to producing new product releases and dealing with the day to day aspects of business, Palladium's annual Christmas Surprise Package starts in October. That means, for us, Christmas starts mid-October and runs till the end of December. It's a lot of work but it is also a joy, because the Christmas Surprise Package brings so much joy to so many people.

We've been doing this for so many years, we can't imagine anyone who doesn't know what the Surprise Package is, but we know there are still some folks who don't. A full description can be found elsewhere in this issue, but here is a brief one:

You place your order for the Christmas Surprise Package, send us $38 (plus shipping and handling; usually around $48 for most customers in the USA), and send us a "wish list" of 10-12 different (available) Palladium products. Then I personally go through your wish list, select 3-4 items from it, may include a surprise item or two (an issue of the Rifter®, art prints, etc.) for a total of $80 or more worth of Palladium product (always more, sometimes often in the neighborhood of $90 or $95 worth of product), and, if you ask us to (and most customers do), the Palladium staff and I, along with available freelancers like Matthew Clements, Mark Dudley, Carmen Bellaire and Chuck Walton, sign each and every book we send you. For many gamers, this is the only way they can get autographs.

We ask for a "wish list" of 10-12 items so that you do NOT know what you are getting. This creates anticipation and the element of surprise just like getting a present on Christmas morning, leaving you pleasantly surprised by what the package contains.

The Christmas Surprise Package is a great way for you to try new Palladium games, sourcebooks and game settings, get Christmas presents for your gaming buddies at a low price, and try books and product like bookmarks, coffee mugs, T-shirts, greeting cards, art prints, etc., that you've been interested in, but haven't yet purchased.

Be a hero. That's right, by ordering a Surprise Package for one or more of your gaming pals, you spend $38 (plus handling and shipping), but you look like a hero when you hand him or her several items worth $80-90! How cool is that?

The Palladium Christmas Surprise Package is Palladium's way of doing something special for our fans and saying *thank you* to our many loyal and wonderful customers. I love it, because it captures the essence of giving and joy of the holidays, and not just Christmas; these Palladium Surprise Packages are for all gamers, of every faith, everywhere in the world. In fact, because we can't escape the high price of shipping overseas, I always load up on Surprise Packages outside of North America. We're happy to do it.

See the full description elsewhere in this issue, and spread the word, because we only advertise this special offer in The Rifter®, in the Palladium online store and on our website. By the time you read about this in The Rifter®, we'll already be taking orders. So order one or several, and have a wonderful season of holidays and joy.

On a personal note, I already have half of my Christmas shopping done. Ho, ho, ho.

Every day in October is Halloween

Kathy Simmons and I love Halloween. It is a big, important holiday for us. As big as, in some ways *bigger* than, Christmas. You see, Kathy and I have created a massive Halloween display. It is larger (and cooler) than many professional "Haunted Houses" and covers a quarter acre of land.

Kathy is the true genius and maniac behind this amazing display. I'm just her willing Halloween minion.

What makes this sweeping display so different from most, is Kathy creates wonderful vignettes – scenes – with various creatures in settings designed specifically for them. Some are friendly, others are scary, but all are fun.

Here's a very brief and incomplete description:

The Wizard of Oz scene with *Dorothy, the Scarecrow, Tin-Man, Cowardly Lion,* and *Toto,* too, strolling arm-in-arm down the yellow brick road. There is also the *Wicked Witch of the West,* with her hour glass and crystal ball, as a guard stands by and *Flying Monkeys* await her command.

A pirate shipwreck complete with the bow of the ship, tattered sails, crow's nest, and a crew of skeleton pirates guarding their treasure chest and bottles of rum.

The Bug Man covered in insects and spiders. This is one of my few complete creations, and it has been a crowd pleaser for years. He is surrounded by a massive spider web with a half-dozen large spiders crawling out from the webbing.

The Monstrous Trio stand menacingly off to the left of the Bug Man. They include a zombie with a vulture perched on his shoulder, picking at his face, a lizard man, and snake monster.

Slug Monster and Butcher are off to the right. They are a team who prey upon humans and there is a barrel full of hands, arms and feet. The Slug Monster is humanoid and wears a white butcher's jacket. The Butcher has high-top boots and has a stogie in his grinning mouth.

The Ghoul's Card Game is hugely popular. They sit at the table playing cards and they are served drinks by *Charlie Sheen.*

The Witches is an awesome scene with five witches, smoking cauldrons, spell books, candles and black cats.

The Graveyard is alive with zombies and vampires rising from the dead. A ghoulish grave digger and many tombstones and coffins fill out this haunting scene.

Diablo the Hell Hound sits inside his dog house with a pile of bones as *Igor* brings him a bowl of new munchies to chew on.

Dinner is Served. Next to Diablo is *Pee Dee* at the barbecue grill, spatula in hand dishing up skewers of shish kabob bugs, mice, frogs and brains. Yum.

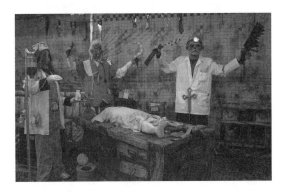

The Chop Shop and Mad Doctor's Laboratory seems to be a favorite of most people who visit, though the zombie horde coming out of the backyard is another, and everyone seems to have their own personal favorite. In addition to spooky lab surroundings, there is a ghoulish *Nurse and Doctor* in the act of chopping up their latest victim lying on the slab before them.

Assisting the gruesome duo is a towering *man-monster* in a lab coat clutching a bloody saw.

To his right is a **gruesome refrigerator** (another one of my creations) filled with strange creatures, severed limbs, brains, organs, eyes and bugs wrapped nicely in butcher packages. There are also bottles of blood and things best left unmentioned.

The Laboratory is next to the fridge where there is a bank of shelves filled with test tubes and dozens of bottles of brews, poison and concoctions. Other containers are filled with liquids of various colors and jars of icky things to make visitors squeal. Rats rim the area and a vulture picks at a finger it has snatched from the slab.

In front of the lab shelves is a table on which lays a black morgue bag. The head of the ghoul inside is partially out of the bag, eyes glowing red and moaning an eerie warning.

The Frankenstein Monster towers at the end of the lab scene. His arms reaching out at all who pass.

Caged Werewolves. "New" this year, we decided to extend the lab to the front porch. There is another *Frankenstein-like monster* with a metal jaw and implants, a mad doctor with more body parts on a table in front of him, and more bottles and light-up devices. His assistant is a dude in a helmet and gas mask who looks more than sinister. Locked away inside a prison cell are *two werewolves,* their arms reaching out from between the bars.

The zombie horde. This was new last year and visitors went wild over the *dozen zombies* staggering out of the brush in the back yard toward one lone police officer, rifle in hand, but hopelessly outnumbered. This year, we are adding a few new zombies and changing the scene a bit to make it even more scary and dramatic.

Hundreds of people come to visit our Halloween display for weeks before Halloween. We try to put the display up at least two weeks before Halloween. There are more than 100 life-sized props/figures and many elaborate scenes which take us a few weekends and a couple of full weeks to set it all up. Kathy even takes her vacation from her other job in the end of September and early October to get it all done. I mostly help with sets, offer ideas, and paint masks, plastic hands, do blood splatters, tatter zombie clothing and set up the fridge, laboratory and other scenes, as well as the webbing and a few other odds and ends. Kathy is the real genius who makes the life-sized figures and creates most of the props and scenes. She is also the master of lighting that makes it all pop at night.

The display has gotten so popular that last year, we even had a *school bus* load of children wander our front yard and enjoy the fun. We had approximately 250-300 children of all ages show up Halloween night, and we get approximately one hundred people a day who come by during the weeks prior to Halloween. A few locals bring their children over every day or two after school because the kids love it so much. Thank goodness our neighbors appreciate the display too. The lady next door has a pretty sweet display, and several other houses on the block also put up nice displays.

This year there has been so much anticipation that we had neighbors and locals coming by the house since Labor Day asking if we were doing our display again this year. A few pretty much insisted we must do it again. And not just two or three people, but a couple dozen. Yikes, it was only September, but they wanted to make sure we were going to do it, because they had already invited friends and family to come and see it in October and wanted to know when it would be ready. Funny.

Of course, we do it to bring joy and spooky fun to children of all ages. That's why Kathy has been nicknamed the "Queen of Ghouls." And since people love her creations so much, I convinced her to create an Ebay store (Queenofghouls.com) to sell some of her spectacular props. They look good in photos, but snapshots do NOT do them justice. In person, they look so real it's amazing. Regrettably, the amount of work and cost involved in each ghoul requires Kathy to charge $175-$250 for most of her life-sized Halloween props, but are they ever worth it. Her props look much more real than most of what you see in the stores or online. And when placed in scenes we make and lit up right at night, oh man, they look awesome.

That's my holiday report. See News and Coming Attractions for data about new product releases. Palladium is getting stronger every day thanks to the support of gamers like you.

Happy Holidays from all of us at Palladium Books. May they be full of love, friendship, joy and gaming.

– Kevin Siembieda, Publisher and Ghoulmaster

Palladium News

By Kevin Siembieda, the guy who should know

Palladium Christmas Surprise Package

No other game company does anything like it, and certainly not for 15 years running. It's our way of giving back to you, our fans. Order one, order several. Get them as gifts for your gaming comrades and loved ones or as a gift for yourself. Use it to fill holes in your collection or to try new world settings, but make sure you get at least one.

See the full description of this popular Christmas season tradition from Palladium Books. You'll be glad you did.

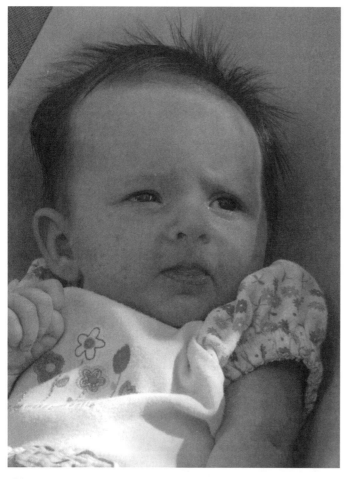

Granddaughter Update

I'm happy to report that my daughter *Monica* and baby granddaughter, *Chloe Sage* (born July 5, 2012), are both doing great. According to Monica, Chloe is growing like a weed. The family has recently moved, and I hope to visit them in Arizona around Thanksgiving Day or possibly January.

Robotech® Update

I reported last issue that Palladium Books was planning to launch a line of *Robotech® mecha* and *spaceship* game pieces in 1/285th scale. Well, plans are moving forward quickly. The initial release is what we are tentatively calling the **Robotech® Tactical Role-Playing Game: Defense of Macross Island.** It will have many figures (Valkyries, Destroids, Zentraedi Battle Pods, Fighter Pods, etc.) and probably retail in the $120-$130 price range. It will be a big boxed set that can be played as a stand-alone game or as game pieces in your ongoing *Robotech® RPG campaign*, other *mass combat battles*, and as *display pieces* for your desk or shelf. They'll be beautiful, and followed by additional sets of mecha (and spaceships) to quickly expand your Robotech® universe. We're still waiting for price quotes from manufacturers, so we don't want to say what you'll get in the box, just yet.

Of course, the initial set, planned as a Summer 2013 launch, will be followed by the mecha from ALL eras of Robotech: The Masters Saga, New Generation and Shadow Chronicles. And all to scale.

In fact, I have been spending a lot of time trying to set everything up for the production of the Robotech® game pieces. There has been a lot of communication with Harmony Gold, conversations and emails with the lead line developers, review of work contracts, discussions with my attorney, writing product outlines and proposals, and similar stuff. I'm waiting on a number of things from a few different people, but I feel like we are making excellent progress.

My goal with these figures and the Robotech® Tactical RPG is to launch a line of new games and pieces that will send Robotech® fans into ecstacy. I'm not kidding. I want to exceed everyone's expectations. And that's what Palladium's development partner wants too. Wish I could reveal more, but too many details to nail down yet. Heck, the readers of The Rifter® are getting the inside track, as I had yet to announce the title of the game or many of the details presented here. Inside information is another reason to subscribe.

Robotech® Genesis Pits Sourcebook

By the time you read this, the **Robotech® Genesis Pits Sourcebook** should be completely written, edited and waiting for final approval by *Harmony Gold*. It is an outstanding book with a lot of fun, new source material about the Invid, their Genesis Pits, mutants, monsters and adventure. If you are a Robotech® fan, you'll want this book.

Robotech® UEEF Marines Sourcebook

The Robotech® UEEF Marines Sourcebook has been expanded into two Robotech Marine books and will include space adventures, aliens and conflicts with the Invid, Robotech Masters and other malevolent forces.

Palladium Books is shooting for an early 2013 release for both books as we work hard at giving Robotech® fans something to cheer about on all fronts. Game on!

Rifts® Pewter Miniatures

Don't forget Palladium has re-released the old **Rifts® miniatures** that went out of production years ago. Figures like the *Glitter Boy, Coalition Soldiers, Cyborgs, the Kydian Overlord,* and others. Plus ten never released Rifts® minis that include the

Mystic Knight, Magus, Shadow Beast, Psi-Stalker, and several *new Dog Boy* minis.

Keeping in step with current market trends, Palladium is selling individual figures in the $6-$8 price range for human-size figures, and $12 or more for larger figures. The Glitter Boy, for example, sells for $20. There are also ten NEW, different and variant Rifts® figures. All made their debut at the Palladium Open House and are available on the Palladium website. **Note:** The Glitter Boy Pilot miniature is temporarily sold out, but we expect to have it back in print before long.

Rifts® Vampires Sourcebook

As you read this, I'll be putting the finishing touches on this book. Heck, with any luck, it will already be at the printer. Another epic book that should shock and delight you with the new information.

Feeling positive about Palladium's future

2012 has been a good year. Things have gotten much better for Palladium Books. **Palladium's crowdfunding efforts** were of huge benefit and helped on many fronts. *Dynamic new releases* like **Rifts® Lemuria, Rifts® Black Market** and **Endless Dead**™, that wowed and created buzz, helped a great deal too. Our sales have steadily increased all year long. Gamers, retailers and distributors are excited about Palladium product again. That leads to more buzz, new customers and more sales. With stronger financial resources at our disposal, we've been able to do more. More advertising, more reprints, more artwork in books, paying down debt, etc., and that leads to more buzz and stronger sales.

The momentum is building and releases like **Rifts® Vampires Sourcebook, Rifts® Northern Gun**™ **One** and **Two**, exciting new **Robotech®** game products, and a commitment to support as many game lines as possible next year, including **Beyond the Supernatural**™, **Dead Reign**™, **Nightbane®, Chaos Earth**™, **Splicers®, Palladium Fantasy®** and others, means fans are going to flip out with delight.

On the creative front, Palladium's talented freelancers have never been more galvanized and motivated. The same is true of the Palladium staff. I wish you knew everything we are talking about and working on.

Online Palladium Interaction

Don't forget that you can get the latest happenings at Palladium Books any time online. We post a comprehensive **Weekly Update** every Thursday containing the latest news, progress reports and product descriptions, plus I post smaller updates and musing 3-6 times a week in my **Murmurs from the Megaverse®** as well as pop in on **Facebook** several times a week. Other Palladium creators like *Mike Mumah, Brandon Aten, Carl Gleba, Irvin Jackson* and others are also active in making appearances to chat and share their views on Facebook and on Palladium's message boards. Our website is **www.palladiumbooks.com** and has links to the Palladium Facebook Page, online store and other good stuff.

In addition, *Carmen Bellaire* and *Wylliam Johnson* have more than two dozen video interviews with Palladium creators and personalities, as well and video overviews of numerous Palladium role-playing games and sourcebooks, at **youtube.com/user/ Maloquinn/videos.**

Gen Con® Indy was a smashing success

Gen Con Indy was awesome. Sales were up, Palladium's booth was busy all the time, we had fun talking with fans and signing books, and we have already reserved our booth for next year. We're even wondering if we shouldn't expand the size of the booth next year.

Youmacon – Next Convention Appearance

Detroit – November 1-4 – www.youmacon.com

Our next convention appearance will be November 1-4 in downtown Detroit for **Youmacon.** It is a big anime and media convention that includes gaming and is estimating 15,000-20,000 people will attend this year. Palladium Books will be exhibiting with a good number of Palladium staffers on hand to sign books and chat with fans. That includes me (Kevin Siembieda), Wayne Smith, the enigmatic Alex Marciniszyn, Julius Rosenstein and Ben Rodriguez, among others (I think Mark Dudley and some other Palladium crew will be on hand as well).

If you live in the Detroit area and enjoy anime, cosplay, gaming and fun, come on over and join in. Note: The event is getting so large it is spread out between a couple hotels and the Cobo Hall convention center. Palladium and the Exhibitors' Hall are in Cobo Hall. Discount parking is available for the event.

Anime North – Start planning now

May 24-26, 2013 – Toronto, Canada

Canadian fans of Palladium, plan to see us at **Anime North** where I'll be one of the many guests. This will be my first time back at a Canadian convention in 15 years and I hope to visit with a great many of you at this fun event. Wayne Smith and I will both be there, along with a few other Palladium people. Hmmm, you might be the first to see some Robotech® prototypes or advance copies of Robotech game pieces. For more information, go to **www.animenorth.com**.

Coming Soon

- **The Rifter® #60** – in your hands
- **The Rifter® #50 Anniversary Issue** – now back in print
- **Rifts® Black Market Sourcebook** – Available now
- **Rifts® Logo T-Shirt (in all sizes)** – End of October
- **Rifts® Vampires Sourcebook** – November
- **Robotech® Genesis Pits Sourcebook** – November
- **Rifts® Northern Gun**™ **One** – November or December
- **Rifts® Northern Gun**™ **Two** – December
- **Prints of the Two Wraparound Northern Gun Covers** – December
- **Rifts® Megaverse® in Flames** – January, 2013
- **The Rifter® #61** – January, 2013

Coming Attractions

Palladium's 2012 Release Checklist

Recent Releases

- **The Rifter® #59**
- **The Rifter® #60**
- **Rifts® Bookmarks Set 2** – available only from Palladium Books.
- **Rifts® World Book 32: Lemuria** – available now.
- **Dead Reign™ Sourcebook Three: Endless Dead™** – available now.
- **Rifts® Black Market** – available now.
- **Rifts® Black Market Gold Hardcover** – available now.
- Several new T-shirts – available now.
- Back in print – **Mutant Underground™** for Heroes Unlimited™
- Back in print – **Wolfen Empire™** for Palladium Fantasy RPG®
- Back in print – **Old Ones™** for Palladium Fantasy RPG®
- Back in print – **Rifts® World Book 21: Splynn Dimensional Market™**
- Back in print – **Rifts® World Book 22: Free Quebec™**
- Back in print – **Rifts® World Book 23: Xiticix Invasion™**
- Back in print – **Rifts® World Book 31: Triax™ 2**
- Back in print – **Rifts® Mercenaries™**
- Back in print – **Rifts® Black Vault™**
- Back in print – **Rifts® Sourcebook 2: The Mechanoids®**
- Back in print – **Rifts® Sourcebook 3: Mindwerks™**
- Back in print – **Rifts® Sourcebook: Cyber-Knights™**
- Back in print – **Rifts® Dimension Book: Three Galaxies™**
- Back in print – **Rifts® Dimensional Book: Anvil Galaxy™**
- Back in print – **Rifts® Dice Bags** (gold logo on black)
- Back in print – **Rifts® miniatures** (Glitter Boy, CS soldiers, plus new Shadow Beast, Magus and others)

October or November Releases

- **Rifts® Vampires Sourcebook™** – New - in final production.
- **Rifts® Logo T-Shirt (in all sizes)** – End of October.

November Release

- **Robotech® Genesis Pits™ Sourcebook** – New – in final production.
- **Rifts® World Book: Northern Gun™ One** – New.

December

- **Rifts® Northern Gun™ Two** – New – in final production.

January, 2013 Release

- **Rifts®/Minion War™: Megaverse® in Flames™** – New (tentative).

Also for 2013 Release

- **Rifts® Chaos Earth Sourcebook: First Responders**
- **Rifts® Chaos Earth Sourcebook: The Resurrection**
- **Robotech® UEEF Marines Sourcebooks** (two)
- **Rifts® sourcebooks** (many)

- **Splicers® Sourcebooks** (many)
- **Dead Reign™ Sourcebook**
- **Nightbane® Sourcebook**
- **Beyond the Supernatural™ Sourcebook: Beyond Arcanum**
- **Beyond the Supernatural™ Sourcebook: Tome Grotesque**
- **Heroes Unlimited™ Sourcebook**
- **Palladium Fantasy®: Sourcebooks and other good stuff.**

Available in many hobby and game stores around the world. We encourage people to support their local stores. Going to a store enables you to see the product before purchasing it, and many stores are happy to place special orders for you, provided you pay in advance, enabling you to avoid the cost of shipping and possible damage in the mail.

Ordering from Palladium Books: You can also order directly from Palladium Books, but you will pay extra for shipping. For customers with access to a computer, we recommend ordering online to get the most accurate shipping costs (or by telephone; 734-721-2903, order line only). For customers without such access, use the following "mail order" process.

In the USA: 1. Send the cost of the books or items being ordered. **2.** Add $5 for orders totaling $1-$50 to cover shipping and handling. Add $9 for orders totaling $51-$100. Add $15 for orders totaling $101-$200. **Outside the USA:** Double the shipping amount for orders going to Canada, and triple it for overseas orders. Any and all additional costs incurred as a result of Customs fees and taxes is the responsibility of the foreign customer, NOT Palladium Books. **3.** Make checks or money orders payable to *Palladium Books*. **4.** Please make sure to send us your complete and correct address. **Note:** These costs are for the least expensive and slowest method of shipping only. Allow 2-4 weeks for delivery. Order online or call the office for a superior but more costly shipping method.

Rifts® Vampires Sourcebook™

Unknown to most humans, deep within Mexico the vampires have established entire kingdoms. There they live like tyrants and gods, dominating an underclass of cattle people used as slaves and food stock. Learn more about the vampires, their rivals, allies and the humans who willingly serve their supernatural masters for a chance to join the undead. A must-have guide for those who wish to travel deeper into the Vampire Kingdoms or play as vampires and their human minions.

- **More human kingdoms within Mexico like the Tampico Military Protectorate and Durango, the Silver City.**
- **Firefighting robots, hover firetrucks and more anti-vampire gear.**
- **Magic based Vampire Hunters and human strongholds.**
- **Techno-Wizard anti-vampire weapons and magical devices.**
- **Profiles for Doc Reid and Reid's Rangers, the world's most famous Vampire Hunters.**
- **Fort Reid, an entire city devoted to hunting the undead.**
- **The Bloodwatch, a secret vampire intelligence agency that tracks down and exterminates Vampire Hunters.**
- **The Yucatan Peninsula, a mysterious dimensional pocket overrun by strange demons known as Xibalbans.**
- **The return of the Mayan god Camazotz, Lord of Bats and Darkness.**
- **The werebeasts of Mexico and Central America; those who assist the vampires and those who fight against them.**
- **Written by Kevin Siembieda, Matthew Clements and Braden Campbell.**
- **128 pages – $16.95 – Cat. No. 884. October or November release.**

Robotech® Genesis Pits™ Sourcebook

An in-depth look at the Invid Genesis Pits, their purpose, function and the creatures they create. Many, many avenues of adventure and ideas to spice up your Robotech® campaign with unexpected menaces and intrigue. In production right now!

- **Secrets of the Invid.**
- **Notable Genesis Pits of Earth.**
- **Genesis Pit mutations and monsters.**
- **Different types of Genesis Pits from across the galaxy.**
- **Inorganics and other war machines of the Invid Regent.**
- **Ways to destroy a Genesis Pit.**
- **Genesis Pit Monster creation tables and rules.**
- **Bioroid and Zentraedi mutants, Simulagents and more.**
- **Written by Irvin Jackson. 8½ x 11 inch book format. Available only in the USA and Canada.**
- **$16.95 – 96 pages. Cat. No. 555 – November release.**

Rifts® World Book 33:

Northern Gun™ One

Northern Gun™ is the largest independent manufacturer of high-tech weapons, robots and vehicles in North America. Outside of the Coalition States, one could argue, no other kingdom is as powerful or influential, at least when it comes to technology and weapons. The manufacture and sale of Northern Gun weapons and vehicles has given virtually every kingdom, town, colony of settlers and adventurer group a chance to survive and prosper. Located in Michigan's Upper Peninsula, NG has been the premier outfitter of mercenaries, adventurers and upstart kingdoms for generations. Now, for the first time ever, learn Northern Gun's history, goals and plans for the future. Of course, that means new weapons, robots, power armor, vehicles and gear.

- **In-depth look at Northern Gun: its business operations & community.**

- **Bionic and cybernetic services.**
- **Weapons and combat gear; new and old.**
- **Robot drones; new and old.**
- **Giant combat robots; new and old.**
- **Freighters and hover trains.**
- **Northern Gun character classes and more.**
- **Key locations, people and sales outlets in and around Northern Gun.**
- **Northern Gun's relationship with the Coalition States, Triax Industries, the Black Market and others.**
- **The Kingdom of Ishpeming, a puppet-state propped up by NG.**
- **The Ishpeming military and more.**
- **Written by Matthew Clements, Kevin Siembieda and others.**
- **Interior Artwork by Chuck Walton, Manning Brothers, and others.**
- **Wraparound cover by Chuck Walton.**
- **160 pages – $20.95 retail – Cat. No. 887 – Fall release.**

Palladium Books® Presents:
Rifts® World Book 33:
Rifts® Northern Gun™ 1
By Matthew Clements & Kevin Siembieda

Palladium Books® Presents:
Rifts® World Book 34:
Rifts® Northern Gun™ 2
By Matthew Clements & Kevin Siembieda

Rifts® World Book 34:

Northern Gun™ Two

More information about the weapons, vehicles and practices of Northern Gun, including the new rage of robot gladiatorial combat.

- **Power armors; new and old.**
- **Hovercycles and vehicles; new and old.**
- **Aircraft; new and old.**
- **Boats, ships and submarines; new and old.**
- **Robot Gladiatorial Arena; new!**
- **Robot Gladiator O.C.C. and some notable gladiators.**

- The NG Bounty Board, the largest collection of bounties and mercenary contracts anywhere on Rifts® Earth.
- Mercenaries, pirates and more.
- Written by Matthew Clements, Kevin Siembieda and others.
- Interior Artwork by Chuck Walton, Nick Bradshaw, and others.
- Wraparound cover by John Zeleznik.
- 160 pages – $20.95 retail – Cat. No. 888 – December release.

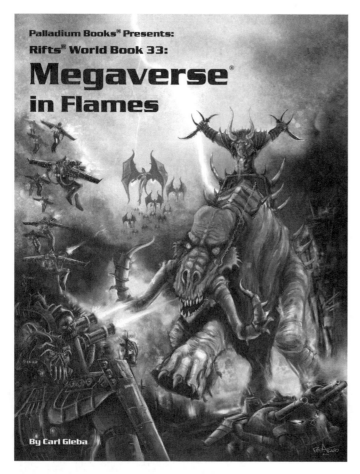

Rifts® World Book 35:

Megaverse® in Flames™

The Minion War spills across Rifts Earth, where demons and infernals hope to recruit allies and use the Rifts as gateways of destruction. Their influence shakes things up across the planet, especially at locations where demons and Deevils already have a strong presence. Demons, Deevils and supernatural beings run rampant and wreak havoc across the world.

- Demon plagues and mystic blights.
- Soulmancy and Blood Magic revealed.
- Magical and demonic weapons and war machines.
- Demonic armies, strongholds and places of evil.
- Hell Pits and Rune Forges.
- Many Demon Lords, their minions and plans.
- Calgary, the Kingdom of Monsters; in detail.
- Ciudad de Diablo, Harpies' Island and other notable Hell holes on Earth.
- Lord Doom, Pain and other demonic leaders.
- Horune treachery, Dimension Stormers and other villains.

- Notable demonic generals, mercenaries, people and places.
- Battleground: Earth – as demons and infernals amass their legions.
- Global chaos and the places most dramatically affected by the Demon Plagues.
- Epic battles and adventure ideas galore.
- Written by Carl Gleba. Part of the Minion War "Cross-over" series.
- 192 pages – $24.95 retail – Cat. No. 876. January, 2013 release.

The Rifter® #61

Looking for new ideas and material for your campaign? Then you want **The Rifter®.** The greatest value of **The Rifter®** is that every issue offers new and different ideas, and gets your imagination running in directions you might not have considered. It's an idea factory that will help you generate new ideas of your own, and it also presents valuable source material you can drop right into your games.

- Rifts® and source material for 2-3 other game settings.
- News, coming attractions, and more.
- 96 pages – still only $11.95 retail – Cat. No. 161. January, 2013.

Rifts® Chaos Earth™ Sourcebook:

First Responders

Data about the chaos and madness of the early days of the Great Cataclysm, and the brave men and women who tried to stem the tide of destruction and save lives, the First Responders.

- Apocalypse Plagues: Strange diseases, symbiotes and mutations that transform, torment, harm and kill Earth's survivors.
- First Responder O.C.C.s, skills and special equipment.
- Civilian O.C.C.s, skills and orientation.
- Notable rescue vehicles, robot drones, and technology.
- New weapons, vehicles, mecha and more.
- Character modification and enhancement rules.
- Creatures from the Rifts and adventure ideas galore.
- Written by Jason Richards & Kevin Siembieda.
- 96 to 128 pages – $16.95 retail – Cat. No. 665. 2013 release.

Recent Product Releases & Notable Books Back in Print

Rifts® Black Market *Hardcover*
– *Gold Contraband Edition* – Available now!

Everything you want to know about the Black Market of Rifts® North America presented inside a pair of gorgeous black leatherette covers. Gold foil embossing on front cover and spine. Historically, gold collector editions only increase in value on the collector's market, and often quickly. This is the lowest number of a Collector's Gold Edition that Palladium has ever printed.

- Striking Black leatherette cover with gold foil embossing.
- Limited "Collector's Edition."

- 250 signed and numbered copies.
- 8 signatures, including main authors Kevin Siembieda, Matthew Clements and Carmen Bellaire, plus Chuck Walton and the Palladium staff.
- Exactly the same content as the softcover book described below.
- 192 pages – $60.00 retail – Cat. No. 886HC. Available now. Sold ONLY from Palladium Books via our online store and mail order.

work, The Immaterial Hand, El Oculta, and Le Marche Noir.
- Black Market internal operations and security.
- Black Market services, products, practices and customers.
- New weapons and equipment of Bandito Arms/Black Market.
- A wide range of BigBore weapons and other merc weapons.
- New power armor, vehicles and robot riding animals.
- Black Market criminal assignments, jobs and mercenary bounties.
- Major Black Market smuggling corridors and routes.
- Smuggling methods, both magical and conventional.
- Traveling Shows: Freak Shows, Medicine Shows and Circuses.
- Traveling Shows as fronts for the Black Market.
- Traveling Black Market Merchants, Market Towns and Market Outlets.
- Written by Clements, Siembieda, Bellaire and others.
- 192 pages – $24.95 retail – Cat. No. 886. Available now.

Rifts® World Book 32: Lemuria™

– Available now

Rifts® **Lemuria** is a smash hit. We have only heard rants and raves about it from gamers. New magic, weapons, living power armor, monstrous war steeds, dragons, sea monsters, weapons and gear. The Lemurians are an amphibious people with floating cities and magic-based technology that allows for land and underwater adventures alike.
- **The Lemurians, their race, history and society.**
- **New aquatic races – Lemurians, Junk Crabs, and others.**
- **8 expansive, new O.C.C.s including the Serpent Hunter, Spouter, Oceanic Guardsman, Biomancer Gene-Mage, Birdman and others.**
- **9 monstrous and wondrous Lemurian War Steeds.**
- **10 suits of living Bio-Armor, plus the Wave Strider & Bio-Skins.**
- **10 Biomancy plants and creatures from Lemurian Gardens.**
- **19 types of Lemurian weapons, herbs and magic.**

Rifts® Black Market™

A Rifts® Sourcebook

Gamers have gone wild over **Rifts® Black Market™**. It contains a wealth of information about the inner workings of the Black Market, the Five Factions, new Bandito Arms/Black Market weapons and gear, how to make *any* O.C.C. a Black Marketeer, special abilities of the Black Marketeer, criminal enterprises, Black Market loans, merc and crime jobs, and much more. This book has it all. AND best of all, a lot of it can be easily adapted to just about any world setting, not just Rifts Earth.
- **Rules to make any O.C.C. (or R.C.C.) a Black Marketeer.**
- **Special abilities and benefits of the Black Marketeer.**
- **Specialized O.C.C.s of the Black Market.**
- **Criminal enterprises, jobs, and inner workings of the Black Market.**
- **The Five Black Market Factions that wield the greatest power in North America: Bandito Arms, The Chicago Net-**

- **Symbiotic Stone vehicles, Exotic animals and dragons.**
- **50+ new Biomancy spells and a handful of new Ocean Magic spells.**
- **The Stone Guardians of Easter Island and other mysteries.**
- **Symbiotic creatures and Biomancy constructs; some that enable air-breathers to survive underwater indefinitely.**
- **New dangers, new challenges, adventure ideas and more.**
- **Written by Diaczyk, Clements & Siembieda.**
- **224 pages – $24.95 retail – Cat. No. 885. Available now.**

Available now – Dead Reign™ Sourcebook 3:

Endless Dead™

Endless Dead says it all. The zombie hordes grow in number and strangeness. Can humankind survive? Where is the military? What's next for the survivors of the zombie apocalypse?

- **New types of zombies, including the Walking Mass Grave.**
- **New O.C.C.s like the Wheelman, Zombie Hunter and others.**
- **Information on vehicles and anti-zombie defenses.**
- **Random encounter tables galore.**
- **Tables for creating Survivor caravans, hideouts and more.**
- **Timetable for setting campaigns during the Wave, the beginning of the Zombie Apocalypse, or months into the reign of the dead.**
- **Stats for some of North America's dangerous wildlife, a threat to survivors and zombies alike.**
- **Written by Siembieda, Clements and Rosenstein.**
- **96 pages – $16.95 retail – Cat. No. 233. Available now.**

Note: Dead Reign™ RPG provides everything you need to start playing the Zombie Apocalypse and the struggle for human survival, except dice, players and imagination. A complete stand-alone RPG with skills, weapons, game rules and guidelines for using other Palladium settings. 224 pages – $22.95 retail – Cat. No. 230. Available now!

Rifts® Pencil

It's silly, but fun. A standard No. 2 Pencil that reads: DO NOT REMOVE. PROPERTY OF THE CHI-TOWN LIBRARY. Obviously a relic and collector's item from before the famous library burned down. Erin Tarn has a whole desk drawer of these pencils. What about you?

- Offered for the very first time. Fun and useful.
- **Cat. No. 2561.** 50 cents per each pencil.

Palladium Fantasy RPG® Coffee Mug

This mug is gorgeous. It is the same style as previous coffee mugs and captures the classic Palladium Fantasy cover image in red on a black mug. Microwave and dishwasher safe.

- **15.5 ounce mug** perfect for coffee, tea, hot chocolate or soda on game night or any time. Fun and useful.
- **Classic Palladium artwork** depicting the knight and dragon from the cover of the original edition of the Palladium Fantasy RPG® on one side of the mug and *The Palladium Fantasy RPG® logo* on the other side. Nice.
- **Cat. No. 2560 – $10.00.**

Palladium Bookmarks, Set Two

– Available now

They look great. A set of four, 2 x 6 inch bookmarks, printed on both sides, each bookmark depicting a different Palladium game line: **Chaos Earth™, Phase World®, Nightbane®** and **Beyond the Supernatural™.** They are attractive, useful and make a fun collectible. The first set has been so popular, we had to do a second.

- **Designed by Kevin Siembieda and Wayne Smith.**
- **Art by Scott Johnson (Rifts® Chaos Earth™ Glitter Boy cover), Kevin Long (Phase World® Sourcebook cover), Brom (Nightbane®), and John Zeleznik (Beyond the Supernatural™).**
- **Each is 2 x 6 inches, full color, printed on both sides.**
- **Four different bookmarks in the set.**
- **Cat. No. 2555 – $5.00 retail – available now!** Based on what similar bookmarks sell for, we figure the set of four should have an $8.00 value, but Palladium's price is only $5.00.

Palladium Bookmarks, Set One

– Available now

"I love the Palladium bookmarks and use three of the first set all the time." – *Kevin Siembieda*

A set of four, 2 x 6 inch bookmarks, each depicting a different Palladium game line: **Rifts®, Palladium Fantasy®, Heroes Unlimited™** and **Dead Reign™.** They are attractive, useful and make a fun collectible.

- **Designed by Kevin Siembieda and Wayne Smith.**
- **Art by Scott Johnson (Rifts® Ultimate cover), E.M. Gist (Dead Reign™ RPG cover), Mark Evans (Palladium Fantasy®), and Tyler Walpole (Heroes Unlimited™).**
- **Each is 2 x 6 inches, full color, printed on both sides.**
- **Four different bookmarks in the set.**
- **Cat. No. 2554 – $5.00 retail.** Based on what similar bookmarks sell for, we figure the set of four should have an $8.00 value, but Palladium's price is only $5.00. Available now.

Rifts® Dice Bag

– Back in print – Available now

Everyone at Palladium has a **Rifts® Dice Bag**, shouldn't you? It is a good size, sturdy, drawstring bag made of imitation black velvet emblazoned with the famous Rifts® logo in gold.
- 7x9 inches – $8.00 retail – Cat. No. 2539.

Rifts® World Book 23:

Xiticix Invasion™

– Back in print – Available now

One of the strangest and most dangerous alien species on Earth is the Xiticix. Armed with new breeds of aggressive warriors, new weapons and legions of insectoids willing to fight to the death, people are beginning to wonder if they are the next threat to humanity.
- 9 different types of Xiticix, their hierarchy and society.
- Xiticix Hive Cities, defenses and plans for expansion.
- Xiticix powers, abilities and weapons.
- Psi-Stalker Tribes fighting the Xiticix & new R.C.C. data.
- Heroes and Hardcases: groups and 15 Non-Player Characters.
- Plots against the alien invaders by the CS, Lazlo & others.
- Fort Barron of the Coalition Army, mapped and described.
- Adventures, maps and many adventure ideas.
- Written by Kevin Siembieda and Wayne Breaux Jr.
- 160 pages – $20.95 – Cat. No. 838. Available now.

Rifts® Sourcebook 2:

The Mechanoids®

– Back in Print – Available now

Archie 3 and Hagan Lonovich are two of the most beloved villains (anti-heroes?) in the Rifts Earth setting. This sourcebook highlights their strange relationship, plots and blunders. One of which is inadvertently unleashing The Mechanoids® into the world!
- The prophecies of the Seven Dangers.
- 20+ Mechanoids and their robot legion.
- Optional Mechanoids® Player Characters and character sheets.
- Archie Three and Hagan: Heroes or villains?
- The weapons and robot minions of Hagan Lonovich.
- New creations from Archie Three and Hagan, plus more history and insight about the unlikely duo.
- Five adventures, random encounter tables and adventure ideas.
- Written by Kevin Siembieda.
- 112 pages – $16.95 – Cat. No. 805. Available now.

Rifts® World Book 18:

Mystic Russia™

Back in Print – Available now

Russian mythology and magic come to life in this fan favorite Rifts® World Book. The book includes all kinds of demons, monsters, new magic character classes (O.C.C.s), and nine different types of gypsies – some of whom are adventurers, others mystics and mages, some psychics and one is even a beguiling shapeshifter. Plus more background about Russia and the Sovietski.
- 36 Fire Magic spells.
- 29 Nature Magic spells.
- 18 Russian Demons, their powers and hierarchy.
- 10 Russian Woodland spirits, including the Man-Wolf and Werebeasts.
- The Night Witch, Hidden Witch and Born Mystic O.C.C.s.
- Necromancy and Necromancers expanded and their place in Russia.
- The Russian Ley Line Walker character class (O.C.C.).
- The Russian Shifter/Summoner O.C.C. (and all those demons to call upon).
- Mystic Kuznya O.C.C.: Warrior and maker of magic weapons.
- Plus Gypsy O.C.C.s, combat vehicles of the Sovietski, and more.
- Written by Kevin Siembieda.
- 176 pages – $20.95 – Cat. No. 833. Available now.

Rifts® Sourcebook Three:

Mindwerks™

Available now – Back in print

The Brodkil Empire, Angel of Death, Gene-Splicers, monsters and dangers that haunt Poland and other regions around the New German Republic.
- 14 O.C.C.s and R.C.C.s, including a dozen D-Bee races.
- Mindwerks 'bots, cyborgs, weapons & equipment.
- Mindwerks M.O.M. conversions, Crazies and insanity.
- Gene-Splicers and their presence on Rifts® Earth.
- An evil Millenium Tree and Germany's infamous Black Forest.
- Massive, new war machines for the Gargoyles and the NGR.
- The Kingdom of Tarnow, its namesake magical crystal and anti-Gargoyle weapons and equipment.
- More information on Europe after the Coming of the Rifts®.
- Written by Kevin Siembieda.
- 112 pages – $16.95 retail – Cat. No. 812. Available now.

Rifts® Coalition Wars® 1: Sedition™

– Back in print – Available now

Magic vs Technology. The infamous Coalition/Siege on Tolkeen story arc starts with this 160 page sourcebook. Not only does it lay the groundwork for the Coalition's all-out siege on the kingdom of magic, but it includes a vast number of Techno-Wizard weapons and vehicles, powerful magic artifacts, demons, monsters, magic and a historic Crisis Time-Line from 12 P.A. to 106 P.A.
- 15 Rift and Ley Line Magic spells.
- 10 Spells of Legend and six powerful magic artifacts.
- 50+ Techno-Wizard weapons including Goblin Bombs.
- 12 Techno-Wizard vehicles and TW vehicle conversion rules.
- Iron Juggernauts – Techno-Wizard giant combat robots.

- The war plans of the Coalition Army.
- Background on the Kingdom of Tolkeen and its inhuman allies.
- Key places, maps, adventure ideas and more.
- Written by Kevin Siembieda and Bill Coffin.
- 160 pages – $20.95 – Cat. No. 839. Available now.

Rifts® Coalition Wars® 2:

Coalition Overkill™

– Back in Print – Available now

The Siege on Tolkeen goes into full swing as the Coalition Army makes the first devastating attacks on Tolkeen. Coalition Generals, Special Forces squads, strategies and adventure ideas.

- Key Coalition leaders and power players and their stats.
- The Dirty Thirty, the most vile and deadly of CS Special Forces.
- Coalition Bounty Hunters and Mercenaries.
- The Daemonix – one of Tolkeen's unholy alliances.
- Stats for dozens of NPCs, adventure ideas, and more.
- Written by Kevin Siembieda and Bill Coffin.
- 112 pages – $16.95 – Cat. No. 840. Available now.

Coalition Wars® 4: Cyber-Knights™

– Back in Print – Available now

The history and secrets of the Cyber-Knights, and more.

- Cyber-Knight O.C.C., secrets and powers revealed.
- In-depth examination of the Code of Chivalry.
- Cyber-Knight Factions and rules of combat.
- Crusaders, Fallen Knights, Robber Knights and Despoilers.
- Lord Coake statted out, along with stats for other Cyber-Knights.
- Notable weapons and armor of the Cyber-Knights.
- Story background, adventure outlines, ideas and more.
- Written by Kevin Siembieda.
- 112 pages – $16.95 – Cat. No. 842. Available now.

Rifts® Mercenaries

This fan favorite sourcebook is packed with information about mercenaries, creating mercenary companies, merc O.C.C.s and a vast array of weapons, vehicles, armor and equipment.

- 9 O.C.C.s including Master Assassin, Smuggler, Super-Spy, Forger, Thief, Bounty Hunter and others.
- 7 Mercenary companies, including Larsen's Brigade.
- The weapons and vehicles of Golden Age Weaponsmiths.
- The weapons and explosives of Wellington Industries.
- The weapons and vehicles of Iron Heart Armaments.
- The weapons, force fields and vehicles of Naruni Enterprises.
- The weapons and gear of Northern Gun.
- Angrar Robotics and Chipwell Armaments.
- A few Coalition vehicles.
- A mercenary adventure and more. Many adventure ideas.
- Written by C.J. Carella.
- 160 pages – $20.95 retail – Cat. No. 813. Available now.

World Book 21:

Rifts® Splynn Dimensional Market™

Another fan favorite packed with information about the Splynn Dimensional Market, its merchants, D-Bee slaves and lots and lots of magic items.

- Splynn Dimensional Market described.
- 30+ Splynn merchants and key locations in Splynn.
- Splynn underground, the authorities and NPC characters.
- 14 alien R.C.C.s; Splugorth slave stock.
- 30 Bio-Wizard organisms: 19 Parasites and 11 Symbiotes.
- 26 Bio-Wizard weapons, restraints & Bio-Borg creation rules.
- Tattooed Archer O.C.C. and 20 Magic Tattoos.
- Notable Kittani and other weapons and vehicles.
- Written by Mark Sumimoto and Kevin Siembieda.
- 192 pages – $24.95 retail – Cat. No. 836. Available now.

Rifts® World Book 22:

Free Quebec™

This World Book contains a wealth of information about Free Quebec, Glitter Boys and notable people and places.

- Overview of Free Quebec and its military.
- 6 Quebec Military O.C.C.s including variant Glitter Boy Pilots.
- 6 types of Glitter Boys plus the Glitter Boy Sidekick.
- Pale Death SAMAS and other Quebec power armor.
- Free Quebec's Navy, Cyborgs and technology.
- Notable places including Old Bones & various combat groups.
- Many adventure ideas and more.
- Written by Kevin Siembieda and Francois DesRochers.
- 192 pages – $24.95 retail – Cat. No. 837. Available now.

Rifts® World Book 31: Triax™ 2

The Gargoyle War rages on. The NGR appears to be winning. When you see the myriad new robots, power armor and vehicles, you'll know why.

- Overview of the New German Republic, circa 109 P.A.
- 27 new Triax weapons plus body armor & additional gear.
- 10 new Triax giant robots including the Talon and Devastator Mk II.
- 10 cars and commercial vehicles, plus more than 50 special features.
- 9 new robot drones including robot pets, assistants and spy-bots.
- 6 new types of power armor, 5 aircraft and other combat vehicles.
- NGR mobile fortress, many adventure ideas and more.
- Written by Taylor White and Brandon Aten.
- 192 pages – $24.95 retail – Cat. No. 881. Available now.

Rifts® Black Vault™

There is a wealth of information packed into this 48 page adventure sourcebook that makes it a perennial favorite.

- Overview of the Black Vault – the Coalition's warehouse of captured magic items.
- The Black Vault and CS Anti-Magic Recovery Squad.

- 101 magic items, including magic potions, scrolls, Techno-Wizard devices, magic weapons and more.
- An overview of the Coalition's love/hate relationship with magic.
- Written by Kevin Siembieda.
- 48 pages – $9.95 retail – Cat. No. 855. Available now.

Rifts® Dimension Book™ 6:

Three Galaxies™

A guide to the Three Galaxies, this book takes a look at dozens of solar systems, notable planets, select alien races, people, civilizations and monsters, as well as space anomalies, spaceships and more. This is another sourcebook that is ideal for campaigns involving the **Minion War™**, the **Thundercloud Galaxy™**, **Phase World®** and adventures in the **Three Galaxies.**

- An overview of the Three Galaxies.
- 16 O.C.C.s/R.C.C.s including the Obsidian Spell Thief and Space Warlock.
- A half dozen monsters plus the mysterious Necrol.
- Galactic Organizations (Atorian Empire and more).
- More information on the Intruders, Kreeghor, Splugorth and others.
- Draygon Industries and their weapons.
- Demon Stars, Demon Planets and magic starships.
- Notable spaceships and weapon systems.
- The monstrous Necrol and their living weapons and space-craft.
- Notable equipment of the Three Galaxies, and adventure ideas.
- Written by Carl Gleba.
- 160 pages – $20.95 retail – Cat. No. 851. Available now.

Rifts® Dimension Book™ 5:

Anvil Galaxy™

– Available now – Back in print

This popular, fan-favorite **Phase World®** sourcebook presents a dynamic overview of the *Anvil Galaxy™* and its many alien races, technologies, conflicts and secrets. A great resource for any Phase World® fan and valuable addition for campaigns involving the Minion War™.

- Legends of the Cosmic Forge™ and the Forge War™.
- Nearly 20 alien races & an overview of the Anvil Galaxy™.
- Transgalactic Empire and Consortium of Civilized Worlds.
- Overview of the Three Galaxies.
- Planet Creation Tables and more. By Bill Coffin.
- 160 pages – $20.95 retail – Cat. No. 847. Available now.

Old Ones™

A big sourcebook for the Palladium Fantasy RPG®

This is a massive adventure book with maps and descriptions of more than 50 locations in the *Timiro Kingdom*. As if that were not enough to make this the ultimate adventure book, there is also information about the Old Ones and a few O.C.C.s.

- 50+ cities, towns, and forts described and mapped. Each suitable as a place for adventure.

- 7 fully fleshed out adventures and scores of adventure ideas.
- Includes the fabled "Place of Magic," an ancient Dwarven Ruin reputed to date back to the Elf-Dwarf War.
- Minotaur R.C.C., Illusionist P.C.C. and Monk/Scholar O.C.C.
- Background and rumors about the Old Ones and adventure galore.
- Travel notes, world information about Timiro and more.
- Written by Kevin Siembieda.
- 224 pages – $24.95 retail – Cat. No. 453. Available now.

Wolfen Empire™

A sourcebook for the Palladium Fantasy RPG®

Back in print! This juicy adventure-sourcebook is authored by *Erick Wujcik, Kevin Siembieda* and *Bill Coffin*. It presents a comprehensive background and history of the Wolfen Empire, the Wolfen tribes, their military and their plans for the future. It also includes several adventures, strange animals, random encounter tables and more. Wolfen Empire is a fan favorite, and one of Erick Wujcik's last published role-playing works.

- 101 Adventures Table.
- 4 fully-fleshed out adventures plus a few notable places, including the Bones of Belimar, the Village of Wrijin and the town of Badd Land (a Bandit's Paradise).
- 13 notable animals of the North.
- The Great Northern Wilderness and Killer Winters.
- Wolfen history, religion and economics.
- Wolfen military, ranks and types.
- Written by Erick Wujcik, Kevin Siembieda and Bill Coffin.
- 160 pages – $20.95 retail – Cat. No. 471. Available now.

Mutant Underground™

A sourcebook for Heroes Unlimited™

Advancements in genetic engineering have created an array of mutants and superhumans. Some are heroes. Some are villains. Others are monsters. Many have gone underground and begun to build a secret mutant society and subculture. A sourcebook for Heroes Unlimited™.

- The Mutant Underground, its champions and its enemies.
- Genetic Mutation Tables for creating mutants of all kinds.
- The mutant slave trade.
- Mutant Recovery Teams and government agents.
- 20+ superhumans and mutant characters.
- New combinations of super abilities plus genetic mishaps.
- Mutant animals with super abilities and more.
- Background and campaign information. Many adventure ideas.
- Written by Kevin Siembieda. Based on ideas by Mike Wilson.
- 96 pages – $16.95 retail – Cat. No. 520. Available now.

www.palladiumbooks.com

2012 Christmas Surprise Package

Available now till December 23, 2012

Every year for the last 14 or 15 years now, Palladium offers a **Christmas Surprise Package** – our way of saying thank you to our fans and helping to make your Christmas a little more special.

What is a Palladium Christmas Surprise Package?

$80 or more worth of Palladium Books product for only *$38 plus shipping!* A minimum of *$80 retail.* Sometimes much more! Santa Kevin wants to make gamers delighted and often packs in $90-$100 worth.

- **Autographs** from Kevin Siembieda, available staff and freelance artists and writers. If you "request" autographs we'll sign *every* book in your box! For many, especially those across the country and overseas, this is the *only* way to get autographs from Kevin Siembieda and crew. *Take advantage of it.*
  If you do *NOT* want autographs, please state – "No autographs."
  If you do NOT want T-shirts, please write – "No T-shirts."
- **Each order is hand-picked by** *Kevin Siembieda* from a "wish list" *you* provide! Please list at least 8-12 items that you know are in stock. PLEASE do not list books you know are *out of print*; you will not get them.
- **The Grab Bag makes a wonderful gift for** Christmas, Hanukkah, birthdays, anniversaries, etc., for the gamers in your life. Since there will be so much in every Surprise Package, ordering just one might enable you to give books to two or more pals.
- **Impress your friends with a gift worth $80** *or more* for a cost of only $38 (plus shipping and handling).
- **Fill holes in your own collection** or get books and product you've been meaning to try or have been eyeballing longingly.

It's a surprise package because you never know exactly what you're going to get or who will sign your books. We try to include *many* of the items on your "wish list," but we may surprise you with stuff you are not expecting. Extra items may include other *RPG books, The Rifter®, posters, prints, art books, greeting cards, T-shirts, back stock items,* and other things. Some items may be slightly damaged so we can send you more.

Spread the word. The Christmas Surprise Package is only publicized by word of mouth, to readers of **The Rifter®** and on **Palladium's website – www.palladiumbooks.com –** so tell everyone you know. Buy one for *every gamer you know* and *have a very Merry Christmas.*

Multiple orders WILL result in some duplication.

The Cost

$38.00 plus $10.00 for shipping and handling in the USA; $48 total.

$38.00 plus $30.00 estimated for shipping and handling to CANADA; $68 total.

$38.00 plus $52.00 estimated for shipping and handling OVERSEAS; $90 total. **Note:** Sorry, we are only passing along the postal rates of Priority Mail International (typically 4-10 days delivery). We always try to load up on orders going overseas, so you can expect at least $90 worth of product with *autographs* and items you might not normally be able to get.

All North American orders are shipped U.S.P.S. Media Mail (the "slow" Book Rate), or UPS, <u>or</u> the way *Palladium* decides is best. Those ordering online can select the desired method of shipping, but will pay accordingly. We strongly suggest **UPS** because it is fast, reliable and *can be tracked.* Media Mail cannot be tracked, takes 10-21 days to arrive, and one-of-a-kind items like artwork or a gold edition can <u>NOT</u> be replaced if lost.

Credit card orders are welcomed. Visa and MasterCard are preferred, but we accept all. Order by mail, telephone or online.

No C.O.D. orders.

We must have YOUR *street address* (no P.O. Box) to ship via *UPS.* Make sure you give us your entire, correct street address and APARTMENT NUMBER! Palladium is NOT responsible for loss if you give us an *incorrect* or *incomplete address,* or if you *move* <u>after</u> you place the order.

Note: Orders received by Palladium after December 14th can *NOT* be *guaranteed* to arrive *before Christmas.* Palladium makes no promise that foreign or military base orders will be received before December 25th regardless of when they are placed. Rare books and one-of-a-kind items, like art prints or gold editions, can NOT be replaced if lost in the mail.

Send Mail Orders to: *Palladium Books – Dept. X – 39074 Webb Court – Westland, MI 48185-7606.* **Or e-mail** using the ordering info in our online store at *www.palladiumbooks.com –* or call **(734) 721-2903 to place orders by telephone** using a credit card.

Ideas for "Special Wants"

To insure your X-Mas Surprise Package is everything you want it to be, send us a *wish list* of your "wants." **The more items listed,** the more likely you are to get items *you want.* List them in order of preference (at least 8 items, but 10 or more is better). That way, you don't know what you're getting and we have a large selection to choose from, making it fun for you and easier on us. Thanks.

PLEASE do *not* ask for books you *know* are not yet available or out of print like *Tome Grotesque* or *Mechanoid Space®.*

Note: Santa Kev and his elves are NOT mind readers. If you do not give us a clear idea of your wants, you *may* be disappointed by what comes in your Surprise Package. You do NOT make our job easier when you say something like "I own everything, surprise me." Please provide a list of 8-12 books and other items!

- **Rifts® Ultimate Edition** and core books like **Rifts® G.M. Guide, Rifts® Book of Magic,** and **Rifts® Adventure Guide.**
- <u>For Rifts®:</u> **Rifts® Vampire Kindgoms™ Expanded, Rifts® Vampires Sourcebook** (an October release), **Rifts® Lemuria** (new), **Triax 2™, D-Bees of North America, Shemarrian Nation™, Dimensional Outbreak™, Thundercloud Galaxy™, Fleets of the Three Galaxies™, Heroes of the Megaverse®, Three Galaxies™, Tales of the Chi-Town 'Burbs™** (short stories), **Rifts® Machinations of Doom™** (graphic novel & sourcebook by award winning artist Ramon Perez), **Rifts® & the Megaverse® –** the Art of John Zeleznik (softcover art book or the $50 hardcover), **the Zeleznik Coloring Book, Rifts® Sourcebook One Revised, Juicer Uprising™, Coalition War Campaign, Rifts® South America, Rifts® Australia, Rifts® Mercenaries, Rifts® MercTown™, Rifts® Merc Ops™, Rifts® Merc Adventures, Rifts® Black Market™** (new), **Siege on Tolkeen/Coalition Wars® series,** and more!

We have big plans for the **Chaos Earth™ RPG** in 2013, so you might want to snag the RPG and the **Creatures of Chaos** sourcebook.

Looking for *high-tech,* consider **Rifts® Game Master Guide, Naruni Wave 2™, Rifts® Sourcebook One, Coalition War Campaign™, Coalition Navy™, Free Quebec, Triax & the NGR™, Triax™ 2, Rifts® Black Market, Rifts® Mercenaries, Rifts® New West™, Rifts® Atlantis,** among others.

Looking for magic and monsters, consider **Rifts® Book of Magic, Federation of Magic™, Rifts® Atlantis, Rifts® Lemuria, Rifts® South America Two, Rifts® Spirit West™, Rifts® Mystic Russia.** Emphasis on monsters and D-Bees: **Rifts® Conversion Books**

1, 2 & 3, **D-Bees of North America**™, **Psyscape**™, **New West**™, **Rifts® Dinosaur Swamp**™, *Adventures* in **Dinosaur Swamp**™, **Rifts® Atlantis**, **Splynn Dimensional Market**™, **Phase World®**, **Hades**, and **Dyval**™, among others.

Want space adventure? See **Phase World®** and most of the other **Dimension Books**™ like **Skraypers**™, **Three Galaxies**™, **Megaverse® Builder** and **Thundercloud Galaxy**™.

- **Minion War**™ **titles.** With **Megaverse® in Flames** coming soon, you may want to get all the books in the series: **Hades, Dyval**™, **Dimensional Outbreak**™, **Heroes of the Megaverse®** and **Armageddon Unlimited**™.
- **Rifts® Dimension Books**™ are always fun: **Thundercloud Galaxy**™, **Naruni Wave 2**™, **Wormwood**™, **Skraypers**™, **Phase World®**, **Phase World® Sourcebook**, **Three Galaxies**™, **Anvil Galaxy**™, **Megaverse® Builder**™, **Heroes of the Megaverse®** and others.
- **Rifts® Conversion Books** include **Rifts® Conversion Book One**, **Conversion Book 2: Pantheons of the Megaverse®** and **Rifts® Dark Conversions**™.
- **Robotech® Gold Edition.** A dozen or so are available for Grab Bags. With a value of $70, you are likely to get only one other item in your X-Mas Surprise Package.
- **Robotech® RPG – Manga Edition** and a couple dozen of the 8½ x 11 inch *Hardcover editions* are available. So are the Robotech® Sourcebooks: **Macross Saga**™, **The Masters Saga**™ and **New Generation**™.
- **Heroes Unlimited**™. Any of the following make for great superhero gaming! **Armageddon Unlimited**™, **Heroes Unlimited**™ **G.M.'s Guide**, **Powers Unlimited**™ **1, 2 & 3**, **Villains Unlimited**™ **Revised**, **Century Station**™, **Gramercy Island**™, **Aliens Unlimited Galaxy Guide**™, **Compendium of Contemporary Weapons**, **Ninjas & Superspies**™ **RPG**, and **Mystic China**™, among others. **Heroes of the Megaverse®** and **Skraypers**™ include alien superheroes and villains easy to adapt to HU2.
- **Palladium Fantasy RPG®** **and sourcebooks.** A unique fantasy world with human and non-human races like the Wolfen. **Mysteries of Magic**™ **Book One**, the **Palladium Fantasy RPG®** itself, plus epic sourcebooks like **Western Empire**™, **Northern Hinterlands**™, **Land of the Damned**™ **One** and **Two**, **Monsters & Animals**™, **Dragons & Gods**™, and others.
- **Dead Reign**™ **RPG**, the zombie apocalypse, is the game you WANT to try. **Civilization Gone, Dark Places** and **Endless Dead** sourcebooks.
- **Beyond the Supernatural**™ **RPG**: Modern day horror and weirdness reminiscent of the TV shows, **Fringe** and **Supernatural**. Can be used with *Dead Reign*™ and *Nightbane*®. Big plans for it in 2013.
- **Nightbane® RPG and sourcebooks** including the popular **Nightbane® Survival Guide**. All Nightbane® titles are in stock except the discontinued *Shadows of Light*. Suitable for easy use with *Heroes Unlimited*™, *Ninjas & Superspies*™, and *Beyond the Supernatural*™.
- **Back stock:** This is the time to get RPGs, sourcebooks, world books, and supplements you've been wanting. Fill those holes in your collection, get hard to find back stock items or try a new game like **Robotech®, Dead Reign®, Rifts®, Palladium Fantasy®, Nightbane®, Heroes Unlimited**™, **Ninjas & Superspies**™, **Beyond the Supernatural**™, **Chaos Earth**™, **After the Bomb®, RECON®** or **Splicers®**.
- *Rifter*® **back issues** are available (issues 1-13 only in the X-Mas Surprise Package). Many issues are sold out, including issues #4, #8, #19, #21-26, #28-35, #38, #46-48, and others.

- **Original art** by select artists. We don't know everyone who may be contributing, but we have some art by *Mike Wilson* and *Kent Burles*. Art is donated by the artists. Each is an original, signed, one-of-a-kind illustration from a printed book or an unpublished sketch made by the artist. Value ranges from $20-$100. *Only people who request original art will be* **considered**.
- **Art Prints** – we have a variety of black & white prints from Rifts® Lemuria (unsigned), the color Dog Boy print (unsigned) and other odds and ends with an average value of $5-$6 each. Plus the Palladium Zombie prints (signed by the staff), the Mike Mumah Rifts® Anniversary print ($10, color, signed) and a few others. Most have print runs of fewer than 500 copies. *Only people who request prints will be* **considered**.
- **Non-Book Palladium Products and Novelty Items.** Don't forget about the awesome **bookmarks** (Set #1 & #2), **magnet set** (four), **Rifts® baseball cap**, **Chi-Town Library pencil**, various **coffee mugs**, **Rifts® black dice bag** (gold imprint), **A+Plus comic books** (out of print for decades, $12+ value each) and **Rifts® Christmas cards**. All limited print items.
- **Palladium T-Shirts.** Select T-shirts are available while supplies last; some sizes are already gone; first come, first served. All have a $20+ value.
  - Coalition Christmas – Small to 5XL.
  - Gamer – Medium to 3XL.
  - Gamer "Zombie" – Small and XL to 3XL.
  - Hell was full so I came back (color!) – Small to XL.
  - Lazlo Society – XL only.
  - Rifts® is F'in Brilliant - Medium and XL to 4XL.

Ordering the 2012 Surprise Package

Include *ALL* of the following information . . .

- *Special Wants* – list *several* specific books, new and old, or other items like Rifts® coffee mugs, dice bag, art prints, etc. – at least 8-10 items please.
- Indicate "No T-shirt" if you don't want to be considered for one. If you *DO WANT* a T-shirt include *your size* (many shirts are limited to only XL).
- Your favorite Palladium games.
- Palladium games you have *not* played but you might want to try.
- Indicate if you want autographs.
- Comments and suggestions.
- Accurate & complete mailing address! UPS cannot ship to a P.O. Box; provide a *street* address. Include your APARTMENT number! Palladium is NOT responsible for *loss* if you give us an *incorrect* or *incomplete address*, or if you *move*.

Total Cost: $48 USA ($38.00 + $10 estimated for shipping & handling), $68 to Canada, $90 overseas. Multiple orders *will* result in duplication.

Credit cards are welcomed: Visa and MasterCard preferred, but most major credit cards are accepted. Go to the Palladium website (www.palladiumbooks.com) and fill out the **2012 Christmas Surprise Package Order Form** and pay with a credit card. **Or order by telephone** (734-721-2903); this is an *order line* only.

Place orders by mail by enclosing a check or money order along with your wish list, the info above *and address*, and send to:

Palladium Books® – Dept. X – 39074 Webb Court – Westland, MI 48185, USA

Kids' Game: Something Wonderful!

How to Immerse Barely Teenage or Younger Role-Playing Novices in the Game

By Hendrik Härterich

This article was written as a "how to" for facilitating a game with kids, especially when those kids are your own.

My daughters had always wondered what that strange hobby of mine was, and recently we talked about it. They were 13 and 10 then and – to my surprise – wanted to play. I confess that I was terribly excited and a bit mortified at the same time because I was at a loss as to how to do that best.

I asked myself and later, on the brilliant Forums of the Megaverse (http://forums.palladium-megaverse.com), whether anybody had played with their own kids and whether anybody could give me some advice. I wondered about what kind of game and what setting to play best and whether there is a Palladium system light version. I received wonderful answers. None was a patent remedy, but all were very encouraging. That thread can be found here: http://forums.palladium-megaverse.com/viewtopic.php?f=1&t=122083

This article is not about Palladium light rules or a new O.C.C., but rather how to allow child novice gamers easy access to the game.

I found out that it is less about how lightly to apply the rules, but to let loose and concentrate on the role-playing aspects, especially in character generation. The actual game after character generation will then be much easier. Gaming is for kids like driving a car is for most of us. You turn the key, the engine starts and you drive. You do not need to know why the engine works, you just literally roll (pun intended) with it. Let the mechanic worry about the rest; and the mechanic is you as the G.M. The G.M. takes care of the engine, the children should just concentrate on their characters and playing. You will find that your children have a natural knack for playing an adventure; do not let the rules get in the way of that. I would advise against explaining the rules. They will want to know about them soon enough. Be patient and wait for the children's impatience to work for you.

Parents, especially, will understand why I have been so terribly excited. To role-play with your own children is such a new and great opportunity to interface with them. To share something that is very dear to you. It is to me. After almost 30 years of gaming, it is the hobby for me and, I would say, has become part of my very fabric. So, you really do not want to botch this! Yet exactly that line of thought and strain makes a botch even more likely.

The purpose of this article is to give advice on how to game with kids. I will share my experience and how it worked out for me, so that you may have some aid in making a game with your own kids work.

Step 1: "Meditation & Ritual"

1 - Calm down. Start by sticking to your G.M. routines.

If you are as stupefied as I was when game day came, do what you need to do to put this special form of stage fright out of your mind. Relax! The first thing I put on my table was my (Coalition) coffee mug and a bowl with baby Oreos, but any other cookie would, of course, have worked. I placed the *Palladium Fantasy RPG®* and *After the Bomb®* books neatly beside my two dice sets chosen for the day. The routine calmed me some.

Purposefully, I went to the kitchen to give the girls a chance to settle in. Besides, everybody was thirsty and I had to get the drinks (juice, of course). When I came back I saw my kids riffling through the *After the Bomb* book with glee. A good start!

Whatever calms you down at that stage is good. The children will probably be just as excited as you. You may want to read your adventure again, watch a movie first (especially if the tone is similar to the game you plan), you may want to turn on some relaxing or motivating music, etc. With music I would be careful, as your music taste will likely not be the same as your kids' – especially with teenagers.

And finally, I know this will sound stupid, but many people forget: have enough paper, pens and dice ready!

2 – Let your kids get a feel (meant literally!) for the game.

Give your kids a chance to hold the minis, see the props (mats and such) and let them look at the books.

Their curiosity will win and they will get an idea by the pictures what the game is about. Mind, choose the book carefully, not every role-playing book has art fit for the young or very young. In my assessment, *After the Bomb* ("AtB") is fine and my daughters love *Palladium Fantasy*. I think that *Heroes Unlimited* ("HU") would also work extremely well because of the excellent and familiar superhero comic book style of the art. It really depends on what you want to allow and what links best with the interests of the children, e.g. a child loving superhero comics would likely dig HU.

3 – Take care of the youngest (and any pets) who do not play.

This may not seem so important a point, but having a whirlwind of a dog and a quicksilver-like youngest daughter, I learned the hard way that you need to find ways to take care of sufficient peace to game.

If you have several children, especially the very young can be a problem for the game, depending on their nature. The solutions are to find a baby-sitter, try to involve them as well (I even allowed my youngest – 3 ½, so she does not swallow dice – to play with my dice while we were gaming), get the youngling to do something else such as listening to an audio book, meet a friend during game time, or flat-out "bribe" them. For my youngest, milk and Oreos helped her to settle down, but it was impossible to get her away from the gaming table, which is ok.

If you have pets, such as a dog, make sure they are calm, too. Take the dog for a good, long walk before gaming, so that he is in a resting mood and does not disturb the game. Throwing the dog a bone is surely a classic as well.

4 – Have sufficient pencils & paper ready and give each kid his or her own set of dice.

This one is a natural, right? Have enough pencils and paper ready!

I would not give them character sheets at this point. A character sheet can be confusing to the uninitiated: too many numbers and too many terms they will not know. You do not want to confuse or overwhelm your kids.

It deserves mentioning that you should yourself not be surprised how many terms they already know. Today's kids have often some knowledge of standard role-playing terms; mine know a lot from their Nintendo DS. That said, you definitely want to avoid entering into a discussion of why your game does not allow the same as game X or Y. That would serve no purpose; you would only start a potential conflict instead of focusing on the game.

Give each kid his or her own set of dice! That is important – the feel and color(s) of the polyhedrons is unique and the dice will work their own magic just like they did 30 years ago!

I gave my daughters their dice one week before the game, right after they had gotten interested for the first time. One week after that, when we actually gamed, they had themselves gotten their own dice bags – which they had surely seen me use – which was another good sign. As I said, I really recommend to do what you can to let the children's active mind and natural eagerness work for you. Giving them dice in advance made them proud. They know how seriously I take my own dice, getting some from me was special for them and the timing worked up their curiosity.

Step 2: Character Generation Quiz

1 – Simple Rules / Rules are entirely secondary for now.

I recommend not to go by a specific system, but simply and very generally S.D.C. and Megaversal, to keep their and my mind free. Of course, it is a good idea to choose a game line for the setting, but the rules, as such, should be applied with a light touch. Always remember, the children are eager to learn, but must not be overwhelmed as that may quench the flame of gaming.

Another good piece of advice is to give the children no rules rundown. Just tell them "you will learn that as we go, on the fly, it is easy." Your children will be fine with that. Children learn a lot of things in that way. Curiosity and soaking things up is second nature to most children; use that.

Take them "by the hand" and when they need to roll a skill check or to hit, just tell them which dice to use and what number they must make. After having done that just a couple of times, they will know that a D20 is used to hit the monster and percentiles to check whether riding that horse works.

Hence, my main worry was not the rules, but how to get them in the game without burdening them with too many concepts at once. An example is the Teenybopper adventure in the first edition of *Beyond the Supernatural™* (TEENY-BOPPER TERROR OR THE TOMB OF THE PERPETUALLY COOL ADOLESCENTS by Erick Wujick, *Beyond the Supernatural™, 1st Edition*, pages 205-211; you can get BtS 1st ed. via http://rpg.drive-thrustuff.com/product_info.php?products_id=60668), which is great fun. A note of caution: that adventure may not work in all cases. My oldest IS a teenager and does not – surprise, surprise – want to be told that she is sometimes hysterical.

I wanted to make the character generation less "dry" – and it is dry for the uninitiated. I wanted my kids to be able to interface with the characters as quickly and smoothly as possible.

2 – Game World:
For the 1st step – the here and now!

The easiest way to transport them to the game is to make the first step in the game as close to reality as possible. Not a fantasy world, no Rifts realities, nothing. I went very simply with a today's suburban U.S. normal family as a background, to which I shortly introduced them. They know normal, it is an easy start. It will also make them itch more for when the adventure begins.

3 – Who are you?

Next, ask them very simply, "who are you?" That question will give them a stop, but it really is the core of character creation. They will likely ask you what you mean. That, in turn, gives you the chance to tell them (again) that they are not playing themselves but a made-up / make believe character. To make it simple, do not confuse them by telling them that you can actually play what you want in a role-playing game, but narrow it down to playing a person about their age. Children have no problem with make believe, they just need the cue that in your game you allow exactly that.

How to create the character?

The answer is so simple it may surprise you: Go with a questionnaire approach!

I know, this sounds even dryer than any standard procedure, but it really is not. It is lots of fun. It also works so well because it allows your kids to talk about something that interests every teen or younger, i.e. him or herself, but in a fantasy way. They can say what they want because it is just for the character, to make up a story. What could be better? It is a free for all. Let the kids be kids and let them make lots of active choices.

Questionnaire
(character generation by "creativity quiz")

Character Name

An inevitable first, right? But this naming is very important; it gives the other "me" its own life.

Character Age

Usually kids will want to be 2 or 3 years older than they are. It is also a very important first question, because it shows them just how free they are in the game.

Favorites

A no-brainer as well. Every kid has something they are really "totally into" at the moment. Your kids can use that or cook something up. Make that clear to them, but it will be easy; they will fill that in quickly.
- **Music/song** – When the first of my kid gamers had answered that, I put that music on as background music. I guess it helps to get into the groove – depending on the music, of course. Anyway, the answer to this question will provide you with a neat character jingle, maybe even serve as a soundtrack.
- **Color** – An easy question that has virtually no game relevance but for my daughters is very important.
- **Animal(s)** – This one is easy to answer for kids, especially girls, I find, but it was a really important question for me. I needed to know what animal I could turn them into later, as my plan was to let them play *After the Bomb®*.

Does he/she like to read?

A library rat, like my middle daughter, will know a lot of stuff that is not necessarily typical for her age – consequently, she has some lore skills if "library rat" is chosen for a character. Make sure to ask for things like, does [character name] – always use the character name when talking to your kids, it will get them into the groove! – read much? What does he/she read? Is she often in the library? And so on.

Dislikes

An idea by my kids: everyone has them, dislikes. As mentioned, my eldest is a teenager and, naturally, has formed some dislikes. I really advise you to put this in because it helps to create that 3rd dimension for the character.

Hobbies/Active Sports

You see what this does? It is essentially a skill selection program. My oldest chose fencing, dancing and riding. My second daughter chose Karate, riding and reading. I proceeded to ask them to fill in how many years they have been doing their hobbies for, which is certainly very important to gauge quality of Physical skills that can easily be derived from this information.

Student Job

Well, lots of teens work. I did. The job choice must not be game relevant, but some will provide additional skills for the character. In any case, a student job fleshes out the character a tad bit more.

Star Sign

My daughters came up with this. It is unimportant to me whether someone is Capricorn or Sagittarius, but it is of interest to them. That is another thing: stay open for suggestions and the interests of your kids. If needs be, tailor the game – or in this case the character generation process – to your kid gamers' needs and interests.

Fears

Another suggestion by my daughters. I would not have asked this because I did not necessarily want to go that "deep," but they thought, rightly, that fears are part of the fabric of a person (although they phrased it differently and said "everyone is afraid of something, right?").

I actually let my daughters only roll for the basic stats. The remainder of the typical minutiae of the O.C.C.s is in my head and will find its why onto their "character sheets" step by step. I advise you to do the same, depending on the age and interest of the kids you play with, of course. Some love numbers more than others, and all are, in my experience, quite creative and (still) attuned to what a mind can conjure up.

You may want to write the characters up for them afterwards. I do not mean writing them up on a "real" character sheet but in the simple form of the questionnaire. I did not do that because I felt that leaving the sheets in their own handwriting gives them something familiar to come back to (as in, "this is mine").

If your children like to draw, invite them (but do not demand) to draw up their characters. You may want to be careful if the drawing skills of the children at the gaming table are not equal, as a child who has no or little talent may feel left out, especially if a sibling would draw his or her character with skill. In such – presumably likely – cases, you may want to hold drawing characters for a while or invite the talented one to draw the whole party – a family portrait, if you will. However, so that the game is not held up and to keep the interest going between sessions, perhaps that is some nice (voluntary!) homework. Do not use the word "homework," rather suggest it by saying, for example, "how cool would a portrait be?"

Step 3: Let the Games Begin!

1 – A warning: Do not make too many assumptions.

Your kids will surprise you. That was fair warning given to me and, very simply put, it is completely true. Kids will surprise you more than any other party you have Game Mastered for so far. You can be sure of that. They will act more intelligently and far more creatively than you thought, and they will get into the game much more quickly than you prayed for. It is a pleasant surprise. To keep it pleasant, do not make too many assumptions, and especially do not tailor the adventure to what you think your children like, unless you know that for sure.

Even if you know what makes them tick, think twice if you want to make an adventure in "their world." Think back a couple of years. Would your parents have been able to tell you what Luke said when he met Han for the first time? Would you be able to give them the "Hogwarts experience"? Being honest to myself, I would not. I love the Harry Potter books, have read them all and saw the movies, too, but I never immersed myself so completely

in them as my kids did. My girls listen to the audio books daily. I can never reach their knowledge level. Remember what happens when you read your child the same story every evening – kids love to hear the same story for days on end – and because you are tired you skip half a page or rephrase a sentence? Your child will correct you. Do you want to repeat the experience when you G.M.? I don't.

Consequently, I counsel giving your kids a game in either the real world or on a new, make-believe world, which could be fantasy or science fiction depending on your children's interest and your preferences.

2 – Game World:
The 2ⁿᵈ step – out of the here and now!

Well, I think that today and normal do not make for a great adventure. Again, I had thought long and hard and decided to use a tool often used in the classics.

In C.S. Lewis's Narnia series, notably in "The Lion, the Witch and the Wardrobe," a closet is a portal to the fantasy world, and children from the here and now walk through it to their adventure. In J.M. Barrie's "Peter Pan," the children follow the boy-who-wouldn't-grow-up by magical flight from the real world to the fantasy realm Neverland. In L. Frank Baum's "The Wonderful Wizard of Oz," it takes a tornado to blow the protagonist-kid Dorothy from real Kansas to the fantasy world Oz. Lewis Carroll's Alice falls down a rabbit hole to get to Wonderland. In the Chronicles of Thomas Covenant by Stephen R. Donaldson, the hero dreams himself into the fantasy realm "the Land," which may or may not be real. (I know this is a subject of avid discussion, or once was.)

I am sure a hundred more examples can be found.

The device is always the same. The transition from reality to a fantasy world is experienced by the heroes of the story. It makes the transition part of the story and allows the reader to share that experience. I think that description fits for **Rifts**® very well. However, personally, I would caution against giving them a *Rifts* adventure just yet. *Rifts* is an exciting but also brutal world with a confusing array of creatures and mixture of genres. That is wonderful, but may not be suited for your children yet. Again, you do not want to overwhelm them.

I thought to apply and advocate that same principle here.

With my daughters it worked out like this:

An Example

The setting I gave my young players was a normal house in a nice suburb in the Ann Arbor / Detroit area, their mother "Em" being a journalist at a newspaper in Ann Arbor, their father "Ted" being an engineer with Ford. Both girls were coming home from their student jobs as the game opened. The oldest one, "Lily" (real name Charlotte), came home from the ice cream parlor, went straight to her room without saying much but "hi Mum," and started listening to an audio book (quite realistic role-playing, that). The younger one, "Sarah" (real name Paula), trotted home from the library, continuing to read on the way (to which the G.M. asked whether she was careful with the road crossings, which she was, so no rolls needed for random encounters there), and then sat down in the kitchen to chat with her Mama (also quite realistic role-playing, that).

I happily noted that the girls jumped right into the game.

I had told them that they had found out at work that the people seemed unusually cranky today and that not so many as usual showed up. Then, when their father came home, that he was in a bad mood, too, and excused himself from the table early, which I said was also unusual. This information had no meaning at all, just to put them on edge a little and to tell them "something is about to happen" as well as to make them curious.

After dinner, the girls wanted to go to their rooms, naturally. "Lily" went first, "Sarah" staying behind with her mother for a moment. Lily found that the door to the cellar, where their father had that secret room for himself – I mentioned that here for the first time – was slightly ajar and that she heard a sound like a steam engine, hammering pistons and steam being emitted. She also saw some eerie bluish light flicker under the door in rhythm with the humming and hammering from the cellar.

While I was describing this, she shouted, "I go upstairs and get my foil." Her character has fencing as a hobby, so that made sense. Meanwhile, her sister pleads, "Am I there, am I there, do I see this?" and my youngest looks at me completely transfixed. Nice!!! That was a moment of very intense pride and serenity for me.

As simple as the whole setup was, it was very exciting for all of us when they went slowly downstairs. **Note:** Simple is good!

The tension could almost be touched, especially when they saw that there was ankle-high "fog" on the ground and the door to the "secret" work room of their father was maybe open, there was even more blue light and it smelled, oddly, of a forest.

Well, they found their father lying semi-conscious on the steps of a big steam engine, babbling, "don't go near," which my daughters flatly denied in chorus. *Huzzah!* I thought, but did not say. And after a little to-and-fro with their father, who tries to crawl up the stairs, coughing, "must save the world" but always breaks down again, my daughters actually say, "Papa, you stay here, we'll save the world!" *Well, go girls,* I think – *to the rescue!*

On the top of the mechanical thing is a Rift to another dimension.

What did my girls do? They went to their rooms and packed their bags without stopping for anyone or anything. They went down and ... off through the Rift they went ... only to find out that after breathing the air for a moment, "Lily" changes into a (fencing) human-squirrel and "Sarah" to a (5 year Karate trainee) human-wolf.

I had not asked their favorite animals for nothing. Hello, *After the Bomb*® setting!

3 – What happens after the first session?

I would not get too ambitious. Plan the whole adventure as a one-shot that can be extended to go on for several sessions. The children you play with may not like role-playing, and that is ok. My guess is that they will, but do not put yourself, and thus them, under pressure. Concentrate, as they do, on the here and now.

Should the children literally inhale the role-playing experience, and if and when it has gone well for at least 2 or 3 sessions with unbroken interest from all parties involved (be honest, including yourself), then I would think about starting a small campaign, let's say 4-6 sessions, and see how that goes before you plan the campaign that takes them through college...

Recaps are also important. You may find your children to remember the game more vividly than you do yourself. Children have the easiest time in the world to treat fantasy as a part of reality, so do not be surprised. You should still keep careful notes, just in case.

Can age difference be a problem? Well, I don't think I can really say it could not be a problem, but I have never found it to be an issue. You just have to be aware that you play with children and not adults. On the contrary, though, the active minds of children and the absence of adult cynicism lend themselves extremely well to a great gaming experience.

I strongly suggest toning down the violence to a 1950s movie level. While I would not rule out character death completely – it happens in children's books, too, see *Harry Potter* for example – but I recommend to avoid it for a while. The children have just made the characters; a character death would just hold the game back and may actually frustrate them without (educational) need. Let them feel the danger, but allow them to prevail. By all means, make it challenging... but survivable. It is an adventure! If Robin Hood dies on page 2, where is the adventure?

Naturally, and I am just saying this for the sake of completeness, if you play with children, keep the maturity level appropriate.

As your players are children, do not be put out when they sometimes get distracted. It is ok to demand their attention, but if they are really drawn to something else, gracefully back out and suggest continuing on another day (or later). Make that suggestion before they ask, themselves; you keep the upper hand that way.

Try to make it so that they do not split the party. It may be interesting to see what happens, as much for them as for you. Notwithstanding, I suggest to encourage them to stay together.

I have found that the children have played as a team more smoothly and quickly than most grown-ups do.

Their decisions were very creative and sometimes quite unexpected. As they do not know the rules yet, they might try to change the "fabric of the universe" according to their wishes; remember, for them it is make-believe, and in that you can do anything. That does not work in role-playing games so well, and you will need to (gently) teach them the limits of what they can do. However, if they have good ideas – such as what may be found behind that corner (anyone remember the *Princes of Amber*?) – it will be worthwhile to listen to them and you may want to incorporate some (!) of that into your game.

I find children difficult to predict, but that makes it even more interesting to play with them. My advice as to that: roll with it!

My daughters could hardly wait for next time!

Let me end this small article by wishing you and yours the same!

HOUSE PANDORUM

Optional Source Material for the Splicers® RPG

(Game Master's eyes only!)

By Kris Tipping

Saints, Librarians and Engineers see more than their fair share of the darker side of human nature; a nature that still lingers, even when faced with a common enemy. These beings are rarely killed when it is Splicer against Splicer. They are simply too valuable for the Resistance. However, they are often seen as mere tools; tools for power-hungry men and women, blinded by the desire to rule the world. That perspective changes you.

"It's funny; the human race finally has a common enemy and we still fight amongst ourselves like children" – *quote from a Saint after being liberated from a band of Waste Crawlers*

House Pandorum learned the critical lesson that the universe is a cruel, indifferent place and you must be strong to survive. But humans, as we are, are weak and frail. It was this simple belief which was to become the cornerstone of their goal. If humans could create a machine that can obliterate them, then Splicers could create a new race: a race of humanity that could once again dominate this planet, a race that would mean the stepping aside of the present day homo-sapiens.

"We still haven't learned our lesson and for that the human race is doomed to extinction. We intend to expedite that extinction" – *Chaos Lord*

House Pandorum's prime objective, their ultimate goal, is to herald in the dawn of a new age of man. They wish to "evolve" the human race into something else: Neo-Sapiens. To Pandorum, a Neo-Sapien is simply the next step; an evolved human that has:

- A physically perfect M.D.C. body.
- Equivalent Supernatural Strength and Endurance.
- Accelerated healing and regenerative capabilities.
- Resistance to disease, toxins, poisons and radiation.
- Increased longevity.
- And above all, "Psychic Abilities."

To achieve their goal of an evolved human, they study every facet of the human genome: genetic defects, mutations, abnormal susceptibility (weaknesses), etc. To expand their understanding of the many facets of the human genome, they attempt to collect as many DNA samples from as far and wide as possible. This practice even includes kidnaping and experimenting on people. They conduct a multitude of genetic testing and cloning and due to these practices have created some formidable *template* Biotics to breed a bit of chaos in the land. This research is also coupled with extensive and continuous investigations on the native and alien fauna of this planet. (**Note:** As an option you could give House Pandorum an edge by allowing them access to a cryo-zoo that has either been liberated or discovered.)

"We have the knowledge, skills and tools to accelerate the evolution of the human species, and we have liberated ourselves from the bindings of human morality." – *Librarian Hope*

House Pandorum has a noble goal but they are deluded and misguided; their methods cold and destructive. They are stable, driven and focused on their goal. Though they are not diabolical, they are apathetic and indifferent. Despite this, they are not crazy, nor cruel. They don't torture or kill for the fun of it. They simply see humans as weak, and little more than either potential test subjects or Biotics for their defenses. Much like the fabled Pandora's Box, they release chaos upon the land while holding a glimmer of hope that they can achieve their goals.

"What better way to distract your enemy than to unleash chaos upon them!" – *Chaos Lord*

Meeting their enemies on the battlefield is not their way. Though they are capable and formidable opponents, their preferred weapons are subterfuge, distraction and misdirection. They believe that the human race will soon be silenced by the machines. So until then they stay hidden, and patiently wait for their goal to be achieved.

For a while, Librarian Hope thought she hated the human race nearly as much as she does the machine; but she realized that hate was the wrong word. What she truly felt was angered disappointment towards the many who hunger for power and control; those who will do anything to obtain it. Even in the face of an enemy that wants all human life extinguished.

Optional Origins of House Pandorum

In actuality, House Pandorum is more of an idea or philosophy than a true, physical "House." Therefore, it can be represented in the game in many different ways. Regardless of which manifestation you choose for your game, the ideas behind Pandorum originate from a single Librarian: a female who gave herself a new name, Hope. Hope shed her old name to reflect the Greek Myth of Pandora's Box and what was kept inside of it when all the evil was unleashed upon the earth. Hope has not gone "*Megalo,*" nor has she been influenced by Kali or any of the other personalities. She has simply made a profound philosophical decision based on her observations.

What other characters are a part of Pandorum? That will depend on how you implement the House into your game. But above all, Pandorum should be a shadowy House, a force that can never truly be defeated; its location should not be known or discovered. Yet its damage and legacy should be witnessed by all.

The following is a list of starting ideas regarding the origins and elusive tactics for House Pandorum:

- **From Chaos Born**: You could have a region in your game that is constantly torn apart by conflict amongst Splicers. The remnants from countless Houses that had tried and failed to get a foothold in the region gradually came together to form a new House. This mysterious shadow House can use intermediaries to be the distraction and misdirection they need, so they can go about their business and not be disturbed.

If you choose this option, the House can be the proverbial "puppet master." While they stay in the shadows, they can either control a Waste Crawler Tribe or House (or both) or create a whole other House with the open desire to conquer all other Splicers. This false front gets all the attention while they are left to their devices.

If you choose this option, House Pandorum will always have a small population (see later description) while the *puppet House* can have a considerable population.

- **The Devil Within**: A Pandorum Faction can begin in one of your Houses by Librarian Hope and while the House goes about its merry way, this faction goes about achieving their goal.

    A more benevolent House might not want to use the type of *Template Biotics* listed later but a malevolent one definitely will.

    In this scenario the population will be the same as '*In Bed with the Enemy*' with the exception that Hope would have a significant number of Scarecrows.

    The faction will always have a number of 'damage control' and 'exit strategies' set in place for them to vanish in the middle of the night if the House is ever in the situation of being compromised or their goal is discovered.

- **On Wind and Wave:** In this version, the House is always on the move, whether it be in the ocean or roaming beneath the dunes of a grand desert. It will require a Kraken or equivalent. The House can either purchase one or procure it through a mutiny. This can also be a mobile version of '*The Devil Within.*'

    If you choose this option the House will always be a small population (see later description) or faction.

- **In Bed/League with the Enemy:** Hope can be fictitious and play the part of a 'Megalo' Librarian and gain the support of the Machine, giving her freedom and security to carry out her master plan. She unleashes chaos upon Splicers while N.E.X.U.S. provides various degrees of support, whether it is protection, reinforcements, or even facilities. The exact details and level of support I leave to the Game Master.

    If this option is chosen then the population of the House would be Hope, a couple of Engineers and a handful of Geneticists and worker Biotics.

Government

How the House is run is dependent on the *Origin* in which you choose for your game.
- For "*The Devil Within*" and "*In Bed/League with the Enemy,*" the main characters will only be Hope and a couple of Engineers, so Hope would just play along with whoever is in charge.
- For "*From Chaos Born,*" the *family* could create the front and be the dominant rulers, directing them in accordance with the tasks necessary for the fruition of Hope's goal.
- For "*On Wind and Wave*" (without "*The Devil Within*" angle), the House runs more like a business, with each department focusing on their component towards achieving the common goal. Hope would run the laboratories and cloning facilities, while the Chaos Lord, with the help of his family, would be responsible for the everyday operations of the House.

Bear in mind that Hope has no interest in ruling or commanding a House, she only wishes to devote her time towards achieving her goal; and that is why she needs the assistance of others. Hope is quite content to be engrossed in her work and leave the rest to someone else. It takes a significant amount of time and resources to employ the tactics required for Hope to conduct her experiments in secrecy.

Factors to be aware of in the operations of the House are:

- The immense resources required for the laboratory testing and cloning.
- The diligent mission to keep the House a secret. Elements such as how hidden and secure their entry/exit points to the House are, and employing their weapons of subterfuge, distraction and misdirection to minimize unwanted attention, such as the release of the Template Biotics upon their fellow Splicers.
- The amount of time and planning involved in the Geneticists' excursions.

Society and Culture

All that are a part of Pandorum have a common attitude; they are tired of war against their fellow humans, and they resent the nature within many, which cannot see the futility of that path. It is that attitude that unites them in the fundamental idea that is, House Pandorum.

They believe they are the minority, surrounded on all sides by those that harbor a war-like nature. A key part to their common attitude is that they believe homo-sapiens have failed as a race; so Pandorum wages a cold war against humanity, with the laboratory as their war factories.

Due to their common goal, Pandorum is a close-knit population. All work tirelessly for that goal, but they do take time off to recharge their batteries once in a while. They are not arrogant or driven by pride; the mood, and tone of the House is calm and focused; the people are not loud or boisterous, nor are their hobbies and recreational activities flamboyant or extreme.

Because secrecy is extremely important in achieving their objective, the best way to describe the general nature of the population would be that they are isolationists. Many do not leave or stray far from the House's prime area of operations for fear of being discovered.

House Pandorum has one goal, one focus, and though there is always collateral damage on the path to the eventual rise of a new sapient race, they *tend* to leave alone (sometimes aid) any who try to live a peaceful existence and who focus on the Machine. They do not harbor that same attitude towards any who seek to conquer, enslave or destroy their fellow humans. The latter experience a quick death, or are used for their experiments or biotic conversion.

To emphasize their nature again, they are not monsters. They merely accept the fact that peaceful and innocent humans will die due to their actions. If you choose the origin "*From Chaos Born*" and you choose to create a front that is war-like, it will be unavoidable that the innocent will suffer. Though they might have agents working in the shadows (hidden by stealth fields) stealing the children away from attacks by other humans, the *family* accepts and understands that they have to pick their battles if they are to avoid being discovered.

Change of Heart

"A philosophy, an ideal has many contradictions and convolutions, because there is never a straight line in one's train of thought." – Librarian Hope

Throughout this article, House Pandorum is portrayed as willing to watch the human race fade into oblivion, whilst they give birth to a new sapient species to dominate the planet. Instead, they could have a completely different philosophy:

"Some of us have to enter the darkness if we are to rid ourselves of all our demons" – Librarian Hope

They can be a force of good, a House trying to make amends for the mistakes that we, as a race, made in the past (pre-N.E.X.U.S.), where we lost focus and became complacent. They can work in the shadows to fight against the Machine and defend those who are not interested in conquering humanity. They would continue to expand their understanding of the human genome, but for the betterment of humankind, and not aid in its extinction.

Population Breakdown:

- The Family: Warlord (Chaos or Shadow Lord), his wife (Lady of Chaos) and 4 children: 3 daughters and a son (the birth order is left to the G.M.).
- 1 Librarian: Female, named Hope.
- 80 Scarecrows who act mainly as protection for the Geneticists when on excursions or to handle the occasional genetic experiment gone wild.
- 2 Engineers: 1 Male: Cyclonus, 1 Female: Typhus.
- 12 Geneticists: Due to their role, they also have the title of *Doctor*, *Shaman*, *Witch Doctor*, *Healer*, etc.
- 60-100 Biotics as worker drones and extra protection if something gets out of containment.
- 5 Saints.
- 6 Deliverymen.

The Family

We must be Strong: To achieve their ultimate goal, all among the House have been augmented to various degrees. The only individuals who have not yet undergone any form of full conversion are the children of the Chaos Lord. The children are all Dreadguards, outfitted with unique and powerful Host Armor. When they reach a certain age, they, like their parents before them, will become heavily augmented, non-mind-wiped Biotics. This transformation makes them stronger but it is not natural; but it will do to help them succeed.

Please Note: The names of the following characters have been left out, and their stats have been left at level one for the purpose of allowing the Game Master to add some of his or her own personal touch to House Pandorum.

As a House, Pandorum is small, yet they spared no expense when they *remade* the Chaos Lord, the Lady of Chaos, and the Host Armors for the children of the Chaos Lord (only four Dreadguards). If ever any of the children of chaos were to lose their Host Armor, another would be provided with all the enhancements it had upon its death.

Chaos Lord/Shadow Lord

Before his transformation, the Chaos Lord was a Roughneck; one who grew tired of the battles between rival Houses and the constant ambushes and tactical strikes from the many Waste Crawler tribes in the region. Much of his anger grew from witnessing the continuous blind arrogance and pride portrayed by superior officers and Warlords. When approached by Hope, he immediately understood her goal and agreed to help her cause. Like his wife, he volunteered to be remade into a powerful Biotic. However, the Lord is a non-mind-wiped Biotic; all his memories and skills have been retained and are now in a new and powerful body.

Class: Non-Mind-Wiped Biotic.
Alignment: Was Unprincipled, but now Anarchist.
Disposition: The Chaos Lord is a skilled fighter with a tactical mind who has grown in confidence since his transformation. He knows how to utilize any troops and arsenal at his disposal to its fullest. He has devoted himself to Hope, and would gladly sacrifice himself to protect her and his new family. He is a humble servant who works tirelessly towards the many

responsibilities of the House. He has also raised his children to understand the path and to serve Hope. Though he has given up on humanity, he hasn't lost *his*.

He is normally direct and swift on the battlefield, but occasionally a savage streak emerges and he sometimes makes his foes suffer a little before he kills them. That cruel streak is directed towards those that remind him of why he turned his back on humanity.

When the House needs more test subjects, the Chaos Lord intentionally selects those that prey on their fellow man. Children are NEVER taken as test subjects and to the best of their ability, not to be harmed. He will leave alone any House or village that he deems are peaceful (focus on the Machine), but on the other hand, he will let them fall at the hands of the Machine. He only considers involving himself and the House if children are threatened by other humans.

Description: For his form, he chose a winged demon; even his face has been altered to look demonic; with a skin tone of charcoal black with deep, blood red tints. Though the form has wings to suit the style, he uses *organic thrusters* as his main means of flight. The wings are fully functional but he mainly uses them during combat; not to mention the awe factor of a giant demon spreading its wings.

Level: One. **Note:** The Chaos Lord was a level eight Roughneck prior to his transformation and the skills below reflect that. Though he is a Biotic, his mind was not wiped so he retains the skills of his past and they continue to advance as if he were a Roughneck as shown on page 156 of the **Splicers® Role-Playing Game**.

Initial Cost of 'Remaking': Insignificant due to the amount of resources House Pandorum has for such a small population.

Non-Modified Attributes: I.Q. 11, M.E. 14, M.A. 9.

Modified Biotic Attributes: P.S. 36, P.E. 20, P.P. 20, P.B. 4 (Demonic), Spd 130 mph (208 km) running and 200 mph (320 km) flying (with a maximum altitude of 25,000 feet/7,620 m).

Height: 10 feet (3.05 m), **Weight:** 1,760 lbs (792 kg).

Biotic O.C.C. Bonuses: Splicer P.S., +1 attack per melee round, +2 on initiative, +2 strike, parry and dodge, +4 pull punch, +1 to roll with punch/impact/fall, +6 save vs toxins/poisons and drugs, +3 save vs Magic, Automatic Dodge, +25% save vs coma and death, +6 save vs Horror factor. These are in addition to any bonuses received through enhancements, skill selection and previous O.C.C.

Base M.D.C.: P.E.x15 +2D8 per level of experience, starting at level two. The Chaos Lord regenerates at 1D6+3 M.D. per melee round and can last ten times longer than normal during strenuous exercise/activity before feeling the effects of exhaustion. This means he can remain alert and operate at full efficiency for three entire days (72 hours) without sleep.

Biotic Biological Enhancements: Elongated Running Legs, Reinforced Exoskeleton, Wings, Organic Thrusters, Quick Clotting Blood, Resistance to Kinetic Energy/Attacks, Resistance to Physical Attacks, Resistance to Lasers, Advanced Senses, Ambidextrous*, Prehensile Tail, Bone Blades for both Forearms, Bone Blades for the Wings, Flame Breath, Bio-Force Field, Omega Blaster (in center of the chest), 15 Organic Rockets, 3 Pairs of Large Horns, Large Clawed Hands, Bio-Energy Expulsion Vent, Reinforced: Wrist/Hand, Elbow, Knee, and Ankle.

* It's a combination of this new body, and the training involved, to become accustomed to the new form. The bonuses from this enhancement have already been included into combat bonuses listed below.

Recommended/Suggested Enhancements: Supernatural P.S. and P.E., Regeneration: Superior, Plasma Breath, Increased speed to Organic Thrusters, Combat Tail, max out Bio-Force Field, Enhancements to Ranged Weapons.

Bio-Enhancement: Starting at level two, the Chaos Lord receives 5D6+10 Bio-E points per level of experience (in addition, he will receive many bonuses from those that can provide them) to enhance his already powerful Biotic form.

Skills of Note: First Aid (95%), Forced March, Running, W.P. Bio-Weapons: Light, Boxing, Kick Boxing and Wrestling, Recognize Weapon Quality, W.P. Knife, W.P. Paired Weapons, W.P. Sword, W.P. Whip, Blind Fighting (75%), Military Fortification (75%), Swimming (85%), Land Navigation (64%), Wilderness Survival (65%), Bio-Comms (55%), and Trap Construction (30%).

Note: These skills are from his life as a Roughneck (level eight) and he was also taught Hand to Hand: Expert as part of his training but focused on his Hand to Hand: Martial Arts.

Secondary Skills: Brewing 60%/65%, Cook (70%), Fishing 75%, Gardening (54%), and Fasting.

His Ambidextrous ability will provide a bonus of +5% to the following skills when selected: Climbing, Demolitions, Escape Artist, Pick Locks, Concealment and other sleight of hand skills.

Weapons and Equipment: The Chaos Lord has full access to the entire arsenal of the House. It is not uncommon for him to wear custom armor and wield a variety of weapons to a battle.

Combat Bonuses (P.P. bonus has been included): Automatic Dodge, W.P. Paired Weapons. +3 on initiative, +7 to strike, +10 to parry, +3 to parry with horns, +10 to dodge, +8 to roll with punch/fall, +7 roll with impact, +7 to pull punch, +2 to disarm, +3 to entangle, and a Critical Strike on an unmodified roll of 18, 19 or 20.

Combat Training: Hand to Hand: Martial Arts; 9 attacks (10 with Flame Breath) per melee round.

Bio-Weapon Systems (Level One):
1. Forearm Blades: +4D6 M.D.
2. Wing Blades: +6D6 M.D.
3. Flame Breath: 3D12 M.D.
4. Bio-Energy Expulsion Vent: 2D8+20 M.D.
5. Organic Rockets: 5D6 M.D. each.
6. Omega Blaster: 2D8x10 M.D.
7. Large-sized Horns: +9D6 M.D. to head butt damage (+1D6 M.D. from *Reinforced Exoskeleton*) for a total of 1D6x10 M.D.
8. Large-Clawed Hands: +2D6+6 M.D. to punch (+2D6 M.D. from *Reinforced Exoskeleton* and +1D6 M.D. from *Reinforced Wrist/Hand*), making it a combined +5D6+6 M.D. to punch damage.

Lady of Chaos

The Lady of Chaos was a soldier's wife, and mother to two children. A non-combatant, she was a laborer, skilled in many crafts required in the running of a House.

A quick and merciful death is what awaits any faced against her. A cold and methodical fighter; she has adapted well to her new role and Biotic form.

When it comes to children, the Lady is a study in contrasts. She feels sorrow for those who fall by the hands of the Machine but will not get involved. However, she will often protect them when they are attacked by humans or fauna. Those rescued are delivered to the many Retro-villages visited by the Geneticists when they are on their rounds (see later description).

She works diligently alongside her husband, carrying out the many responsibilities (military and nonmilitary) of the House. Though she is devoted to Hope's goal, she may not sacrifice herself for her but she would lay down her life to defend her family.

Description: Though she has taken on demonic features in the form of red skin, a crown of horns, two pairs of arms and a tail, her face still has the beauty she possessed before her transformation.

Level: One. **Note:** Before her transformation she could be described as a level 5 Laborer, something akin to the Vagabond O.C.C. as described in the **Rifts® RPG**.

Initial Cost of 'Remaking': Insignificant due to the amount of resources House Pandorum has for such a small population.

Non-Modified Attributes: I.Q. 14, M.E. 13, M.A. 15, P.B. 23 (24 with Wardrobe & Grooming skill).

Modified Biotic Attributes: P.S. 30, P.E. 20, P.P. 22, Spd 100 mph (160 km) running and 200 mph (320 km) flying (with a maximum altitude of 25,000 feet, 7,620 m).

Height: 8 feet, 6 inches (2.6 m). **Weight:** 770 lbs (347 kg).

Biotic O.C.C. Bonuses: Splicer P.S., +1 attack per melee round, +2 on initiative, +2 strike, parry and dodge, +4 pull punch, +1 to roll with punch/impact/fall, +6 save vs toxins/poisons and drugs, +3 save vs magic, Automatic Dodge, +25% save vs coma and death, and +6 save vs Horror Factor. These are in addition to any bonuses received through enhancements, skill selection and previous O.C.C.

Base M.D.C.: P.E.x12 +2D6 M.D.C. per level of experience, starting at level two. The Lady of Chaos regenerates at a rate of 1D4+3 M.D. per melee round and can last ten times longer than normal during strenuous exercise/activity before feeling the effects of exhaustion. This means she can remain alert and operate at full efficiency for three entire days (72 hours) without sleep.

Biotic Biological Enhancements: Elongated Running Legs, Prehensile Tail, Additional Pair of Arms, Ambidextrous*, Flame Breath, Chemical Spray, Resistance to Kinetic Energy/Attack, Resistance to Lasers, Four Pairs of Medium Horns, Organic Thrusters, four Bio-Energy Expulsion Vents (one for each forearm), Bio-Force Field, Combat Spurs on all four forearms, Combat Spurs on shins, Advanced Senses, Cosmetic: Red Skin, numerous tattoos covering her body, silvery white hair, and indigo eyes that can glow.

* It's a combination of this new body, and the training involved to become accustomed to the new form. The bonuses from this enhancement have already been included into combat bonuses listed below.

Some Recommended/Suggested Enhancements: Plasma Breath, Flame Halo, Bio-Energy Blades for each Bio-Energy

Watching her friends and family die fighting against the machine was one thing, but Splicer against Splicer was too much. Following the death of her husband and children by a rival House, a deep sorrow and a bitter disappointment in humanity swept over her. Ultimately, like her new husband, she has embraced Hope's dream of a new species, and gladly accepted the transformation to aid in that goal.

Even though she was only a laborer, she still knew how to fight. Thanks to her first husband, she was trained in Hand to Hand: Martial Arts and a couple of Weapon Proficiencies.

Class: Non-Mind-Wiped Biotic. She had her four children with the Chaos Lord before she was *remade*. Though she can still procreate, she does not wish to have any more children, and is focused on the goal and her family. Option: The Lady chose not to have any children with the Chaos Lord and their children are all adopted.

Alignment: Was Scrupulous but she is now Aberrant.

Disposition: She holds great resentment towards the nature of the beast in our hearts. She simply cannot fathom that for some reason, humans do not rise above primal instincts and a foolish desire for conquest and power over fellow human beings.

Expulsion Vent, Regeneration: Superior, Leaping Legs, and Bone Blade claw hands for one pair of arms.

Bio-Enhancement: Starting at level two, the Lady of Chaos receives 5D6+10 Bio-E per level of experience (in addition, she will receive many bonuses from those that can provide them) to enhance her already powerful Biotic form.

Skills of Note: <u>Common Skills</u>: Standard. <u>Skill Programs</u>: Domestic and Naturalist/Nomad. Wardrobe & Grooming, Sewing 80% (professional level), Cook 75% (professional level, +10% to cook game animals), Gardening 70% (professional level), Brewing (55%/60%), Hunting, Identify Plants and Fruits (45%), Land Navigation (52%), Preserve Food (50%), First Aid (65%), Holistic Medicine (55%/45%), Brewing: Medicinal (45%/50%), W.P. Knife, W.P. Bio-weapons: Light, and Hand to Hand: Martial Arts.

<u>Secondary Skills of Note</u>: Swimming (70%), Physical Labor, Fasting.

A bonus of +5% can be added to the following skills due to the *Ambidextrous* enhancement: Climbing, Demolitions, Escape Artist, Pick Locks, Concealment and other sleight of hand skills.

Weapons and Equipment: The Lady of Chaos has full access to the entire arsenal of the House. It is not uncommon for her to wear custom armor and wield a variety of weapons in battle.

Combat Bonuses: (P.P. and Ambidextrous bonuses have been included): Automatic Dodge, W.P. Paired Weapons, +2 to initiative, +8 to strike, +9 to parry, +9 to dodge, +7 pull punch, +3 to roll with punch/impact/fall, +1 to entangle, and +2 to disarm.

Combat Training: Hand to Hand: Martial Art; 9 attacks (10 with Flame Breath) per melee round.

Bio-Weapon Systems (Level One):
1. Combat Spurs: +4D6 M.D.
2. Flame Breath: 3D12 M.D.
3. Bio-Energy Expulsion Vents: 2D8+20 M.D.
4. Medium-sized Horns: +8D6 M.D. to head butt damage.

The Son of Chaos

Their son designed a unique Host Armor to suit his flair: a savage Were-Bat with two pairs of arms. The lower pair are standard arms, while the top pair are elongated, winged arms that provide him with flight.

Class: Host Armor.
Crew: One Human Pilot.
Level: One Dreadguard.
Total Bio-E Spent: 280 (Factoring in: 40 for metabolism, 10 from Librarian Hope, 40 from the Engineers and 20 from one of the Geneticists).
Bio-E Remaining: None.

Base M.D.C. by Location*:
Hands – 67 each
Upper Pair of Winged Arms – 147 each
Wings on the Upper Pair of Arms – 67 each
Lower Pair of Arms – 117 each
Legs – 207 each
Feet – 87 each
**Head – 187
Main Body – 330

* The bonus to the M.D.C. of the Host Armor from *Reinforced Exoskeleton* has already been calculated in.

** If the Head of the Host Armor is completely destroyed, though he loses nearly all his senses, the pilot would not die as his head is tucked safely away in the chest cavity of the Host Armor. As the son advances, he could possibly add a couple more pairs of eyes on the Host Armor to enable him to still see even if the head is completely destroyed. Truly a terrifying sight, seeing a decapitated Host Armor rising up to continue the fight.

Note: The Additional Pair of arms that are incorporated into the initial design of the Host Armor are placed above the standard pair for the pilot. What this does is expands the thorax of the Host Armor, therefore placing the head of the pilot in the chest cavity of the Host Armor instead of its head. Because of this approach to additional limbs, extra M.D.C. has been added (factored in to above stats) to the Main Body and the Head of the Host armor.

Speed:
Running: 120 mph (192 km).
Leaping: The Host Armor can leap up to 20 feet (6.1 m) high or 40 feet (12.2 m) across from a standing position.
Digging: 20 mph (32 km) through sand or dirt, but *one quarter* as fast through rock and concrete. Digging tires out its pilot, but at half the usual fatigue rate. To dig down enough to adequately hide from enemies on the surface takes 3D6 melee rounds.
Swimming: The powerful pair of elongated upper arms provide the Host Armor with a decent swimming speed of 50 mph (80 km). Swimming tires the pilot but at 10% the usual rate.
Underwater Depth: The Host Armor can withstand pressures up to 700 feet (213 m).
Flying: With the leathery wings being part of the elongated upper pair of arms, his initial speed is 120 mph (192 km) with a maximum altitude of 15,000 feet (4,572 m).

Statistical Data:
Height: 13 feet (4 m).
Width: 4 feet (1.2 m) at the upper pair of arms, 3 feet (0.9 m) at the standard pair of arms.
Length: 3 feet (0.9 m).
Weight: Adds 800 pounds (360 kg) to the weight of the pilot.
Cargo: None.
Physical Strength: Standard pair of arms has a Splicer P.S. of 30 while the upper pair of winged arms has a Splicer P.S. of 35.
Operational Lifetime: 15 years. This is short because this is a transitional period for the children of Chaos before they become non-mind-wiped Biotics.
Bio-Regeneration Rate: 1D6 M.D.C. per minute for the main body and 1 M.D.C. per minute for all other locations.
Horror Factor: 9

Senses and Features:
Inclusive of the standard Senses and Features from page 72 of the Splicers® Main Book, Enhanced Passive Nightvision (light amplification; Range: 6,000 feet/1,829 m). Additional Pair of Arms, Elongated Arms (towards the additional pair of arms), Fully Functioning Wings on elongated arms, Elongated Running Legs (+3 feet/0.9 m to height), Enhanced Neurological Connection, Ambidextrous (for original pair of arms), Regeneration: Enhanced, Chameleon Skin, Resist Electricity, Resist Heat, Resist

Kinetic Energy/Attacks, Resist Physical Attack, Armored Eyes, Quick Clotting Blood, Righting Reflex, Circadian Rhythm, and Reinforced Exoskeleton.

Feeding: Carnivorous metabolism.

Sleep Requirements: The Host Armor requires 2D4 hours of sleep/rest/inactivity per day, generally during daylight hours.

Level 1 Host Armor Combat Bonuses: +1 attack per melee round, +5 initiative, +2 to strike, +1 to parry, +1 to dodge, +1 to pull punch, +1 to entangle, +1 to disarm, +2 to Automatic Dodge, +6 to roll with fall, +4 roll with punch or impact, and +1 disarm.

The Reinforced Exoskeleton also provides +1D6 M.D. to a head butt, and +2D6 M.D. to punches, elbows and kicks.

Note: Any bonuses from Hand to Hand combat, skill selection or P.P. have not been added, but *Enhancements* have been added.

Instinctive Skills: Land Navigation 70%, Track (people) 65%, Track Animals 80%, and Wilderness Survival 60%.

Due to the *Ambidextrous* Enhancement, the pilot automatically gets W.P. Paired Weapons when in the Host Armor and an additional +5% is added to the following skills: Climbing, Demolitions, Escape Artist, Pick Locks, Concealment and other sleight of hand skills.

Bio-Weapon Systems (Level One):

1. Modified Saber Teeth: The natural bite of the Carnivorous Host Armor combined with Saber Teeth provides a bite damage of 7D8 M.D. (If *Reinforced* at a later date, the damage will become 8D8 M.D.)

2. Two Bio-Energy Expulsion Vents (one for each of the lower pair of arms): Each of these weapons delivers a damage of 2D8 + P.E. M.D.

3. Flame Breath: 3D12 M.D.

4. Casting Thrower: 1D8 M.D. per single shot or a four pellet burst inflicts 3D8 M.D.

Some Recommended/Suggested Enhancements: Stealth Field, max out speed of Winged Arms, Bio-Force Field, Leaping Legs, Additional Pairs of Eyes.

Bio-Enhancements: Starting at level two, the Son of Chaos receives 5D6+10 Bio-E per level of experience (in addition, he will receive many bonuses from those that can provide them) to enhance his already powerful Host Armor.

Weapons and Equipment: The Son of Chaos has full access to the entire arsenal of the House. It is not uncommon for him to wield a variety of weapons in battle. One of his favorite weapons at the moment are a pair of detachable *Bone Blades* that have been customized to attach to the winged arms, adding an extra +6D6 M.D. to strike.

The Daughters of Chaos

Two of the daughters of the Chaos Lord are Gardener Dreadguards with a unique version of Host Armor. Part of their philosophy in selecting the Gardener Host Armor is based on the inconspicuous nature of the many plants that can aid in the defense of their loosely designated territory.

The standard Gardener Host Armor is limited to either a Photosynthetic or Thermosynthetic metabolism. Much like the many plants of this planet, the Daughters' Host Armors have Carnivorous metabolisms. There is also a slight modification to the digestive system of the Host Armor. When it feeds upon any victim with considerable neural (brain) tissue, the Host Armor can process the neurochemicals and store them in a specialized gland. These chemicals can then be secreted onto the palm of the Host Armor for the Furies to feed on (see later description of Furies), with the Armor being able to store 16 doses.

The following are the modifications to the initial construction of the *Gardener Host Armor* from pages 65-66 of **The Rifter®
#50.**

Step 1: Standard and unchanged.

Step 2: These Gardener Host Armors have a *Carnivorous Metabolism* and all the bonuses attributed to that metabolism (pages 72-73 of the **Splicers® RPG**).

Step 3: Available Bio-E points for the Gardener are M.E. attribute number plus the P.E. attribute number, +2D4x10+20 Bio-E. In addition, they also receive +40 for Carnivorous Metabolism, +10 from Librarian Hope, and +40 from the Engineers.

The Gardener also starts with 3D6x10+80 (20 was given by a Geneticist) that are used to purchase Plant Fortifications for the character's personal garden.

Step 4: Unchanged.

Note: The Gardener Host Armor might not be the best option for those who choose the *On Wind and Wave* origin.

Extra Protection: Acting as bodyguards for the daughters are the *Template Biotics* known as **Furies** (see later description). Furies are the epitome of savagery and are loyal (bonded) to the Daughters.

Weapons and Equipment: The two Gardeners of House Pandorum have full access to the entire arsenal of the House.

The Third Daughter

Like her brother, one of the daughters designed a unique Host Armor. She based it on the *Parasitic* metabolism knowing that, like her parents, she too will become a Biotic someday. The House also created a specialized chamber for her to step into prior to entering her Host Armor. The chamber acts like a spray tan booth in which skin cells are "sprayed" onto her body to provide a delayed effect of the Parasitic metabolism eating into her skin. This layer of spray-on skin allows her to stay in her Host Armor for up to 11 days before her Armor begins to feed on her. For long missions, she brings along a small spray bottle that can provide an additional three days of feeding for the Host Armor.

Though not converted like her parents, she has had a slight enhancement to help her to be able to stay in her Host Armor for an extended period of time without ill effect (save for cosmetic damage). A series of small nutrient storage organs have been incorporated into her digestive system and limbs, allowing her to go without food for up to a week (it takes a couple of days of considerable eating to replenish the storage organs).

Her Host Armor also has a small modification to its design; though she cannot enhance her Armor with *Symbiotic Nourish-*

ment, part of the water lost from the pilot is recycled for drinking water (she normally water loads before getting into her armor) and a small amount is also processed from the humidity in the air when the Host Armor Breathes. This enables the Host Armor to provide the necessary water the pilot needs to survive for up to 21 days.

With all these modifications to herself and the base design of the Host Armor, when she selects the *Fasting* skill, she will eventually be able to stay in her Armor for weeks at a time.

Though the Parasitic Metabolism does not have a mouth, the daughter had a detachable demonic faceplate (similar to the samurai of old) designed, with a mouthful of fangs for the *Horror Factor* and to provide an additional 60 M.D.C. towards protecting the head of the Host Armor.

When she is not in her Armor she wears a form-fitting bodysuit with a mask and long, flowing gown, very similar to what Hope's Scarecrows wear when on excursion.

Class: Host Armor.
Crew: One Human Pilot.
Level: One Dreadguard.
Total Bio-E Spent: 300 (Factoring in 40 from metabolism, 10 from Librarian Hope, 40 from the Engineers and 20 from one of the Geneticists.)
Bio-E Remaining: None.
Base M.D.C. by Location*:
Hands – 67 each
Pair of Arms – 117 each
Legs – 207 each
Feet – 87 each
Head – 137 (197 with the detachable faceplate, which must be destroyed before damage is inflicted to the head.)
**Main Body – 380

* The bonus to the M.D.C. of the Host Armor from *Reinforced Exoskeleton* has already been calculated in.

** The bonus +1D6x10 M.D.C. from metabolism has been added.

Speed:
Running: 120 mph (192 km).
Leaping: The Host Armor can leap up to 20 feet (6.1 m) high or 40 feet (12.2 m) across from a standing position.
Digging: 20 mph (32 km) through sand or dirt, but *one quarter* as fast through rock and concrete. Digging tires out its pilot, but at half the usual fatigue rate. To dig down enough to adequately hide from enemies on the surface takes 3D6 melee rounds.
Swimming: 30 mph (48 km/26 knots); swimming tires the pilot but at 10% the usual rate. Alternatively, she can use her *Organic Thrusters* to reach an initial speed of 100 mph (160 km).
Underwater Depth: The Host Armor can withstand pressures up to 700 feet (213 m).
Flying: With the *Organic Thrusters,* her initial speed is 200 mph (320 km) with a maximum altitude of 25,000 feet (7,620 m).

Statistical Data:
Height: 11 feet (3.4 m).
Width: 3 feet (0.9 m).
Length: 3 feet (0.9 m).
Weight: Adds 600 pounds (270 kg) to the weight of the pilot.
Cargo: None.
Physical Strength: Splicer P.S. of 30.

Operational Lifetime: 15 years. This is short because this is a transitional period for the children of Chaos before they become non-mind-wiped Biotics. More time can be added to the lifetime of the Host Armor, usually in five year blocks.
Bio-Regeneration Rate: 1D6 M.D.C. per minute for the main body and 1 M.D.C. per minute for all other locations.
Horror Factor: 9

Senses and Features:
The Host Armor does not receive any natural additions (from metabolism) to the standard *Senses and Features* from page 72 of the **Splicers® RPG**. Organic Thrusters, Bio-Force Field, Elongated Running Legs (+3 feet/0.9 m to height has already been incorporated into the **Statistical Data** above), Enhanced Neurological Connection, Ambidextrous, Regeneration: Enhanced, Chameleon Skin, Resist Kinetic Energy/Attacks, Resist Physical Attack, Armored Eyes, Quick Clotting Blood, Righting Reflex, Circadian Rhythm, and Reinforced Exoskeleton.

Feeding: Parasitic Metabolism.

Sleep Requirements: The Host Armor does *not* require sleep or rest, but the pilot does. With the inclusion of *Circadian Rhythm* into the design of the Host Armor, it can help her stay awake for up to four days straight without any ill effect (recovers from days of sleep deprivation after only ten hours of sleep). **Note:** When a *Stealth Field* is implemented into the design, a system will be incorporated that will engage the Stealth Field automatically when the daughter needs to sleep for when she is on long-term missions.

Level 1 Host Armor Combat Bonuses: +3 attacks per melee round, +5 initiative, +2 to strike, +1 to parry, +1 to dodge, +7 to roll with fall, +3 to roll with punch or impact, with +3 to pull punch, +3 to disarm, +1 to entangle, +2 to Automatic Dodge.

Note: Any bonuses from Hand to Hand combat, skill selection or P.P. have not been added, but *Enhancements* have been added.

Instinctive Skills: Escape Artist 55%, Camouflage 50% and Wilderness Survival (70%).

Due to the *Ambidextrous* Enhancement, the pilot automatically gets W.P. Paired Weapons when in the Host Armor and an additional +5% is added to the following skills: Climbing, Demolitions, Escape Artist, Pick Locks, Concealment and other sleight of hand skills.

Bio-Weapon Systems (Level One):
1. Needle Death Blossom: A single needle does one M.D., a small volley does 1D8 M.D., a medium volley does 2D8 M.D., and a large volley does 4D8 M.D. Releasing most (80-100%) at once inflicts 1D12x10 M.D.
2. Bio-Energy Expulsion Vent: 2D8 + P.E. M.D.
3. Light Bore Cannon (mounted on the forearm): 2D10 for each grub fired. The Bore round does an additional 1D10 M.D. for the next 1D4 melee rounds, after the initial shot.
4. 3 Organic Rockets: Each rocket does 5D6 M.D.

Some Recommended/Suggested Enhancements: Stealth Field, max out Organic Thruster speed, max out Bio-Force Field, Leaping Legs.

Bio-Enhancements: Starting at level two, the Daughter of Chaos receives 5D6+10 Bio-E per level of experience (in addition, she will receive many bonuses from those that can provide them) to enhance her already powerful Host Armor.

Weapons and Equipment: The Daughter of Chaos has full access to the entire arsenal of the House. It is not uncommon for her to wield a variety of weapons in battle.

The Geneticists and the Traveling Party

Whether they are cloned or recruited, Geneticists play a crucial role in the potential fruition of House Pandorum's goal. Regardless of background, Geneticists are all trained doctors and herbal experts who travel the land visiting retro-villages and the like, to aid the sick and injured and provide much needed inoculations. However, all the while they are collecting DNA samples from as many humans as possible, as well as engaging in the occasional kidnaping of people as well. When not on excursions, they are at the sides of the Engineers and Librarian Hope, assisting in the countless experiments being conducted.

The typical Traveling Party is a small band that normally includes one Geneticist, 4-5 Scarecrows, and the occasional Saint and/or Deliveryman who comes along for the ride. Their standard means of transport are enhanced Mega-Horses (page 122 of the **Splicers® RPG**).

While at least one of the Scarecrows is constantly by the Geneticist's side, acting as his assistant, it is not uncommon for the other Scarecrows to hang back and stay hidden with the aid of form-fitting *Stealth Field* Body Suits.

No more than four of these parties travel the land (commonly two) at any one time. These excursions are always planned well in advance, factoring in components such as the path in which they return home, the length of the excursion, and also the pickup point with secondary pick-up points decided as well.

There is always an element of risk during every excursion with regards to encountering the Machine or a malevolent group of Splicers. Most parties are left to fend for themselves but these parties are usually well armed and skilled fighters; they will not go without a fight. **Note**: The daughter with the parasitic metabolism could sometimes join the excursion for additional support.

A Geneticist and his Dog: Much like the famous *Deliveryman* being given a *Black Talon War Hawk*, the Geneticist is given an enhanced dog to act as a personal bodyguard and aid in the collection of DNA samples from the human populace. The best description for this dog is a *hidden* Gorehound, one that has the basic enhancements of a Gorehound but looks completely normal in appearance, for a canine. The breed of dog is always selected from the larger specimens such as Alsatians, Dobermans, Irish Wolf Hounds, etc.

The dog can be bio-engineered any way the character desires (though they never alter the natural appearance of the dog) – they have 5D6+30 Bio-E available plus another 1D6+2 Bio-E points per level of the character's experience on additional enhancements. If the dog is lost another will be provided with all the enhancements given to the initial dog.

To aid in the Geneticist's work, every time the dog licks someone it collects hundreds of skin cells; more than enough to get a viable DNA sample. So, while the dog is being playful, it is also collecting DNA.

Unique Plant Creations of House Pandorum

Though House Pandorum prefers to avoid combat and has implemented many strategies to minimize the risk, combat is inevitable. With that in mind, the *Daughters of Chaos* have access to some unique and powerful plants to help tip the balance in their favor.

Seeds of Doubt

"Putting doubt in your enemy is one of the best weapons you can have." – Chaos Lord

This interesting plant design contributes towards the defense of the pilot, and as the name suggests, it makes attackers think twice before they go toe to toe with one of the Daughters of Chaos. The *Seeds of Doubt* act like a parasitic plant and are imbedded into the skin of the Host Armor like a barnacle; they are not meant to be removed and planted. This is a passive defense plant to defend the Gardener whenever engaged in close-quarters combat.

When someone comes in contact with a *Seed of Doubt*, a strong adhesive produced by the plant enables it to stick to the attacker. Once the seed is *uprooted* from the hide of the Gardener, it "activates." Four barbed tentacle vines latch onto the victim to help keep the plant from being torn off. The seed then proceeds to burrows into the attacker in the same fashion as a *Bore Grub*. These seeds are equally effective against the Machine and Splicers alike.

The Seeds can placed anywhere on the Host Armor besides the hands, feet and face, so not as to interfere with other weapons or sensory systems.

If one of these plants sticks to an attacker, the victim has 2 actions/attacks in which to remove it before it begins to burrow into him/her/it. A combined Splicer P.S. of 34 is required to remove the plant.

Bio-E Cost: 5 per seed.

Growth Time: Any seed that is removed from the Gardener grows back in one hour.

M.D.C.: The Seeds of Doubt have a strong fibrous casing that provides them with 10 M.D.C.

Damage: 1D10+3 M.D. for 1D6+1 melee rounds. **Note:** The first action/attack is when the seed latches on. Damage begins on the second action/attack. If the victim is strong and quick enough to remove the seed in one action then they receive no damage from that seed. (Any removed seeds remain active for 7 melee rounds before they die.) If the victim is successful in removing the seed by the second action, the minimum damage they will receive is 1D10+3 M.D. If by the second action the seed is not removed, it must be destroyed by other means, as the seed would have burrowed in too deep for mere fingers to remove it.

The seed will continue to burrow deeper until either destroyed or it runs its life cycle. Any M.D. directed at the seed that exceeds its M.D.C. is carried over to the region of the body in which the seed is attached.

For every melee round that an enemy is engaged in physical combat, 1D4 of these seeds will latch onto them.

Explosive End: For an extra cost of 5 Bio-E points per seed, the *Seeds of Doubt* can be upgraded to explode when they have finished their life cycle, causing an additional 2D4+4 M.D.

Range: The Seed is only activated with direct physical contact.

Payload: There are two factors that limit the number of these barnacle style plants a Host Armor can have. First is the available surface area of the Armor, whilst not interfering with weapons and sensory systems. The second is the increased demand on the Host Armor's feeding requirements. For each Seed imbedded in the Armor, the feeding requirements increase by seven ounces (198 grams) per day. So, five Seeds would increase the daily feeding requirement by 2.2 lbs (1 kg).

Number of Seeds per Region: Head: 5, Arms: 5 each, Torso: 11, Legs and ankles: 7 each – for a total of 40.

Cape Fear

Based off the plant **Drosera capensis**, Cape Fear is a carnivorous plant housed in a bone shell, with four vine tentacles that protrude from the casing. Each tentacle sprouts hundreds of small, flexible stalks resembling the eye stalks of a snail. With the shell casing buried deep beneath the surface, the only visible part of the plant is the vine tentacles that emerge from the ground.

The plant has a pleasant aroma that attracts many forms of insects, and the flexible stalks secrete an extremely viscous and sticky fluid, which is one of the elements the plant uses to catch prey.

This fluid alone is enough to trap smaller prey such as rodents and insects for the plant to feed on. However, *Cape Fear* is capable of capturing and restraining larger prey (even up to Host Armor and small War Mounts). The vine tentacles act like those of an octopus and can entangle/constrict prey.

Cape Fear appears on the Gardener as a baseball-sized coconut, with four holes on its crown like those on a bowling ball.

Bio-E Cost: 30

Growth Time: 2D4+12 days from sapling to immature, 2D4+2 weeks from immature to mature.

The bulb is placed just below the surface and by the time it reaches its immature stage it has reached a depth of 6.5 feet (2 m). When it reaches its mature stage it has reached a depth of 13 feet (4 m). Until it reaches its immature stage, the plant's main form of nutrients is provided by insects that get stuck to the stalks, and the occasional rodent that comes to feed on the insects.

M.D.C.: If the bulb, the heart of the plant, isn't destroyed, the plant can grow back.

Immature Plant: The bulb itself has 30 M.D.C. while the shell has 150 M.D.C. with each of the four vine tentacles having 30 M.D.C. per meter of their length.

Mature Plant: The bulb has 60 M.D.C. while the shell has 300 M.D.C. with each of the four vine tentacles having 60 M.D.C. per meter of their length.

Natural Abilities: The plant is designed to be *impervious to acid*.

Damage: Anything that comes in contact with the plant will first notice that something is sticking to them. The thick, viscous fluid is extremely sticky; as the victim wriggles and thrashes its body or limbs to remove the plant, it actually causes more

sticky stalks to attach (this is due. in part. to the actions of the victim and subtle undulations of the vine tentacle). A combined Splicer P.S. of 23 is required to pull a victim out of the fluid. This does not change as the plant matures.

To deliver the appropriate level of attack response to a victim, the plant has a remarkable sensory system to monitor the activities around it. Mechano-receptors are situated in every stalk that emerges from the vine tentacles, subtly measuring every movement that occurs from contact with the plant. There is also an internal pressure sensing system in the form of Baro-receptors located along the length of the vine tentacles that help the plant determine the weight of its prey (if it is ever stepped on). Thermal receptors act like *Heat-Pits*, enabling it to sense heat in a 30 foot (9.2 m) radius around each vine tentacle. This means if something as large as a Host Armor steps on the tip of one of the vine tentacles, the plant won't attempt to entangle the victim. But, if the same Host Armor stepped closer to where the tentacle emerges, it would automatically coil up and attempt to entangle the victim. If something like a rabbit comes in contact with the fluid, when it begins to struggle, the only response by the plant would be a slight undulation of the vine tentacle in order to increase the number of stalks involved.

When the plant entangles a victim, the sticky fluid now becomes a nuisance as it significantly reduces the ability to escape the grasp of the vine tentacles. Anything caught in the vine tentacles will incur a penalty of -40% to *Escape Artist*. If the victim has *Slime Coating* they still receive a penalty of -25% to *Escape Artist*.

Once entangled, the plant begins its feeding process. The victim suffers damage both from the crushing attack of the plant, as well as secreted acids used to digest the victim. Each vine tentacle is filled with muscle, providing a Splicer P.S. of 30 that attempts to crush the victim quickly so as to minimize damage to the plant from a struggling victim.

Crush Attack: 4D6 M.D. per attack.

Digestion: 6D8 M.D. per melee round.

Duration: This process continues until the victim is fully digested.

Range: The vine tentacles for immature plants have a total length of 15 feet (4.6 m), with a reach of 10 feet (3 m) as the rest is below the surface. Mature plants have vine tentacles that have a total length of 33 feet (10.1 m); with a reach of 20 feet (6.1 m) as the rest is below the surface.

Autonomous Combat Capabilities: Immature: Each vine tentacle has 3 attacks per melee round, +5 to entangle. Mature: Each vine tentacle has 5 attacks per melee round, +6 to entangle. The bonus to entangle/strike is so high due to the sticky, viscous fluid.

Though there are a number of attacks per melee round for each primary vine, the attacks are reactive, not active, as there is no sentience. The plant does not simply spring to life and attack anything in its area. Instead, like a mousetrap, it will only attack when triggered. However, when controlled by a Gardener, the plant can be used to attack at any time (See Control Bonus below).

The plant also has a few ingenious abilities to protect itself from excessive levels of damage. If the plant is suffering too much damage it can do one of two things (or both at the same time):

'Tis the Season for ZOMBIES

Dead Reign™ RPG

It is the aftermath of the *zombie apocalypse*. Civilization is gone, the dead reign, and the living fight to survive against impossible odds. Tales of zombies, human survival and horror as a fast-paced, easy to learn game and sourcebooks.

- **Zombie combat rules, vehicles and equipment.**
- **Six iconic Apocalyptic Character Classes and Ordinary People with 40+ occupations to choose from.**
- **Seven types of zombies plus the Half-Living.**
- **Secrets of the Dead and tips on fighting zombies.**
- **Death Cults, their Priests, power over zombies and goals.**
- **101 Random Scenarios, Encounters and Settings.**
- **100 Random Corpse Searches and other tables.**
- **Quick Roll Character Creation tables (10 minutes).**
- **A complete role-playing game by Siembieda and others.**
- **$22.95 retail – 224 pages – Cat. No. 230. Available now.**

Civilization Gone™

Dead Reign™ Sourcebook One

It has been months since the dead rose to attack the living. Civilization has crumbled. There is no army, no government, no help coming. You are on your own and things are only getting worse.

- **Madmen and Psychopaths including the *Zombie Master, Ghost Walker, Backstabber, Messianic Leader, Zombie Lover, Deathbringer* and others.**
- ***Bandits* and *Raiders* who prey upon other survivors.**
- ***Street Gang Protectors* and their mission to save lives.**
- **Phobia and Obsession tables. Many adventure ideas.**
- **House and home resource and encounter tables.**
- **Random encounter and survivor camp creation tables.**
- **Additional world information and survival advice.**
- **$12.92 retail – 64 pages – Cat. No. 231. Available now.**

Dark Places™

Dead Reign™ Sourcebook Two

Secrets of survival, including using railroad tracks and the urban underground to travel unseen and undetected by zombies.

- **Worm Meat, Bug Boy, Sewer Crawler and Impersonator Zombies.**
- **"Live Bait" zombie lures with human beings as bait.**
- **Traveling the rails and boxcar encounter tables.**
- **Traveling sewer tunnels, steam tunnels & other dark places.**
- **The pitfalls and dangers of the urban underground.**
- **Diseases, infection and additional world information.**
- **Random encounter tables, boxcar content tables, and more.**
- **$12.92 retail – 64 pages – Cat. No. 232. Available now.**

Endless Dead™

Dead Reign™ Sourcebook Three

The zombie hordes grow in number and strangeness. Can humankind survive? Where is the military?

- **New types of zombies like Fused Zombies and Walking Mass Grave.**
- **New O.C.C.s including Wheelman and Zombie Hunter.**
- **Info & tables for weaponizing vehicles and vehicle combat rules.**
- **Random encounter tables for military bases, police stations, gun stores, buildings, suburbs, industrial parks, small towns, farmland and wilderness.**
- **Tables to make Survivor caravans, hideouts, Safe Havens & more.**
- **Timetable for setting zombie campaigns & many adventure ideas.**
- **$16.95 retail – 96 pages – Cat. No. 233. Available now.**

New & Coming Soon from Palladium Books®

Rifts® Vampires Sourcebook   Robotech® Genesis Pits™   Rifts® Northern Gun™ 1   Rifts® Northern Gun™ 2   Megaverse in Flames™

If one of the vine tentacles is struggling with a victim too much, it can simply "detach" from the main bulb, similar to a gecko dropping its tail. Amazingly, like an octopus tentacle, it is autonomous and will continue to crush and digest the victim until he is freed. This autonomous ability will last for two minutes (eight melee rounds).

Any other vine tentacles not involved in the attack will expel their viscous fluid onto the ground and retract below the surface, protected by the bone shell below the ground. The expelling of the sticky fluid was suggested by one of the daughters as she saw the tactical advantage of attacking the victim while it attempted to get out of the sticky situation.

Sticky Ground: The viscous, sticky fluid can be expelled from the stalks to coat the surrounding soil. Covering a circular area around the heart of the plant (radius of the vine tentacle), this now tainted soil can impair anything that comes in contact with it. Depending on how much of the victim is in contact with the tainted soil, he will incur a penalty (G.M. discretion) to his combat bonuses and the victim will not be able to run while stuck in the fluid.

Solid Ground: Though the bulb/heart of the plant is safely buried 6.5-13 feet (2-4 m) underground and protected by a tough, bony shell, it wouldn't take long for someone to dig it up and destroy it for good. Librarian Hope thought of a few countermeasures for that exact tactic. The fibrous outer layer of the bone shell grows rapidly and creates a vast, dense M.D.C. root system. This root system is not for nourishment, but to provide a buffer zone in which the area around the plant would take a considerable amount of time to dig through. The layering and density of the M.D.C. fibrous root system reduces the digging speed of any creature to a grinding halt. Penalty: Reduce digging speed to *one thousandth* the normal speed the design has when digging through *rock or concrete*. So a normal Host Armor could only dig 26 feet (eight meters) per hour through the root system.

The root system of the immature plant has a radius of 13 feet (4 m), while the mature plant has a radius of 26 feet (8 m).

Fountain of Acid: If the attacker is hell-bent on digging up the plant, going straight down is the quickest option, but is not the wisest. On the crown of the bone shell are a number of photo-receptors and thermo-receptors that when triggered, activate this defense. When the plant is exposed to enough light or body heat, it spits out a considerable amount of acid. Damage: 4D8 M.D. per melee round for 2D4 melee rounds. Payload: Immature: Enough for four attacks. Mature: Enough for eight attacks. Range: 6.5 foot (2 m) radius for Immature. 13 foot (4 m) radius for Mature.

Control Bonus (in addition to the bonuses above): A Gardener taking control of a *Cape Fear* is something truly terrifying. The vine tentacles become an extension of the Gardener and act like prehensile tentacles and with all four tentacles being controlled simultaneously. A common tactic the daughters employ is to retract the vine tentacles underground and wait for an unsuspecting victim to wander into range. It is not uncommon for them to expel all the sticky fluid onto the ground before they retract the vine tentacles underground.

Immature: +1 attack per melee round for each vine tentacle, +1 to entangle/strike, +5 to parry and dodge. Mature: +1 attack per melee round for each vine tentacle, +2 to entangle/strike, +6 to parry and dodge.

When the vine tentacles are used to strike, the P.S. of the vine tentacle determines the damage.

Note: The Gardener can have up to two of the vine tentacles attacking the same target, or attack 4 targets simultaneously.

Elder Plant Bonus:

Each year:

● The vine tentacles gain another 3 feet (0.9 m) in length until they reach 45 feet (13.7 m), for a total reach of 30 feet (9.2 m) as the rest is under the surface.

● Another 5 M.D.C. is added to each meter of the vine tentacle until it reaches 85 M.D.C. per meter. (Note: This is how much M.D.C. is required to sever the tentacle.)

● Another 10 M.D.C. is added to the bulb until it reaches 120 M.D.C.

● Another 50 M.D.C. is added to the bone shell until it reaches 600 M.D.C.

● The radius of the root system grows 3 feet (0.9 m) until it reaches a radius of 51 feet (15.5 m).

Pilobolus Cannon

"For inspiration; all you have to do is look at nature." – Librarian Hope

By itself, the **Pilobolus Fungus** is an amazing organism; it is recognized as the fastest thing in nature. In the hands of Splicers, this fungus has been used to produce one of the most powerful organic weapons to enter the battlefield. The Pilobolus Cannon is a biological rail gun that delivers pure devastation at long range. Instead of electromagnetic coils, the Pilobolus Cannon uses extremely high water pressure to accelerate dense bone projectiles to immense speed.

Grown with multilayered, reinforced plant fibers along with dense bone and cartilage, the Pilobolus Cannon is mounted over one of the shoulders of the Host Armor, sporting an appearance very similar to the *Casting Weapons* used by many Splicers. When not in use and to not hamper maneuverability, the Cannon has a collapsible barrel and can retract behind the shoulder. When retracted, it sits snugly in a vertical position behind the shoulder; when activated, it reaches over the shoulder and extends the barrel.

To avoid requiring the Host Armor to anchor itself in some fashion in order to use the Cannon, it uses a clever system of recoil barrels and a series of automatic pressure release valves. Though this enables the Host armor to not require anchoring, it still needs a Splicer P.S. of 30 to maintain balance.

Bio-E Cost: 60

Growth Time: Though this is a weapon that is permanently bonded to the Host Armor, it takes 1D4+2 days for the plant to fully mature and be operational. This growth time is important for when the weapon is destroyed and another one has to grow.

M.D.C. of the Cannon: 2D4x10 +100. Any damage inflicted to the cannon will regenerate at a rate of 2D4 M.D.C. per hour.

Range: 11,000 feet (2.1 miles, 3.4 km), with a directional range of 45° above and below the horizontal and 45° to the right and left of the vertical.

Payload: 36 shots per 24 hours. Spent rounds are replaced at a rate of one every 40 minutes.

Rate of Fire: Once every two melee rounds (2 times a minute).

Note: When concerned with *Ranged Weapon Upgrades*, the Pilobolus Cannon can only receive the *Super-Upgrade* and *Ultra-Upgrade* as described on page 107 of the **Splicers® RPG**. Though a Pilobolus Cannon cannot receive the *Mega-Upgrade*, the character can purchase 2 of them, one for each shoulder.

Damage: 2D10x10 M.D.

Additional Combat Bonus: The Gardener receives a +3 to strike when using this weapon.

Control Bonus, Elder Plant Bonus: None.

Grapes of Wrath (and Stone Fruit)

Take heed in the old saying that, "An army marches on its stomach," because this plant exploits that vulnerability.

The *Grapes of Wrath* were designed not to kill the enemy directly but to slow them down and cause mayhem in their numbers. This simple, inconspicuous S.D.C. plant has an insidious purpose that is only revealed a couple of hours after it has been consumed.

Targeted towards any Splicer creation (and any unfortunate human) with *Herbivorous*, *Omnivorous* and even *Vampiric* Metabolism, the plant can be modified to grow a variety of fruits ranging from red and white grapes, plums, some types of berries, even apricots, peaches and nectarines. As little as 3.5 ounces (100 grams) of these fruits will cause the desired effect.

Once inside the belly, they absorb water and swell to several times their original volume and begin to harden, becoming something akin to gall stones. These stones continue to collect in the victim's stomach, effectively blocking the digestive system and inhibiting the ability to eat.

Bio-E Cost: 10, +5 for every variation of the fruit that the plant can grow. When the plant is first purchased, the player must choose what fruit it will have. Each plant can grow up to five different types of fruit. The more plants you purchase, the more types you can grow. So, three plants will allow you to grow 15 different types of fruit.

    Note: If you purchase *Blood Plums* (see later description) you cannot add additional fruit to this version of the plant as it is permanently attached to the Host Armor.

Growth Time: It takes three days for the plant to grow from seedling to a mature, fruit-bearing plant.

M.D.C.: The plant ranges from a vine to a small shrub and has an S.D.C. of 10-30.

Damage: The plant doesn't cause any actual damage per se. Instead, within 10-15 minutes of eating, the victim has the sensation of feeling 'full' and will suffer penalties equating to if they have gorged on a big meal. Two hours after consumption, the fruits will have fully expanded and solidified, completely occluding the digestive system.

    The victim will constantly feel full and suffer the effects of gorging. Even worse, they will not be able to eat again until the blockage is removed. This requires the services of an Engineer or a Saint, which removes them from the equation for an extended period of time while the stone is being removed and the necessary healing period.

If not dealt with in the necessary time frame, the victim will suffer the effects of starvation and eventually die.

Blood Plums: These are a unique version of the *Grapes of Wrath* that specifically targets the *Vampiric* metabolism. This version is permanently attached to the Gardener and exploits the weakness of *Vampiric* metabolism with regards to the *Smell of Blood* (page 76 of the **Splicers® RPG**). *Blood Plums* are commonly placed around the neck or on the forearms of the Host Armor; upon command, the Blood Plums release the scent of blood while also weeping a blood substance. The victim is encouraged to feed on the Gardener. The plums break easily, pouring the imitation blood into the awaiting mouth of the attacker, providing 4 pints (1.9 liters) of blood in one melee round. (The way this fruit is used to goad a victim into attacking is a risky tactic, but it would not work if left growing on a vine.) Whilst it is feeding on the plums, the Gardener can attack the distracted victim.

Upon feeding on the *Blood Plums*, the attacker must follow the *Sleep Requirements* as stipulated on page 75 of the **Splicers® RPG**. This is inclusive to the standard effects that the plant causes as described above.

Payload: Each version of the plant can grow 2D6x100 +600 grams (7-42 +21 ounces) of the chosen fruit. Any fruit eaten will grow back in two days.

Additional Combat Capabilities, Control Bonus, Elder Plant Bonus: None.

Pearls of Wisdom

In many of the manifestations of House Pandorum, the ability to provide the Furies with their necessary neurochemistry will be of little concern. However, considering how quickly the Furies turn when the hunger kicks in, it is always handy to have some in stock. Yet, when out in the field for extended periods of time that might be difficult, so House Pandorum developed a way to aid in the Daughters being able to maintain control of the Furies. To complement the enhancement to their Host Armor that enables them to extract and store the neurochemistry from their victims, this plant was designed to not waste a single source of the neurochemicals.

Much like the butterfly, this plant has two life cycles. This foul creation appears on the Host Armor as a ball the size of a baseball partially imbedded in the skin of the Host Armor. When removed from the Armor it unfurls, appearing to look like a large starfish the size of a dinner plate. The starfish is then placed on the head or neck of the dead victim where it proceeds to envelop the entire head, neck, and spine.

Combining powerful digestive juices in the form of acids and enzymes, this starfish digests the tissue of the corpse and collects the neurochemicals. When finished, the plant breaks down into sludge and leaves a clear, gel-like stone of the processed chemicals. Once it has completed its task, the plant begins the second stage of its life and it grows into a (S.D.C.) shrub or small bush with little white flowers.

Bio-E Cost: 5

Growth Time: the Plant doesn't really have a growth time in the standard sense; instead it takes 1D4x10+20 minutes to digest the corpse. Any *Pearl of Wisdom* removed from the Gardener grows back in one hour.

M.D.C.: The starfish plant has 5 M.D.C.

Natural Abilities: The plant is also impervious to acids.

Damage: As a safeguard, the plant only activates when placed on dead flesh. Once placed, the plant's life cycle will run its course.

Range: Direct contact only. It has to be placed on a corpse.

Additional Combat Capabilities, Control Bonus, Elder Plant Bonus: None.

Template Biotics of House Pandorum

Biotics are used extensively by House Pandorum, with roles ranging from worker drones and domestic duties to bodyguards and soldiers. The range of their use depends on the *origin* of the House. Though their worker drones follow the conversion path set out on pages 146-149 of the **Splicer® RPG**, *Template Biotics* refer to a standardized way in which the Biotic is converted and enhanced. Their *Initial Cost* varies for each, with some costing as much as a Template Host Armor (200-230 Bio-E points). Modifications from the standard construction are provided below for each Template Biotic.

Each Template Biotic has a *Common Enhancement* list. These enhancements can only occur if the House has a front that can provide these upgrades. *Origins* like **On Wind and Wave** might make it highly unlikely to upgrade the Biotics they release upon the land, so instead they would commonly create more Biotics whose *Initial Cost* is equal to a Template Host Armor (adjust accordingly).

Template Biotic: Dryad

These poor souls have their genes altered with a modified form of **Epidermodysplasia verruciformis** (tree man) that makes them susceptible to the human papillomavirus (HPV) of the skin, resulting in an uncontrolled infection and subsequent changes to the skin as a result. The process turns them into something resembling the dryad nymphs of Greek Mythology, with bark-like skin and naturally sharp fingers, elbows, knees, toes and heels.

Class: Template Biotic.

Level: One.

Alignment: Those released to fend for themselves are Diabolical, while those that are a part of a Tribe or House range from Scrupulous (10%), Unprincipled (30%), Anarchist (30%), and Aberrant (30%).

Attribute Requirement: None.

Attribute (conversion) Bonuses: +2D4 P.S. and Spd, and +1D6+1 P.E. All are in addition to any genetic enhancements purchased via Bio-E points and skills selected.

Biotic O.C.C. Bonuses: Splicer P.S., +1 attack per melee round, +1 to initiative, +2 to strike and dodge, +2 to pull punch, +4 to save vs toxins/poison and drugs, +15% to save vs coma and death, and +4 to save vs Horror Factor.

Penalty: Dryads receive a -10% to all skills that involve their hands due to the nature of the mutation and the blade fingers.

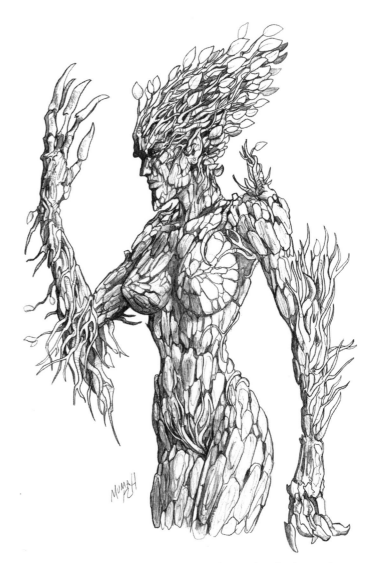

Base M.D.C.: P.E.x15, +3D4 M.D.C. per level of experience starting at level 2. The Dryad regenerates at 1D6+1 per melee round and can last ten times longer than normal during strenuous exercise/activity before feeling the effects of exhaustion. This means most can remain alert and operate at full efficiency for three entire days (72 hours) without sleep.

Biotic Biological Enhancement: The Initial Cost of the Dryad is 130 Bio-E points. Enhancements are: Casting Thrower, Reinforced Exoskeleton, Bone Blades for each hand, Resistance to Kinetic Energy/Attacks, Resistance to Lasers, Resistance to Physical Attack, Reinforced Knuckles, One Bio-Energy Expulsion Vent, Short-Range Spore Discharger, and Elongated Running Legs.

Natural Abilities Due to Transformation: The bark-like skin of the Dryad aids in shielding their thermal and electrical signature (-40% to detect with any Heat-sensing systems and -25% to detect with any Electromagnetic-sensing systems). The bark skin also provides sharp protrusions to the knees, elbows, heels, toes and fingers, adding a natural +2D6 damage to strikes with those appendages.

Common (Additional) Enhancements:

Level 3 – Casting Launcher, Increased M.D.C. (x2), Leaping Legs.

Level 6 – Casting Rifle, Medium-Range Spore Discharger, Increased M.D.C. (x1).

Level 9 – +2D6 M.D. to both Bone Claw Hands, Bio-Force Field.

Level 12 – Long-Range Spore Discharger, +80 M.D.C. towards the Bio-Force Field.

Common Skills: Standard, but with a -10% penalty to each.

O.C.C. Skill Program: Domestic (+10% but Wardrobe & Grooming is replaced with Bio-Comms), Infantryman (+15%), Athletics and Outdoorsman (selecting Land Navigation).

Elective Skills: At Level 1, the Dryad receives Tracking, Camouflage (of self) with a bonus of +30% due to the natural bark-like skin, and Prowl. At Level 3: Detect Ambush. At Level 6: Detect Concealment. At Level 9: Trap and Mine Detection. At Level 12, no skill is selected.

Secondary Skills: The Dryad does not receive any Secondary Skills.

Note: If a Dryad is simply released upon the world (abandoned and left to fend for itself) to cause chaos, it will only have the *Common Skills*, *Skill Programs* and level one *Elective Skills* as stated above. It will not receive any more skills.

M.D.C. Living Body Armor: Generally, the Dryad does not receive any Living Body Armor, but sometimes a Tribe or House may provide the Dryad with one, which would be a standard set with no enhancements.

Standard Equipment: The Dryad is not given any equipment. They need no clothes and armor is rarely given. The exception may be basic toiletries.

Money: No money is ever given to the Dryad, though they may scavenge something off the fallen.

The Upside: Dryads are built tough and resistant, designed to be released into the wild and fend for themselves.

The Downside: Follow the Biotic Insanity list on pages 148 and 149 of the **Splicers® RPG**. Option: Dryads could be cloned and not converted humans, and therefore not susceptible to the standard *Biotic Insanities*.

Template Biotic: Zapper

Hope discovered the debilitating medical condition known as **Neurofibromatosis** (*Reckling-Hansen's disease*); a condition in which tumors made of neural tissue form over the body. Using these tissues as a base, Hope created the Biotics known as "Zappers."

Zappers are extremely powerful electrical generators; quick and agile, but physically frail. Due to the nature of the medical condition (with a little Splicers modification), the Biotic is able to generate a considerable electric field which doubles the power of their *Bio-Force Field* and *Lightning* strikes.

Class: Template Biotic.

Level: One/Two (those released to fend for themselves are held back till level two so *Lightning Discharge* can be implemented into the design).

Alignment: Those released to fend for themselves are Diabolical, while those that are a part of a Tribe or House range from Scrupulous (10%), Unprincipled (30%), Anarchist (30%), and Aberrant (30%).

Attribute Requirement: None.

Attribute (conversion) Bonuses: +1D6 P.S., +5D8+5 to Spd, in addition to any genetic enhancements purchased via Bio-E points or skills selected.

Biotic O.C.C. Bonuses: Splicer P.S., +2 attacks per melee round, +3 to initiative, +3 to strike and dodge, +2 to pull punch, +2

to save vs toxins/poison and drugs, +10% to save vs coma and death, and +4 to save vs Horror Factor. Note: The *Increased Metabolism* bonuses are not added here.

Penalty: Due to the immense electrical charge they generate, any electromagnetic-sensing equipment will be able to detect them at twice the standard distance.

Base M.D.C.: P.E. x5, +1D4 per level of experience starting at level two. The Zapper regenerates at 1D4 per melee round and can last six times longer than normal during strenuous exercise/activity before feeling the effects of exhaustion. This means most can remain alert and operate at full efficiency for two entire days (48 hours) without sleep.

Biotic Biological Enhancement: The Initial Cost of the Zapper is 130 Bio-E points. Enhancements are: *Bio-Force Field, Increased Metabolism, Resistance to Electricity, Electrical Discharge (in initial conversion), **Lightning Discharge (at level two), Short-Range Spore Discharger, and +80 M.D.C. to the Bio-Force Field (for 10 Bio-E points).

* M.D.C. of the Bio-Force Field: Due to their unique conversion, the Bio-Force Field has an initial M.D.C. of 2x(3D6x10) to a maximum of 600 M.D.C. instead of the standard 300 M.D.C. Also, the field is upgraded with 40 M.D.C. per 5 Bio-E points spent instead of the standard 20 M.D.C.

Penalty: If the M.D.C. of the Bio-Force Field is depleted it cannot be reactivated again for 6 hours! As long as the Bio-Force Field's M.D.C. has not been depleted, it regenerates lost M.D.C. at a rate of two points per minute (120 M.D.C. per hour).

** Lightning Discharger: For the Zapper, the initial damage is 8D12 M.D. with a range of 200 feet (61 m).

Common (Additional) Enhancements:

Level 2 – Lightning Discharger.

Level 3 – +240 M.D.C. (30 Bio-E points) is added to the Bio-Force Field, One Bio-Energy Expulsion Vent.

Level 6 – Mega-Upgrade Lightning Discharge, making damage a staggering 1D8x10 +1D10x10 +2D6 M.D., for a grand total of 22–192 M.D. per blast.

Level 9 – Omni-Upgrade to Lightning Discharge, making the range 400 feet (122 m); +40 M.D.C. to Bio-Force Field.

Level 12 – Medium-Range Spore Discharger, Fire Breath, +80 M.D.C. to Bio-Force Field.

<u>Level 13</u> (extra bonus) – If the Zapper ever reaches this level, simply give him the enhancements of *Plasma Breath* and max out the *Bio-Force Field* if it hasn't been done already.

Common Skills: Standard, but with a -10% penalty to each.

O.C.C. Skill Program: Domestic (+10% but Wardrobe and Grooming is replaced with Bio-Comms), Infantryman (+15%), Athletics and Outdoorsman (selecting Land Navigation).

Elective Skills: At Level 1, the Zapper receives Tracking, Blind Fighting, and Trap and Mine Detection. At Level 3: *Detect Concealment*. At Level 6: *Detect Ambush*. At Level 9 and at Level 12, no skill is selected.

Secondary Skills: The Zapper does not receive any Secondary Skills. <u>Note</u>: If a Zapper is simply released upon the world (abandoned and left to fend for itself) to cause chaos, it will only have the *Common Skills*, *Skill Programs* and Level One *Elective Skills* as stated above. It will not receive any more skills.

M.D.C. Living Body Armor: If with a Tribe or House, the Zapper can be given a suit of personalized "living body armor" that is enhanced how the House sees fit, which is usually by increasing the M.D.C. of the armor. **Note:** To not impede the mobility of the Zapper too much, the *Heavy Hide Armor* (Medium) is the preferred choice.

Standard Equipment: The clothes on their back, an extra pair of clothes, and basic toiletries.

Money: No money is ever given to the Zapper, though they may scavenge something off the fallen.

The Upside: Zappers are a force of nature; none can match their raw electrical power and many an enemy will fall.

The Downside: Zappers look hideous with the bulbous neural growths covering their body. Follow the Biotic Insanity list on pages 148-149 of the **Splicers® RPG**. <u>Option</u>: Zappers could be cloned and not converted humans, and therefore not susceptible to the standard *Biotic Insanities*.

Note: The Rare Zapper is sometimes enhanced even further. This is achieved by internalizing the neural lobes to provide the Zapper with a normal outward appearance while their *Lightning Discharge* is enhanced with *Electrical Stunner* as outlined on page 85 of **The Rifter® #50**. This is rarely done as the two enhancements cost a total of 120 Bio-E points, while the Internalizing of the neural lobes has to be done during initial remaking/growing.

Template Biotic: Furies

Due to their meddling with the human brain in an attempt to create psychic abilities, most of House Pandorum's experiments simply generate catatonic, mindless husks, which act like they have been lobotomized.

However, these experiments have also generated the occasional savage; a feral brain-eater. For reasons unknown, their brains lack the ability to produce specific neurochemistry to function properly. Consequently, the Furies are driven by an uncontrollable desire to eat the neural tissue (brain matter) of any living creature (natural or Splicer creation), ranging from humans and fauna, to War Mounts (Host Armor are not a viable option as they do not possess a brain). Without a doubt, these are the most terrifying and horrific Biotics House Pandorum creates.

These Biotics are exclusive to House Pandorum or their *front* House. They are too unstable to be controlled by Waste Crawlers, and their numbers are kept under strict control due to the destruction they can unleash. The two Daughters normally have no more than four active at one time, while the House has another 12 in stasis for each of them (24 in total).

As the Furies are more animal than man, they recognize power and strength, which the Daughters are not lacking in. Combined with the Gardener's ability to administer the necessary neurochemicals, the Furies are kept in check by a hair-thin thread.

When they return to the House, each Fury enters its own stasis pod, where it remains until it is called upon.

Class: Template Biotic.

Level: One.

Alignment: All released to fend for themselves are Diabolical. Those that the Daughters command are Diabolical (20%), Miscreant (40%) or Aberrant (40%), but all are loyal to their master until the *Hunger* overcomes them.

Attribute Requirement: None.

Attribute (conversion) Bonuses: +2D6 P.S. and Spd, +2D4 P.E. All are in addition to any genetic enhancements purchased via Bio-E points and skills selected.

Biotic O.C.C. Bonuses: Splicer P.S., +1 attack per melee round, +2 to initiative, +2 to strike and dodge, +2 to pull punch, +4 to save vs toxins/poison and drugs, +10% to save vs coma and death, and immune to Horror Factor.

Base M.D.C.: P.E.x10 +2D6 M.D.C. per level of experience starting at level two. The Furies regenerate at a rate of 1D6 per melee round and can last ten times longer than normal during strenuous exercise/activity before feeling the effects of exhaustion. This means most can remain alert and operate at full efficiency for three entire days (72 hours) without sleep.

Biotic Biological Enhancement: The initial cost of the Furies is 220 Bio-E Points. Enhancements are: Resin Duct, Chameleon Skin (initial conversion), Stealth Field (at level two), one *Bone Claw* hand at +4D6 M.D., one Bio-Energy Expulsion Vent on the opposite forearm to the bone claw hand, Reinforced Exoskeleton, Reinforced Jaw, Reinforced Knuckles, Bio-Force

Field, Elongated Running Legs, Combat Spurs, Flame Breath, and Quick Clotting Blood.

Note: Furies released onto the land to fend for themselves do not receive the enhancement of *Stealth Field*; that is only for those that are kept by the House.

Natural Abilities Due to Transformation: The Furies are instinctive hunters that need to feed on the neural tissue of others to obtain the required neurochemistry that they cannot produce. Their metabolism has been converted to Carnivorous (all the bonuses have not been added) and the mouth is full of razor sharp teeth to match with a bite equal to that of a carnivorous Host Armor. They can control their temperature (metabolism), making it harder for them to be detected with any Heat-sensing equipment (-25%), and they also have the ability of *Pheromone Masking* equal to the *Nihilist Suicide Beast* as described on pages 24-25 of **The Rifter® #38**.

Common (Additional) Enhancements:

Level 2 – Stealth Field.

Level 3 – Leaping Legs, +2D6 M.D. to Bone Claw hand, Ultra-Upgrade to Flame Breath, +2 Resin Duct Shots.

Level 6 – +2D6 M.D. to Bone Claw hand, +40 M.D.C. to Bio-Force Field, Plasma Breath.

Level 9 – +2D6 M.D. to Bone Claw hand (now at +1D6x10 M.D.), Elongated Arms, Short-Range Spore Discharger, Spines & Blades.

Level 12 – Needle Death Blossom, +40 M.D.C. to Bio-Force Field.

The Hunger and its Penalties: Because the brain of the Furies cannot produce the necessary neurochemistry, they must constantly prey on anything with enough neural tissue (brain matter) to satisfy their requirements.

Following a feeding, the Furies can function normally for a full two days (48 hours), but during the third day they begin to get 'twitchy.' This is the sign that they will need to feed soon. If they are not taken care of within 72 hours of their last feeding, the Furies become crazed, going on the hunt and fearlessly attacking anything in their path.

For an *entire* 24 hour period, the Furies go into survival mode and receive bonuses equal to *Adrenaline Surge* as described on pages 85-86 of the **Splicers® RPG**. If they don't feed by the end of the fourth day, they collapse where they stand and go into something akin to a coma. Unless one of the Daughters or someone else who is part of the House finds them and administers a dose, the Fury will die at the end of the fifth day.

Common Skills: None.

O.C.C. Skill Program: Domestic (+10% but Wardrobe & Grooming is replaced with Bio-Comms), Infantryman (+15%), Athletics and Outdoorsman (these skills are more instinctive than learned).

Elective Skills: At Level 1, the Fury receives Tracking, Prowl, and Blind Fighting or Track & Trap Animals. At Level 3: *Detect Concealment*. At Level 6: *Detect Ambush*. At Level 9 and at Level 12, no skill is selected.

Secondary Skills: Furies do not receive any Secondary Skills. Note: If the Fury is simply released upon the world (abandoned and left to fend for itself) to cause chaos, it will only have the *Common Skills*, *Skill Programs* and level one *Elective Skills* as stated above. It will not receive any more skills.

M.D.C. Living Body Armor: If with a Tribe or House, the Furies can be given a suit of personalized "living body armor" that is enhanced how the House sees fit, which is usually an increase to the M.D.C. of the armor. **Note:** To not impede the mobility of the Furies too much, the Heavy Hide Armor (Medium) is the preferred choice.

Standard Equipment: The clothes on their back, an extra pair of clothes and basic toiletries.

Money: No money is ever given to the Furies, though they may scavenge something off the fallen.

The Upside: Furies are fearless savages that attack on command, tearing and biting away at all in their path.

The Downside: Furies *are always* cloned experiments, not converted humans, so they are not susceptible to the standard insanities. They are savages, though, with the most basic primal instinct: to feed.

Template Biotic: Wrangler

The Wrangler is a Biotic that was specifically designed to get into the face of the enemy, literally tie them up, and tear them to pieces. This monstrosity is a walking pile of tentacle-style weapons.

Class: Template Biotic.

Level: One.

Alignment: Those released to fend for themselves are Diabolical, while those that are a part of a Tribe or House range from Unprincipled (20%), Anarchist (20%), Aberrant (30%), and Miscreant (30%).

Attribute Requirement: None.

Attribute (conversion) Bonuses: +2D4 P.S. and Spd, +1D6+1 P.E. All are in addition to any genetic enhancements purchased via Bio-E points and skills selected.

Biotic O.C.C. Bonuses: Splicer P.S., +1 attack per melee round, +1 to initiative, +2 to strike and dodge, +2 to pull punch, +4 to save vs toxins/poison and drugs, +15% to save vs coma and death, and +4 to save vs Horror Factor.

Base M.D.C.: P.E.x10, +2D4 M.D.C. per level of experience starting at level two. The Wrangler regenerates at 1D6 per melee round and can last ten times longer than normal during strenuous exercise/activity before feeling the effects of exhaustion. This means most can remain alert and operate at full efficiency for three entire days (72 hours) without sleep.

Biotic Biological Enhancement: the Initial Cost of the Wrangler is 210 Bio-E points. Enhancements are: Every finger is given *Stabbing Tendrils*, Tangle Foot (for both feet), 10x *Flying Blades* placed in the back of the neck, one Bio-Energy Expulsion Vent, Short-Range Spore Discharger, Bio-Force Field, +40 M.D.C. to Bio-Force Field, Reinforced Exoskeleton, and 2x *Serrated Whips*.

Common (Additional) Enhancements:
  Level 3 – Both *Serrated Whips* upgraded to *Tentacle Harpoons*.
  Level 6 – Resistance to Kinetic Energy/Attacks, Resistance to Lasers, +20 M.D.C. to Bio-Force Field.
  Level 9 – Resin Duct, +40 M.D.C. to Bio-Force Field.
  Level 12 – +2 Resin Duct Shots, +80 M.D.C. to Bio-Force Field.

Common Skills: Standard, but with a -10% penalty to each.

O.C.C. Skill Program: Domestic (+10% but Wardrobe & Grooming is replaced with Bio-Comms), Infantryman (+15%), Athletics and Outdoorsman (selects Land Navigation).

Elective Skills: At Level 1, the Wrangler receives Tracking, W.P. Whip, and W.P. Bola. At Level 3: Trap & Mine Detection. At Level 6: Detect Ambush. At Level 9: Detect Concealment. At Level 12, no skill is selected.

Secondary Skills: The Wrangler does not receive any Secondary Skills. Note: If a Wrangler is simply released upon the world (abandoned and left to fend for itself) to cause chaos, it will only have the *Common Skills*, *Skill Programs* and Level One *Elective Skills* as stated above. It will not receive any more skills.

M.D.C. Living Body Armor: Generally, the Wrangler does not receive any Living Body Armor but sometimes a Tribe or House may provide them with one, which would have to be custom made so as not to interfere with the many natural weapons built into the Wrangler.

Standard Equipment: The Wrangler is commonly given an M.D. whip and a handful of bola. They rarely wear armor, and are given basic toiletries and a spare pair of clothing.

Money: No money is ever given to the Wrangler, though they may scavenge something off the fallen.

The Upside: In close-quarters combat, the Wranglers are a blur of movement as their many tendril weapons flail around, shredding their victims.

The Downside: Follow the Biotic Insanity list on pages 148-149 of the **Splicers® RPG**. Option: Wranglers could be cloned and not converted humans, and therefore not susceptible to the standard *Biotic Insanities*.

Template Biotic: Dozer

Librarian Hope used a modified version of the syndrome known as *Paget's disease* for the Dozer. A quick description of *Paget's disease* is *"abnormal bone remodeling causing progressive, sometimes painful bone deformities."* Dozers look like hulking, deformed, bone statue humanoids that haven't been completed by their sculptor.

Class: Template Biotic.

Alignment: Those released to fend for themselves are Diabolical, while those who are part of a Tribe or House are Unprincipled (30%), Anarchist (30%), Aberrant (30%), or Miscreant (10%).

Attribute Requirement: None.

Attribute (conversion) Bonuses: +2D4+2 P.S. and Spd, +1D6+1 P.E. All are in addition to any genetic enhancements purchased via Bio-E points and skills selected.

Biotic O.C.C. Bonuses: Splicer P.S., +1 attack per melee round, +1 to initiative, +2 to strike and dodge, +2 to pull punch, +4 to save vs toxins/poison and drugs, +15% to save vs coma and death, and +4 to save vs Horror Factor.

Base M.D.C.: P.E.x20 +3D4 M.D.C. per level starting at Level 2. The Dozer regenerates at 1D6 per melee round and can last ten times longer than normal during strenuous exercise/activity before feeling the effects of exhaustion. This means most can remain alert and operate at full efficiency for three entire days (72 hours) without sleep.

Biotic Biological Enhancement: The initial cost of the Dozer is 116 Bio-E points. The Enhancements are: 3 pairs of Large Horns, Horned Defense, Armored Head Crest, Saber Teeth, Casting Thrower, Short-Range Spore Discharger, and 2x

Spike Launchers. The addition of this modified Paget's Disease provides the Dozer with a natural *Reinforced Exoskeleton* and *Spines & Blades* (for each forearm).

Note: The *Spines & Blades* (as described on pages 103-104 of the **Splicers® RPG**) are made out of bone instead of the normal resin, providing the Dozer with +8 M.D. to its punching and hand to hand attacks, and doing 2D6 M.D. when thrown. Each Spine and Blade has 10 M.D.C.

Common (Additional) Enhancements:

Level 3 – Casting Launcher, Tusk Spears, One Bio-Energy Expulsion Vent.

Level 6 – Casting Rifle, Ultra-Upgrade to Casting Weapon, one Spike Launcher.

Level 9 – Casting Cannon.

Level 12 – Omni-Upgrade to Casting Weapon.

Penalty from Paget's Disease: Every year, the Dozer has to come in for a service from the Engineers. If not serviced annually, they receive these cumulative penalties each year: -10% Spd, -1 to initiative, -1 to strike, parry and dodge, and -5% to any skill that involves the use of the hands.

The penalties max out at -50% to Spd, -5 to initiative, -5 to strike, parry and dodge, and -25% to skills, but the Dozer rarely misses one year of servicing. It's only those who are left to fend for themselves that have to endure.

Common Skills: Standard, but with a -10% penalty to each.

O.C.C. Skill Program: Domestic (+10%, but Wardrobe & Grooming is replaced with Bio-Comms), Infantryman (+15%), Athletics and Outdoorsman (selects Land Navigation).

Elective Skills: At Level 1, the Dozer receives Tracking, W.P. Blunt, and W.P. Bio-Weapons: Heavy. At Level 3: Trap & Mine Detection. At Level 6: Detect Ambush. At Level 9: Detect Concealment. At Level 12, no skill is selected.

Secondary Skills: The Dozer does not receive any Secondary Skills. Note: If a Dozer is simply released upon the world (abandoned and left to fend for itself) to cause chaos, it will only have the *Common Skills* and *Skill Programs* as stated above. It will not receive any more skills.

M.D.C. Living Body Armor: Generally, the Dozer does not receive any Living Body Armor as its body is a living statue of bone.

Standard Equipment: They need no clothes, and armor is rarely given, but they are given the appropriate weapons for their skills, and basic toiletries.

Money: No money is ever given to the Dozer, though they may scavenge something off the fallen.

The Upside: Dozers are powerful and armored Biotics that can take a beating and are built tough and resistant, designed to be living tanks. Most of the time, this type of Biotic is kept close to home due to the penalties of the syndrome that can cripple their body if not kept in check.

The Downside: They will eventually be crippled by pain, and their appearance is frightening with their malformed exoskeletons. Follow the Biotic Insanity list on pages 148-149 of the **Splicers® RPG**. Option: Dozers could be cloned and not converted humans, and therefore not susceptible to the standard *Biotic Insanities*.

Template Biotic: Satyr

"It's amazing that in this day and age, we can bring myth and legend to life." – Librarian Hope

These poor souls are cosmetically altered to look like a were-goat, with the Herbivore metabolism to boot. Hope designed the Satyr as a form of amusement, taking normal humans and converting them into living embodiments of a creature from Greek Mythology.

Class: Template Biotic.

Alignment: Those released to fend for themselves are Diabolical, while those who are part of a Tribe or House are Scrupulous (10%), Unprincipled (20%), Anarchist (30%), Aberrant (30%), or Miscreant (10%).

Attribute Requirement: None.

Attribute (conversion) Bonuses: +2D4 P.S. and Spd, +1D6+1 P.E. All are in addition to any genetic enhancements purchased via Bio-E points and skills selected.

Biotic O.C.C. Bonuses: Splicer P.S., +1 attack per melee round, +1 to initiative, +1 to strike and dodge, +2 to pull punch, +5 to save vs toxins/poison and drugs, +15% to save vs coma and death, and +4 to save vs Horror Factor.

Base M.D.C.: P.E. x10, +2D4 M.D.C. per level of experience starting at level two. The Satyr regenerates at 1D6 M.D.C. per melee round and can last ten times longer than normal during strenuous exercise/activity before feeling the effects of exhaustion. This means most can remain alert and operate at full efficiency for three entire days (72 hours) without sleep.

Biotic Biological Enhancement: Initial Cost is 175. Enhancements are: Hoofed Feet (+40 mph/64 km), Flame Breath, Elongated Running Legs (+20 mph/32 km), Casting Thrower, Modified Light Gore Cannon (from the mouth, not a port on shoulder; +6 damage due to metabolism), 3 pair of Large Horns, one pair of Combat Spurs, one Bio-Energy Expulsion Vent, Reinforced Exoskeleton, Bio-Force Field, Quick Clotting Blood, Cosmetic Alterations: Made to look like a humanoid goat that is covered in thick fur (Resistance to Cold and Fire is incorporated into the fur).

Common (Additional) Enhancements:

Level 3 – Leaping legs, Medium Gore Cannon.

Level 6 – Plasma Breath, Ultra-Upgrade Medium Gore Cannon.

Level 9 – Heavy Gore Cannon, Ultra-Upgrade Plasma Breath.

Level 12 – Casting Launcher, +100 M.D.C. to Bio-Force Field.

Common Skills: Standard, but with a -10% penalty to each.

O.C.C. Skill Program: Athletics and Outdoorsman (selecting Land Navigation).

Elective Skills: At Level 1, the Satyr receives Tracking, Camouflage (of self) with a bonus of +15% due to the fur, and Prowl. At Level 3,: Trap and Mine Detection. At Level 6: Detect Concealment. At Level 9: Detect Ambush. At Level 12, no skill is selected.

Secondary Skills: The Satyr does not receive any Secondary Skills. Note: If a Satyr is simply released upon the world (abandoned and left to fend for itself) to cause chaos, it will only have the *Common Skills* and *Skill Programs* and Level One *Elective Skills* as stated above. It will not receive any more skills.

M.D.C. Living Body Armor: Generally, the Satyr does not receive any Living Body Armor but sometimes a Tribe or House may provide them with one, which would be a standard set with no enhancements.

Standard Equipment: The Satyr has no need of clothes as their bodies are covered in fur, but they receive basic toiletries.

Money: No money is ever given to the Satyr, though they may scavenge something off the fallen.

The Upside: You are a living example of Greek Mythology that is a capable and formidable fighter.

The Downside: Follow the Biotic Insanity list on pages 148-149 of the **Splicers® RPG**. Option: Satyrs could be cloned and not converted humans, and therefore not susceptible to the standard *Biotic Insanities.*

Unleash the Evil from Pandora's Box

The twists and turns of this idea are abounding. The many facets to this idea can spawn a myriad of story plots. Because there are so many ways this idea can be represented in your game, and direction in which you may take them, you can introduce the vilest, nastiest and most evil things imaginable; and House Pandorum can be their creators, and unleash them upon the world of Splicers to generate chaos. So be creative, and put a slice of your madness into House Pandorum. Welcome to my nightmare; I hope you like it.

Trust and Intimidate: A Way of Life

Optional Material for
Use with Any Palladium Game

Especially Useful with the
Rifts®: Black Market Sourcebook

By Liam Gray

Rifts®: Ultimate Edition, page 279, describes Mental Affinity as "the character's likeability, personal charm and charisma." Then it goes on to say that "Natural Leaders, with an M.A. of 16 or higher, have a bonus to invoke trust or intimidation in others." But what exactly does that mean?

I want to start this article by saying that although it is tempting to use an antagonist with high Mental Affinity to win over one of your players (and that can make a great story), Game Masters should handle such things with care. Player Characters are supposed to be heroic, and nothing is lamer than being told that you are unable to fight back or are helpless to defend yourself against the suicidal impulses instilled in you by your new mistress. I'm not saying water down the antagonists, or that all "Bad Guys" need to have low Mental Affinity; on the contrary, a lot of antagonists in modern media and literature are very charming. But use it creatively and use it to tell an interesting story. Mental Affinity should NEVER be reduced to a tool to kill off or railroad player characters.

What is Trust?

Trust is many things. To Joseph Prosek, it is a powerful weapon; to the average Black Market con man, it is a lucrative business tool; but more often than either case, trust is the foundation of friendship. In **Rifts®**, Trust represents a character's dedication to a person and the influence of player characters over NPCs in the world around them.

To help represent this, I use a system a little bit like the way *Favors* work in the Black Market. Player characters may give NPCs a number of "tasks," based on the relationship between the characters, and the player character's M.A. attribute. The number of tasks remaining represents the strength of a friendship or a relationship, and the player's ability to convince an NPC to do something he normally would not do to assist the player. As long as an NPC has unused tasks, then he should be considered friendly or at the very least, cooperative. If a player cashes in the final task "owed" to him by the NPC, then the NPC generally feels disillusioned, used, conned, or that the character owes him something for his efforts, and will not assist the character further without some sort of reason or personal gain. To determine the initial number of tasks, see *Earning Trust* and the *Trust Table*, below. Of course, not all "friendships" should use this system; that is what good role-playing is for!

Levels of Trust

Basic Trust

Basic Trust is the lowest level of trust. It is the general sense that the person engaging you means you well. Earning a character's Basic Trust means that the NPC is convinced that the character has his best interests at heart or is sensitive to the NPC's cause or personal beliefs. Characters who have earned an NPC's Basic Trust can normally convince a character to perform small tasks that would not endanger him or threaten his employment or lifestyle.

Penalties: None.

In life or death situations (when the NPC is threatened or at risk), the character can compel the NPC to overcome his personal fears and doubts or convince him that the immediate threat is a mutual one and warrants cooperation.

Intimate Trust

This level of trust represents an NPC's admiration or a stoic personal belief in the character and his credibility, and often manifests as a drive to please or impress the character. This includes a willingness to share personal or sensitive information with the character. An NPC with an Intimate Trust of a character will do almost anything he asks, but still has his own mind and opinion in any given situation. Asking him to act in a way that could jeopardize his lifestyle, health, or those he cares about, uses up one task. An action resulting in serious damage to one of those things will immediately break his trust (use up all remaining tasks). An NPC with Intimate Trust would consider the character a close personal friend or someone worthy of admiration and even let him live with him (but not indefinitely).

Penalties: If forced to fight the character he trusts, the NPC finds himself nervous or hesitating (no initiative, and bonuses are at half when attacked by the character).

In a life or death situation (when the character is threatened), the NPC will come to the character's defense and put himself in harm's way to ensure the character's safety, though doing so counts as one task.

Total Trust

This represents a blind (but not necessarily unreasonable) level of trust. NPCs with Total Trust for a character will open their homes to them, confidently introduce them to their children, and happily divulge their deepest, darkest secrets. NPCs with Total Trust put their better judgment and opinions to one side when dealing with the character and accept his or her word without compromise. They will care for the character indefinitely (as long as they are able), and put the character's needs before their own (even if this means going hungry or being forced to make an uncomfortable lifestyle change). None of the aforementioned things count as tasks; they are inclusive of this level of loyalty. The only things that do count as tasks for the character are things that would put the character's own life (or those he cares about) at risk, requesting more than HALF of the character's total resources, or attacking him with deadly force (this last one uses up all tasks and breaks the trust).

Penalties: If forced to fight the character he trusts, the NPC finds himself nervous or hesitating (no initiative, and bonuses are at half when attacked by the character), and will only ever attempt to flee or restrain (pull punch or holds) the character until he is at 0 S.D.C., or less than 50% of his total M.D.C., or unarmored and faced with Mega-Damage weaponry.

In a life or death situation (that threatens the character), NPCs with Total Trust will do whatever the character asks, even kill, so long as it does not breach their alignment. This does **NOT** count as a task, but breaking alignment to protect the character will.

Absolute Trust

This is an implicit, uncompromising trust, and unreasonable dedication to the character or his ideals. Many soldiers of the Coalition States feel this trust towards Emperor Karl Prosek. NPCs with Absolute Trust will fight, die, and live as the character dictates without batting an eye, and can even be convinced to murder their own loved ones in the name of the character. However, Absolute Trust is not always evil or negative, and can just as easily represent a faith in one's comrades or an unconditional love and belief in the character. Characters with Absolute Trust will always do whatever the character needs them to do without it counting as a task. The only things that count as completing a task is when the character personally betrays them or intentionally (and sadistically) endangers them for trivial reasons (entertainment, etc.).

On occasion, characters with a Mental Affinity stat of 27 will inspire Absolute Trust for months or years at a time. NPCs so

inspired by the character will remain loyal the entire time or until the time of their death. Deprogramming such a character requires the use of psionics, magic, or intense psychiatric treatment supported by evidence that the character does not care for, or has (in some significant way) betrayed, the victim.

Penalties: If forced to fight the character he trusts, the NPC finds himself nervous or hesitating (no initiative, and bonuses are at half when attacked by the character), and will only ever attempt to flee or restrain (pull punch or holds) the character. Though many might believe the contrary, an NPC with this level of admiration can NEVER bring himself to kill the character, no matter how much he might deserve it.

In a life or death situation (involving the character or the character's reputation), an NPC with Absolute Trust will resort to violence or even murder (if his alignment dictates or he has been asked) without so much as a second thought. Asking an NPC with Absolute Trust to act (or not act, as is sometimes the case) on the character's behalf counts as one of the character's attacks per melee.

Earning Trust

Earning trust is a complicated matter that often takes time. The higher the character's Mental Affinity, the less time it generally takes to earn trust. As a general rule, players should be able to earn the trust of an individual after 3D6 hours of interaction. Characters with a M.A. of 16 or higher reduce this time by HALF!

This interaction can be split up throughout a week however the player likes (assuming he is not antagonizing, or being intentionally dismissive of the NPC). When the time has elapsed, the player then rolls his character's Trust check. The higher the player rolls (while remaining under his base percentage), the better; consult the *Trust Table* below.

All characters have at least a **base 30% chance** of instilling or earning trust in this manner, but characters with an M.A. of 16 or higher have the distinct advantage of being able to instill trust remotely or when rushed (see below), in addition to their higher percentage of success as per the Attribute Bonus Chart in *Rifts® Ultimate Edition*, page 281.

Trust in Life or Death Situations

Characters with a Mental Affinity of 16 or higher have the ability to use the force of their personality to convince people to trust them or help them out when they normally wouldn't. In life or death situations (or when rushed), the character can attempt to sway an NPC's sympathies or earn his or her admiration. Doing so takes one melee round (15 seconds), during which time the character can do nothing else but engage the NPC(s) in conversation and defend himself. At the end of the melee round, the player then rolls his Trust check and if successful, the NPC is now treated as having a Basic Trust (one task).

If the player's roll exceeded the first Basic Trust result (i.e., the roll was 40% or higher) while still being successful, then the player may continue to spend an additional melee round (15 seconds) per level of success on the table to raise the NPC's trust level until it reaches the result he rolled.

For Example: A player who rolled 56% and was still successful could inspire Intimate Trust (1D6 tasks) in an NPC, but doing so would take five melee rounds (75 seconds).

Note: It is impossible to instill Total or Absolute Trust in this manner, and enemies or long-time antagonists can never be raised higher than Basic Trust (one task).

Leaders of Men

Characters with a Mental Affinity of 16 or higher are natural leaders and can attempt to sway large groups at a time. Doing so requires a successful Public Speaking skill check before rolling to determine the level of the audience's trust. Attempting to instill trust in their audience with a speech or a monologue takes 1D6x10 minutes and hinges entirely on the success of the Public Speaking roll, without which there is no Trust roll. However, perhaps most notably, speeches or monologues made may be recorded for future posterity and used to inspire or brainwash others who watch them. NPCs must witness (or watch) the entire speech to be influenced by it or fall under the sway of the character's force of personality.

Trust Table

01-10%: The NPC feels he or she is being threatened or conned and may become hostile.

11-24%: The NPC is unswayed.

25-39%: The character has earned the NPC's Basic Trust for one task.

40-45%: The character has earned the NPC's Basic Trust for 1D4 tasks or until broken.

46-50%: The character has earned the NPC's Basic Trust for 1D6 tasks or until broken.

51-55%: The character has earned the NPC's Intimate Trust for 1D4 tasks or until broken.

56-60%: The character has earned the NPC's Intimate Trust for 1D6 tasks or until broken.

61-65%: The character has earned the NPC's Total Trust for 1D4 days.

66-70%: The character has earned the NPC's Total Trust for 2D6 days.

71-80%: The character has earned the NPC's Absolute Trust for 1D4 tasks or until broken.

81-84%: The character has earned the NPC's Absolute Trust for 2D6 tasks or until broken.

85-88%: The character has earned the NPC's Absolute Trust for 2D4 weeks.

89-92%: The character has earned the NPC's Absolute Trust for 2D6 months.

93-94%: The character has earned the NPC's Absolute Trust for 1D4 years.

95-96%: The character has earned the NPC's Absolute Trust for life.

97-00%: The NPC is obsessed with the character and will willingly change his alignment or abandon previous beliefs in an effort to be more like his new friend and idol.

What is Intimidation?

Intimidation is the ability to wield terror as a weapon against one's enemies, or gain station through fear or sowing discord. Intimidation is the practice of bullies and thugs, and whereas any character can use it, I recommend that Game Masters keep a close eye on the alignment of "Good" characters who use this to extort or assault their way to success.

States of Fear

There are many different kinds of fear, and a lot of different ways people can react towards fear. Intimidation should not be confused with Horror Factor. Although Horror Factor can be used to intimidate, "Intimidation" represents the ability to sociologically predate an individual or person on a deep, psychological level that can leave him quaking in his boots and looking over his shoulder the rest of his life.

Intimidated

An intimidated NPC is a compliant NPC. This does not necessarily mean that he is trembling in his boots or whatever passes for footwear on Rifts Earth these days (but many do). While the character is intimidated, reduce his attacks/actions per round by HALF, and he is "willing" to answer whatever questions the character might ask him. Game Masters should note that intimidated NPCs generally have no love nor loyalty to the character threatening them, and many (especially those being intimidated by bigger, nastier NPCs) will lie, only tell half-truths, or just say whatever they think the character wants to hear – whatever gets the process over as quickly as possible.

Panicked

A panicked NPC is a gibbering mess and would willingly chew off its own arm (or equivalent appendage) to get away from the character intimidating him. Panicked characters are at half Spd (unless moving away from the character) and see their number of attacks/actions per melee reduced by half while in the intimidating character's presence. Additionally, when they are not voiding their bowels, urinating on themselves, or begging for mercy, they are being entirely compliant and truthful and "know better" than to lie to the character.

Inflicting Intimidation

In essence, Intimidation works in the same way Trust does. Which is to say a character attempting to intimidate an NPC must spend one melee round (15 seconds) doing nothing but threatening or roughing up the victim. The player then rolls his Intimidation check with the goal of rolling under his base percentage (with higher rolls being more desirable), and then consults the Intimidation Table. If the check is successful, the NPC has been Intimidated (1D4 days), but the character can increase this by putting a press on the NPC and increasing the fear by one level on the table per melee round (15 seconds) until the level of intimidation matches the result of the character's initial Intimidation roll. The character need roll only once, but if he is stopped or interrupted, he cannot intimidate the NPC further and he must start over. The character does not roll for a new duration each time the fear level is increased; instead, the NPC is considered "Intimi-

dated" until the aggressor has finished his intimidation attempt, however long that may take, or until the character is interrupted.

For Example: If a CS Grunt wanted a young D-Bee in the 'Burbs to tell him where his parents lived, he would need to roll 56% or higher (to "Panic" the child) but under his Intimidation ability, and then "rough up" the youth for four melee rounds (one minute) before the kid would break down and truthfully spill the beans or do whatever else the CS Grunt demanded for the next 1D6 minutes.

Resisting Intimidation or Panic and Conquering Fear

The training and discipline necessary to become a Man-At-Arms means that Intimidation rolls made against these brave individuals are at a -20% penalty and the time they are Intimidated or Panicked is reduced by HALF!

Furthermore, whenever one of the character's friends or objectives is threatened, the player may make a saving throw vs Horror Factor (12 or higher) for his character to completely overcome whatever grip fear or apprehension may have on him so that he can do what must be done.

Finally, although it is easy to intimidate someone (from shaking him down, to late night phone calls), curing intimidation is often just as easy. If an NPC (or character) is "intimidated" by someone or something, he has a few options – ranging from moving house to acquiring better personal protection – it all comes down to confidence and feeling "safe."

If a character has taken appropriate measures so that he believably (within his own mind) feels *safe*, that is enough. Unfortunately, characters who are *"Intimidated for Life"* never feel safe and require 3D4 months of weekly psychiatric care to conquer the fear and paranoia.

Note: Psychic or magical abilities or sedatives that soothe emotion or fear can be used to calm a panicked character, and can serve as a temporary solution or alternative to psychiatric care for Intimidated characters.

Intimidation Table

01-10%: The NPC is amused and openly mocks the character (and will continue to do so in later encounters).

11-24%: The NPC is unimpressed.

25-39%: The NPC is momentarily taken aback and loses initiative and one action.

40-45%: The NPC is Intimidated for 1D4 days.

46-50%: The NPC is Intimidated for 1D6 weeks.

51-55%: The NPC is Intimidated for 1D12 months.

56-60%: The NPC is Intimidated for 2D6 months or Panicked for 1D6 minutes.

61-65%: The NPC is Intimidated for Life or Panicked for 1D20 minutes.

66-70%: The NPC is Intimidated for Life or Panicked for 1D6 hours.

71-80%: The NPC is Intimidated for Life or Panicked for 2D4 days.

81-84%: The NPC is Intimidated for Life and Panicked for 2D6 weeks.

85-88%: The NPC is Intimidated for Life and Panicked for 1D4 months.

89-92%: The NPC is Intimidated and Panicked for Life.

93-94%: The NPC must save vs Insanity (12 or higher) or gain a Phobia of the character.

95-96%: The NPC must save vs Insanity (14 or higher) or gain a Phobia of the character.

97-00%: The NPC and must save vs Insanity (Natural 20 required) or gain a Phobia of the character.

Conflicting Interests

Criminals and Black Marketeers frequently use intimidation as a tool to strike fear into the hearts of their competition, but what happens when two very large and angry men are demanding two very different things?

It is the kind of situation no one wants to be in, and there is no simple answer. The truth is that a character CAN be intimidated by two or more different people at once, and he just has to make a choice between who scares him more. Generally, this should be the person who rolled the highest, but that is not always the case. Intimidation isn't Trust, and whereas it is a powerful tool, it is not flawless or infallible.

This same logic applies where Trust is concerned. Conflicting loyalties and interests make for interesting role-playing tools and there is nothing wrong with indecision. Sometimes, it really adds a level of depth to a scene! At the end of the day, the player's choice needs to be his own and the final choices of the NPCs are left in the hands of the Game Master.

Sorcerer's Forge

The Techno-Magical State

Optional Source Material for Rifts®

By Timothy Dorman

With some additional text and ideas throughout by Kevin Siembieda.

Sorcerer's Forge is a small city-state with fewer than 8,000 residents. It is located in what was western Pennsylvania. The community embraces both technology and magic and is home to a large community of Techno-Wizards. The city produces and sells many common technological and magical goods, as well as many unique Techno-Wizard weapons, vehicles and power armor. The city is largely isolationist, but welcomes travelers they deem trustworthy and willing to purchase or trade for their goods. The community knows of Lazlo, New Lazlo, and the Federation of Magic, but has stayed separate and independent of them.

Sorcerer's Forge is shielded from the outside world by an effect known as "the Shroud," which makes it invisible to anyone more than 5 miles (8 km) away. For those who know of the city, it can be used as a safe harbor during adventures in the northeastern wilderness.

History

With the Coming of the Rifts, western Pennsylvania was devastated by storms and earthquakes. These earthquakes caused a massive uprising of the ground, creating a new branch of the Appalachian Mountains that stretches into the central northwest of the state. As these earthquakes began, part of the industrial city of Pittsburgh (in western Pennsylvania) was inexplicably Rifted 100 miles (160 km) to the northeast. The confused survivors were killed in the chaos that followed, and the city was devastated. The ruins were situated atop the newly formed mountains and obscured by a magical field that would become known as "the Shroud." Aside from the occasional traveler or animal, the site was left largely undisturbed for almost two hundred years.

Around 15 P.A., a town of human practitioners of magic located in eastern Ohio was destroyed by a rival community, and the few dozen survivors fled east. They crossed the Eastern Wall searching for an isolated place to build a new home. While exploring western Pennsylvania they discovered **the Shroud**, and at the center, the reasonably well preserved ruins of a displaced section of Pittsburgh. The settlers salvaged some of the technology from the ruins and augmented it with magic to build a new community. One with a few working factories and remnants of pre-Rifts technology – the perfect home for Techno-Wizards.

Over time, they rebuilt a few of the old factories and machine shops, and began to manufacture various technological items in limited amounts. With many of the settlers being Techno-Wizards, the community became a small manufacturing center and a place for the creation of Techno-Wizard (TW) items. They dubbed their new town **Sorcerer's Forge**, and quietly began to trade goods to the outside world. Its isolation and the cloaking power of the Shroud allowed the town to grow without harassment from outside forces.

By 55 P.A., Techno-Wizardry was the dominant resource of the growing town, embraced as the natural evolution of technology and magic. Sorcerer's Forge has since become wealthy and strong selling magical and technological goods throughout the region, but it still does so under a veil of secrecy. It has invested this wealth in quietly modernizing and expanding the town's manufacturing capabilities.

As Sorcerer's Forge grows, it is starting to attract more attention, both good and bad. However, its leaders have kept growth at a managable rate, while maintaining prosperity for the community and continuing to be inventive. Moreover, their carefully maintained secrecy and little known location has kept most monsters, raiders and rival magic and tech communities from finding them. With the rise of the Coalition States, Federation of Magic and other powers on the continent, the leaders of the little city-state are concerned for their continued safety. To protect their community from attack, they have decided to adopt an isolationist policy. They severely restrict the entry of travelers and sale of goods, and engage in a campaign that actively spreads rumors that the city is a myth and located away from its actual location. When the Federation of Magic and others take credit for their TW creations or they are mistaken for their handiwork, Sorcerer's Forge is pleased to let the mistaken identification stand. They transport goods for sale by indirect routes, and often sell them to the Black Market faction known as the **Immaterial Hand**. The Immaterial Hand is their primary buyer and main link to the outside world. The Black Market faction is happy to keep the community their little secret, and actively work at helping to keep Sorcerer's Forge's existence and location unknown to the world at large. Indeed, the community has been so successful at keeping itself hidden, that few people, let alone the major powers, have heard of them. And those who have, dismiss any rumors of the place as a myth.

As of 109 P.A., Sorcerer's Forge has grown to nearly 8,000 people and is the largest and most advanced community in western Pennsylvania. However, in recent years, the lords of the city have noticed an increased effort from outsiders to find the city. Numerous explorers have been searching the area, some merchants are being questioned as to where their goods originate, and small teams of mercenaries have been spotted in neighboring areas. The leaders suspect many of those searching for them work for one particular person or group, but the identity and motivations of said individual/group remains unknown.

The City of Sorcerer's Forge

Sorcerer's Forge is a predominantly human community. Fewer than 30% of its citizens are D-Bees or mutants, and only 1% are creatures of magic like the *Faeriekin*. Supernatural beings (especially those with evil alignments) are not allowed. The city itself is a small area, but it has citizens and influence in parts of the area around it. Most of this region is forest wilderness broken by the occasional farm or mining community. However, there are only a few small villages and few have more than 100 residents.

The State of Sorcerer's Forge Population:

Permanent residents (circa 109 P.A.): 7,925.
    75% Human.
    12% D-Bees.
    12% Human Mutants, mostly Psi-Stalkers and psychics.
    1% Other; mostly Faeriekin and a few other creatures of magic.

Transient Population: Usually no more than a few dozen visitors can be found in the city at a time, due to the isolationist policy of the ruling powers, and the fact that few people even know it exists.

Sorcerer's Forge is a small city-state located at an extension of the *Appalachian Mountains*. All round it are tall hills covered by lush, dense forest. The perimeter of the city is surrounded by large, Mega-Damage walls of gray stone, 50 feet (15.2 m) high and 15 feet (4.6 m) thick. The walls and entrances are guarded by the military. Visitors are screened by city soldiers and the police force before being allowed to enter.

Beyond the walls of Sorcerer's Forge is a surprisingly modern city, comparable to anything the Coalition States has to offer. There are stores, shops, restaurants, apartments and houses. Most buildings have basic amenities such as indoor plumbing, electricity, central heating and cooling, lights, communication systems, computers and other appliances. Most of the structures are less than five stories high to keep a low profile. Flying vehicles (and flying people) are heavily restricted inside the city, so as not to be seen in the air from afar. Throughout Sorcerer's Forge there are roads for small vehicles and sidewalks for pedestrians.

The western section of the city is the *industrial center* where most of the technological and TW goods are produced.

The eastern section is where the schools, magic colleges and medical facilities are located.

Businesses and housing are scattered throughout Sorcerer's Forge.

The main military and government buildings are located in the center of the city. Military and government buildings are made with M.D.C. materials, while most civilian buildings are not.

To visit Sorcerer's Forge, you must make a formal request via someone who lives there or does business with the city. This representative passes your request to the city council. If you offer a beneficial service or are believed to be a trustworthy, potential customer, you may be granted access. To become a citizen, you must have visited the city several times over the course of several years, not broken any major laws, and have the recommendation of several prominent citizens.

The Shroud

The Shroud is a magical field of some kind that may have its roots in another dimension. It is certainly a dimensional anomaly that no human is known to have a part in creating. On the other hand, it is possible that a Dark Age sorcerer or alien mage may have created the Shroud with a since forgotten spell a hundred or more years ago. The city of Sorcerer's Forge and some of the surrounding area, has been established within the Shroud for the express reason that the magic keeps the city and its population hidden. The city is directly at the center of the Shroud largely because the pre-Rifts ruins of Pittsburgh happened to appear here as well, relocated from its original location. Again, how and why is unknown, but it suggests this was the result of dimensional displacement or magic energy gone wild during or sometime after the Great Cataclysm. This makes the city of Sorcerer's Forge and the 5 mile (8 km) radius around it to appear to be forested wilderness devoid of people and buildings. Moreover, the magic masks the sounds and energy transmissions of the city, so that sensory devices and ordinary senses do NOT detect them. Even aircraft and creatures flying near the city hear only the sound of nature and see forest, not buildings. All forms of technological and magical detection are blocked by the Shroud, including the detection of heat sources, radio waves, radar, light, motion and life. Long-range communication is disrupted once one enters the buffer zone and while radio waves and similar forms of transmission work inside the Shroud, they cannot penetrate the buffer zone dome effect to communicate with people outside the Shroud. Only communications through physical land-lines or via ley lines (such as *Ley Line Transmission*) can transmit beyond the Shroud. Any attempt to send a signal through the Shroud or out of the Shroud from within always fails. **Note:** Sorcerer's Forge maintains several land-lines through the Shroud to a small handful of their own trading posts and bases on the outside of the Shroud for the purpose of communicating to their comrades and as an early warning system should danger arise. The city leaders have been known to add to their concealment via the use of magic and illusions to make the city even harder to find.

The city's leaders have a theory that the magical effect is maintained by several nearby ley lines, but nobody has ever seen or heard of such a magical or dimensional effect. The Shroud appears to be unique to Sorcerer's Forge. In fact, many a mage has tried to figure out and replicate the "reflection" and "masking" effect without success.

The Shroud's outer borders are difficult to define. As a traveler from the outside approaches the buffer zone of the Shroud, he can still see everything that is actually ahead for 300 feet (91.4 m), but beyond that it is obscured by the magical effect, making the area appear as a dense, inhospitable forest. Not only that, it creates a sense of foreboding that causes most intelligent beings to unconsciously turn back or take a path that seems easier and cuts around, and away from, the city nestled within the Shroud. This outer field of the Shroud stretches for about two miles (3.2 km) around the area of habitation for the city-state.

Traveling within the two mile (3.2 km) *buffer zone* is difficult and many travelers get lost, travel in circles and find themselves either back where they started or on the other side of Sorcerer's Forge without ever realizing they've traveled around the concealed city. **Note:** -50% skill penalty to *Tracking* (by all means) and *Land Navigation*. Even compasses are tricked to lead travelers around the Shroud and away from the region it protects.

If one or more travelers manage to penetrate the outer buffer zone, usually by accident, they enter the Shroud and everything returns to normal. It's still possible to travel away from, or skirt past the city at the center of the Shroud, but instruments and senses now work as normal, and a visitor can see everything inside the Shroud and find its inhabitants. The city sits atop an area within the Appalachian Mountains and is surrounded by a forest, so is not easily seen unless one literally stumbles across it. And remember, the weird phenomenon of the Shroud keeps it invisible from the air, unless one is flying at roughly *treetop level*. At treetop level, the flyer *might* notice the city or outlaying farms

or homes, but only if he's paying attention and only if he does not rise higher than treetop level.

Security Patrols. The perimeter around the *buffer zone* is patrolled by city guardians for additional security. These defenders, most of whom are Wilderness Scouts, Psi-Stalkers and others versed in stealth, wilderness travel and combat, have become skilled at leading interlopers away from the city and back into the buffer zone where they are almost certain to become lost and turned away. Persistent outsiders who cannot be misled are either chased away or captured, interrogated and hauled back to the outside world. It is a rare event to be taken to the city itself, though it can happen. Invaders and other obvious malevolent forces are ambushed and destroyed via weapons and magic. As a rule of thumb, they are wiped out to a man and their bodies and possessions disposed of, or taken elsewhere, so their fate cannot be linked to Sorcerer's Forge. A typical patrol is 1D4+6 defenders, one or two of whom is always a mage.

The Surrounding Region

Some of the people living around Sorcerer's Forge are also its citizens. Most of this area is wilderness, with some farming communities and a few tiny villages. The area beyond that is mostly remote, uninhabited forest, with a few tiny settlements, outposts and tribal people. Few of the region's inhabitants outside of the Shroud are aware of the city's existence, something the leaders of Sorcerer's Forge work hard to maintain. Among those who do know there is a "mysterious community of wizards" in the region, most are convinced the place magically moves around throughout the mountains. Only a small number of trusted individuals and a few clans of Psi-Stalkers know the whereabouts of Sorcerer's Forge and how to find it (their penalty for travel in the buffer zone is -22%). So far, the place has even escaped the notice of Archie Three and his Shemarrians, and that is quite a feat.

The city sits in a valley within the Appalachian Mountains. A new branch of mountains that came into existence during the Great Cataclysm, so there are no pre-Rifts road systems. It is only accessible by land via several narrow passes and trails, or via Rifts, providing one knows where to Rift to. The area immediately around Sorcerer's Forge is a dense forest with several paths – some deliberately misleading to carry travelers back out of the Shroud and around and away from the city – others "true paths," as they are known. The forest is referred to by the people in the region as the **Grey Woods**, and is said to be inhabited by a number of fierce predators and magical beings. Several small ley lines are found near and within the Shroud, but do not touch the city itself; the closest being 4 miles (6.4 km away. Sorcerer's Forge maintains a few small observation/military outposts throughout the area to watch for danger, lead outsiders away and to help innocent travelers in distress (and to lead most away from the city).

Government & The Seven Lords

The city-state of Sorcerer's Forge is ruled by a governor, who is appointed by an elected council. However, the true power behind the community are the **Seven Lords**, said to be immortal. The truth behind the Seven Lords is that they were normal humans who lived during the last days of the Golden Age of Man. With the Coming of the Rifts, they were Rifted almost two hundred years into the future (around 20 years before the start of the

P.A. calendar), along with a few dozen other people of their era. Surviving in the world of Rifts was difficult, and many of the displaced people from the Golden Age of Man perished. However, the last of them eventually came upon the already small community forming in the ruins of Pittsburgh. With their understanding of pre-Rifts technology, they were welcomed into the community. Fascinated by Techno-Wizardry, they learned the secrets of its magic and helped build the community that would eventually become known as Sorcerer's Forge. In the years that followed, they discovered after being Rifted through time, for some reason, they did not age (or more accurately, they aged very slowly), and all were gifted with a talent for magic. Moreover, it seems that they were somehow drawn to the ruins and the seven believe they are fated for some grand destiny.

As mentioned, the Seven Lords became enamored with the concept of magic, especially Techno-Wizardry, and all became very skilled in magic and rose to prominence in the community. They were all instrumental in the growth and success of Sorcerer's Forge and earned the title "Seven Lords" because they rose to be leaders within the community. When it was realized they didn't seem to age, this gave them even greater status among the people, many of whom consider the seven to be demigods or at least, chosen leaders.

As the people began to deify the Seven Lords and even worship them, the seven decided it best to take a back seat, became reclusive and adopted a method of indirect rule over the city. They removed themselves from the public spotlight and had a city council elected (new elections are held every eight years). On occasion the city council appoints a governor for a 10 year term, and they all work together to govern the city. However, the real power of the government still lies with the Seven Lords. Minor domestic issues and other day to day matters are handled by the governor and city council. The people of Sorcerer's Forge know the Seven Lords still influence the government, though they believe they mostly play the role of *advisors*. Since the Seven Lords are removed from the public spotlight and all decisions *seem* to come from the city council or governor, the people believe they have a functioning democracy. This is true to a point, since the Seven Lords largely allow the city council to rule by the people's will, but they set strict guidelines that must be followed. If the city council or governor refuse to follow these guidelines, they are removed from office.

The Seven Lords have the legal authority to overrule any decision by the city council or governor that they deem inappropriate, and can directly issue orders to all branches of the government. This is known by the people, but is, to their knowledge, never enforced. Moreover, it is the Seven Lords who quietly established and lead the city's military, from guardians to a secret cadre of mages in charge of the city defenses. The influence of the Seven Lords is palpable. As most citizens and city leaders believe, they are demigods or the immortal chosen. Anything one or more of the Seven Lords suggests is given much greater consideration than any other citizen, and any directive or strong opinion from them is taken as gospel and put into action by the governing body. Overall, the people of Sorcerer's Forge view the Seven Lords favorably, seeing them as protectors, wisemen and very possibly, gods with knowledge of the past, present and, some say, the future. (The latter is not true, and all are mere mortals though they age very slowly and may be fated for something grand or terrible.) They are believed to meet in a secret chamber in a bunker beneath the main government building, issuing orders through messengers. Most visitors to the city have never heard of the Seven Lords, and those who have believe them to be a secret cabal of masked mages who secretly rule the city.

Despite the Seven Lords' shadowy control of the local government, they are benevolent leaders who only want the best for the community. They see Sorcerer's Forge as a bastion of civilization in an insane world, and they seek to nurture and preserve it for as long as they can.

Society and the Law

The people of Sorcerer's Forge embrace both magic and technology equally, so it is normal for a person to cast a spell and use a computer, fly via magic and ride a horse or hovercycle for fun or work. Most of the people own and use technology (computers, radios, etc.), most are unafraid of magic, and a full one third are fully trained practitioners of magic, half of which are Techno-Wizards and another quarter are skilled in other forms of magic, such as the Mystic Soldier and TW Robot Pilot, both of whom know limited magic and have special abilities (they are described later). Most of the population is well educated, can read and write, and appreciate artistry, music, entertainment and magic. The city is modern, clean and well kept. Most citizens are of good alignment and peace-loving; crime is minimal, despite their relationship with the Black Market. However, the people are isolationist, avoid contact with the outside world, and only see outsiders as potential customers or threats.

The population is largely human, with the occasional Psi-Stalker or D-Bee. Most are friendly enough, but wary of strangers, especially non-humans. Most of the people are conservative in the way they dress and tend to wear dull colors, though younger people often defy this trend. Cybernetics are a rarity in Sorcerer's Forge (many of them are practitioners of magic), but not banned. Major Psychics (aside from Psi-Stalkers) are a rarity, but treated as equals. Practitioners of Magic are often looked up to as talented individuals, provided they don't practice any of the banned forms of dark magic, including Necromancy, Bio-Wizardry, Witchery, Temporal Magic and the summoning of supernatural creatures. D-Bees are usually treated with suspicion, being viewed as too alien to be entirely trusted. Supernatural creatures, Creatures of Magic, undead and evil aligned beings are banned from the city as being too unpredictable and a potential threat.

Sorcerer's Forge has a fair justice system very remaniscent to the one in the American Empire prior to the Great Cataclysm; another influence of the Seven Lords. However, there are some limits on personal freedoms, especially when it comes to vice. Gambling, prostitution and drugs are legal, but heavily regulated and relegated to specific locations where the business is allowed.

Bio-Wizardry, Necromancy, Temporal magic, Witchery and the summoning magicks are all banned, and anyone who practices or has items related to these crafts are exiled from the community. Likewise, visitors who dabble in the dark arts are never, knowingly, allowed entry to the city. Slavery is illegal and visitors with slaves are not allowed to bring them into the city. The usual range of crimes are also illegal, but serious crimes are uncommon. Any major infraction at the hands of a visitor will get the perpetrator permanently expelled from the city. The worst crime in Sorcerer's Forge is the intentional unauthorized revealing of the city's location to an outsider. It is punishable by loss of citizenship and permanent expulsion from the city. If the incident results in serious injuries, death and danger at the city, the person responsible is likely to be executed, along with the "enemy" or "villain" given the secret.

Military Defense

The total active military strength of Sorcerer's Forge is 1,000 defenders. This includes Wilderness Scouts, a standing army with a variety of different types of soldiers, and the police force. An additional 2,000 citizens are registered members of the volunteer militia, and will rush to the defense of their city-state, as will the majority of the magic practitioners and psychics. However, few have any combat experience whatsoever in this peaceful, isolated town. Even most of the city defenders are only 1D4 level in experience, with Wilderness Scouts and other types of scouts being 1D4+3 level, but even they have more experience in scouting, tracking, hunting and reconnaissance than actual combat. Though the soldiers use magic weapons as well as technological-based weapons, only 5% are spell casters. The most common weapons are their city's own TW creations. They also buy TW weapons and vehicles from Stormspire, and a variety of other magic and technological fare via the Black Market faction known as the *Immaterial Hand*. Favorite tech weapons, armor and vehicles come from Northern Gun, Wilk's and Triax. They have NEVER purchased any Titan Industries items and tend to avoid the goods of most other manufacturers. Sorcerer's Forge does not normally use Juicers or Crazies, and only has the rare Cyborg. Mercenaries are only used indirectly, via an outside agent like the Immaterial Hand who acts as a middleman for the city without ever revealing their client's identity.

The military of Sorcerer's Forge has two main theaters of operation: patrolling the area around the Shroud to prevent trouble before it finds the city, and within Sorcerer's Forge itself. Wilderness Scouts and Psi-Stalkers seldom patrol more than 20 miles (32 km) away from the Shroud unless there is reason to do so. The perimeter patrols are the light and fast squads trained to move about quietly and unseen unless they want to be seen. They tend to use ambushes, surprise attacks and guerilla tactics to chase or lure intruders away. If a group of travelers approach within 10 miles (16 km) of the Shroud they are turned back or led away. (**Note:** *Eric Walker* leads one of the patrols that make contact with small groups of travelers). The perimeter forces patrol the region to discourage any new settlements and check hostile forces. They are usually only equipped with light equipment (power armor, small vehicles, and handheld weapons). A normal Sorcerer's Forge patrol squad is made up of two Psi-Stalkers 2-4 Wilderness Scouts, 1-2 Mages, and 2 Soldiers (may be any Men-at-Arms O.C.C.). A combat squad or ambush team may be comprised of Scouts as above, but is more often two infantry fire teams, one is a light team with three Mystic Soldiers and one mage or Major or Master Psychic, and one heavy fire team of 2-3 TW Robot Piltos clad in power armor or a combat robot or a light combat vehicle. The combat squad is led by a commanding officer who is usually a 1D4+3 level Ley Line Walker, Mystic, Fusion Elementalist or Warlock (but can be any acceptable practitioner of magic).

The perimeter forces have several small, camouflaged outposts and caches of weapons and equipment within their range of patrol. The reconnaissance squads are less aggressive and usually remain hidden to observe travelers from a distance. They take action only when the intruders appear to be a danger and only if they are confident they can either lure them away or take them down; may pick off a hostile intruder one by one. Otherwise, the recon team will request back-up (one or more combat squads) before launching an attack.

The city defense force is more heavily armed, with power armor, robot vehicles, combat vehicles, and TW weapons, personal armor and other gear. Robots and power armor are mostly conventional Northern Gun product with a third TW modified.

Foreign Relations

Few. Sorcerer's Forge does not have any formal relations with any other major kingdoms or governments. It maintains an isolationist policy so that aggressive states, mercenary companies and adventurer groups will not attack them. However, several groups are aware of its existence or have heard rumors of it.

Frontier Communities

Sorcerer's Forge trades with several small communities in the region, including small human kingdoms, Psi-Stalker tribes, *Blucie* tribes (see **World Book 30: D-Bees of North America**), *Ashen Hunter* tribes, and a few other D-Bee groups or tribes. They have trade/defense alliances with several *Faeriekin* communities in the region. The city also has a trade agreement with the local *Obsedai* (see **D-Bees of North America**) for gems, herbs and other materials. The Native American communities to the north have heard rumors of Sorcerer's Forge, but do not know its precise location and do not trade with them.

The Immaterial Hand

The one group they have strong ties with is the secretive Black Market faction: The Immaterial Hand, who functions as their liaison to the outside world when it comes to trade goods and information. This relationship works great for both groups, as the Immaterial Hand is happy to keep the existence of the Sorcerer's Forge and their unique TW devices their own exclusive secret. As a result, the Black Market faction works just as hard as the Sorcerer's Forge to keep its existence and location a mystery.

Lazlo

Lazlo and Sorcerer's Forge have several shared beliefs; both embrace Techno-Wizardry and wish to be left in peace. However, that's where their common ground ends, as Lazlo welcomes all intelligent beings, while Sorcerer's Forge is mostly human centered. Lazlo has heard rumors of Sorcerer's Forge and buys some of its goods through middlemen, but no citizen, not even Erin Tarn, has traveled there. Most people of Lazlo are unaware of Sorcerer's Forge. On the other hand, the people of Sorcerer's Forge view Lazlo as too idealistic, trusting and open and friendly with Creatures of Magic and "aliens" (i.e. D-Bees).

Federation of Magic

Most of the factions of the Federation of Magic are unaware of Sorcerer's Forge. However, there are some factions and individuals who have heard rumors about a mysterious Techno-Wizard city to the northeast.

The Lords of Dweomer know of the city but choose not to alarm them by revealing their knowledge of it or that they know of its approximate location. Alistair Dunscon is also aware of Sorcerer's Forge, but does not know its location. Nor does he care, since he has more important plans and powerful resources of his own. Master K'zaa of Stormspire does regular business with the city, viewing it as a minor rival and valued customer (Sorcerer's Forge buys many of its magical goods from Stormspire). The people of Sorcerer's Forge view the Federation of Magic as an example of the dangers of magic, and generally avoid it except to trade goods, often through middlemen from Stormspire or the Immaterial Hand. A few dozen mages from Sorcerer's Forge have actually visited Stormspire themselves and a few others originate from the Federation of Magic.

Coalition States

The Coalition has heard rumors of a Techno-Wizard city in the East, but they believe this could be one of many "magical cities" that are said to exist across the eastern half of the continent. Should the Coalition become aware of Sorcerer's Forge, they would add it to their list of enemies. The people of Sorcerer's Forge view the Coalition States as a growing threat. The Seven Lords believe their best chance of survival is to remain hidden, hoping the CS will stay out of the Eastern Wilderness.

A.R.C.H.I.E. Three/Shemarrians

Archie had heard rumors from his spies of a magical city in western Pennsylvania, but was unable to find it until recently. The fact that a large community of practitioners of magic is near his facility in Pennsylvania has motivated Archie to dedicate some of his resources to finding it. So far, the place remains elusive and the sentient machine and his human partner, Hagan, believe it is nothing more than a myth. After all, if such a place really existed, wouldn't the Machine God know it?

The people of Sorcerer's Forge, like the rest of the world, are completely unaware of Archie. They view the Shemarrians with uncertainty, their motivations are vague and their true goals uncertain. With the recent **Shemarrian Declaration of Sovereignty** over the eastern wilderness, the people of Sorcerer's Forge have been disturbed to realize this includes them! As long as the Shemarrians leave Sorcerer's Forge alone, the Seven Lords will take no action against them. They hope the Shemarrian declaration will help to discourage explorers from looking for the city.

O.C.C.s of Sorcerer's Forge

The unique culture of Sorcerer's Forge allows for almost any non-evil O.C.C. in North America, with exceptions for the practitioners of the banned forms of magic (Temporal, Necromancy, Bio-Wizardry, Witchery and the summoning of supernatural creatures). The most common forms of magic users in Sorcerer's Forge are Ley Line Walkers, Mystics and Techno-Wizards. Crazies and Juicers are never created by the city, but are occasionally allowed in the city (as travelers) or hired as mercenaries. Sorcerer's Forge also has a couple of its own unique O.C.C.s that reflect its Techno-Wizard culture.

Mystic Soldier O.C.C.

By Timothy Dorman and Kevin Siembieda

The elite front-line soldiers of the Sorcerer's Forge military are appropriately known as Mystic Soldiers. Their name derives from their skill in the use of select magic combined with conventional military combat training. The Mystic Soldier is a soldier first and a practitioner of magic second. They have the training of a professional soldier, and their know the fundamentals of magic, but know only a few dozen spells. Their special ability and advantage is being able to channel magic to use Techno-Wizard (TW) weapons and devices. Their knowledge of spell magic is very limited and almost exclusive to combat and military applications. Their primary purpose is to keep Sorcerer's Forge hidden and protected from whatever demons, monsters and dangerous outsiders may happen to find their secret community and threaten their existence.

Mystic Soldiers are skilled in the use of both TW and conventional weaponry, using their unique abilities to enhance both in combat. Mystic Soldiers wear a variety of special, full Environmental Body Armor created by the Techno-Wizards of the Sorcerer's Forge that does not interfere with their magic; mainly because their magic abilities are used to enhance the TW weapons and TW armor. However, they are limited to specific types of Techno-Wizard Environmental Body Armor made with a combination of *synthetic and natural materials*, in which they are specially trained to use. The small handful of Mystic Soldiers who have left the Sorcerer's Forge military have gone on to become mercenaries, explorers and heroes, but none of them have ever revealed the existence or location of their homeland. Most tell people the come from *Lazlo* or the *Magic Zone*.

Mystic Soldier O.C.C. Abilities:

The real power of the Mystic Soldier lays in his ability to use and enhance magic weapons and devices. This includes, TW weapons, Rune Weapons, Splugorth Bio-Wizard weapons, Lemurian Biomancy weapons, demon-made weapons, and most other types of magical weapons and artifacts.

1. Enhance Techno-Wizard and Magic Weapon: The Mystic Soldier can increase the damage <u>or</u> the range (not both) of any handheld TW pistol, rifle, rod, Rune weapon or other magic weapon by 25%. To do so, the character must spend an amount of P.P.E. to empower the weapon: 10 P.P.E. for any one-handed weapon, such as a TW knife, sword, or pistol. 20 P.P.E. for any two-handed weapon such as a large TW sword, battle axe or rifle. 40 P.P.E. for any heavy mounted weapon like a *Starfire Pulse Cannon* (Federation of Magic).

The increased damage (or range) lasts for one minute per level of the Mystic Soldier's experience. This effect does not stack with *Power Weapon* or any similar magic spell. Enhancing the damage does not charge or activate the weapon, these things must be done separately. Only the specific Mystic Soldier who empowered the weapon can use the weapon he has enchanted, and only as long as he keeps it in hand or on his body (slung over a his should, held in a holster on his belt, etc.) does the weapon remain so enchanted. **Duration:** The increased damage (or range) capacity lasts only as long as the Mystic Soldier holds/uses the

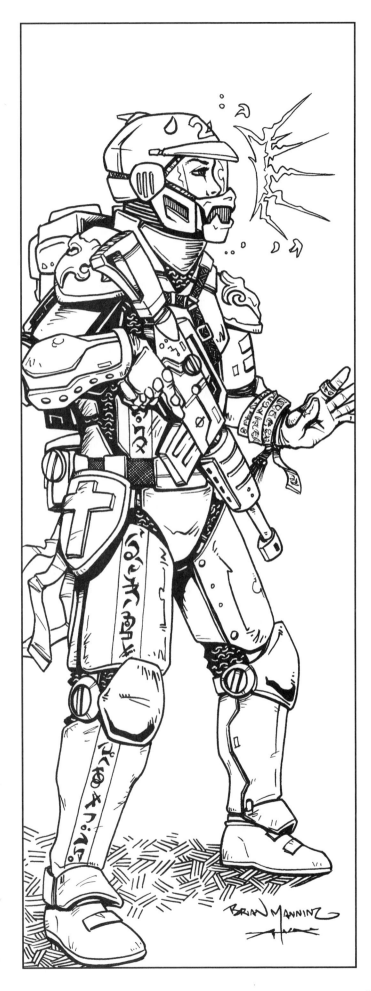

weapon for a total of one melee round per P.P.E. charge. **Note:** Only works on TW weapons.

2. P.P.E. Channeling: This ability is similar to that of the *Mystic Knight*™ (see **Rifts® World Book 16: Federation of Magic**™), except the Mystic Solider can ONLY pump P.P.E. directly *from themselves* into a TW weapon with or without a P.P.E.-Clip, to run, power or recharge the magic weapon. This is a unique power that enables the character to channel and convert P.P.E. energy from his own body into other types of energy with the following affects:

- Can power most, comparatively simple electronic items simply by holding it in his hand and desiring it to function. Such items include: flashlight, radio, video camera, portable computer, language translator, electric shaver, etc. at a P.P.E. cost of one point for up to 10 minutes per level of experience.
- Can recharge most types of conventional and TW batteries: One small, S.D.C. energy battery per level of experience at a total costs three P.P.E. points.
- One large S.D.C. battery (the equivalent of a automobile battery) costs 5 P.P.E. points.
- Standard E-Clip (M.D. energy): 15 P.P.E.
- Long-E-Clip (M.D. energy): 30 P.P.E.
- Energy Cannister or Rail Gun: 50 P.P.E.
- Recharge a high powered energy cannon with one blast (1D6x10 to 2D6x10 M.D.; two blasts if the energy beam does 6D6 to 1D4x10 M.D.) costs 60 P.P.E.
- The Mystic Soldier can also fire energy bolts from his hands or eyes (2D6 M.D., +1 M.D. at levels 3, 6, 9, 12 and 15 up to a range of 300 feet/91.5 m). P.P.E. Cost: 10 points per blast, but half that (5 P.P.E.) if channeled through an enchanted melee weapon or minor magic item (he uses the magic item as a conduit with which to focus, channel and fire the magic energy bolt; point and shoot). An additional 300 feet (91.5 m) range can be added for the cost of another 10 P.P.E. **Note:** there is no cost of personal P.P.E. for the increased that range when the Mystic Soldier is on a ley line or at a nexus point because he channels the ambient magic energy of the ley line through is body and into the weapon.

3. Enhance Tech Energy Weapon Damage: Basically the same as *#1 Enhance TW Weapons* (see above), except it requires 50% MORE P.P.E. and applies to non-magical, technological energy weapons like lasers, ion blasters, plasma rifles and similar. Not applicable to rail guns or other projectile weapons.

4. Enchant Armor: A Mystic Soldier can enhance any *TW M.D.C. armor* he is wearing with an effect similar to *Armor of Ithan*, except this armor has 100 M.D.C. +5 M.D.C. per level of his experience. It costs 10 P.P.E. to activate the magic M.D.C. which lasts for 20 minutes or until the M.D.C. of the magic armor field is reduced to zero, whichever comes first. **Note:** For the enchantment to work, the Mystic Soldier must be wearing some sort of TW or magic body armor, even if it only has a few (at least 3) M.D.C. points. Does not work on ordinary clothing, conventional armor or bare skin.

5. Parry M.D. attacks with M.D.C. Gauntlets: The Mystic Soldier can parry M.D. attacks from M.D. weapons such as magic swords, Vibro-Blades, and the punches or blades of cyborgs and supernatural opponents, provided he is wearing any kind of gauntlets/armored gloves with at least 3 M.D.C. each, by channeling magic energy (5 P.P.E.) into them. Duration: Five minutes per charge of 5 P.P.E.

6. Initial Spell Knowledge: The Mystic Soldier starts with the following Magic Invocations: Breathe Without Air (5), Climb (3), Cloud of Smoke (2), Globe of Daylight (2) Sense Evil (2), Sense Magic (4) and See the Invisible (4).

7. Learning New Spells: The Mystic Soldiers's spell knowledge comes from within the character himself on an intuitive level. The character spends years pondering life, his place in it, and how magic might help him find that place in the world. Then, when he is ready to find his place, he spends 48 hours in meditation. At the end of that he intuitively knows the spells listed above. Then, when he has reached a new metaphysical plateau in his life (a new level of experience), the character finds the time to meditate on combat, his goals and magic to receive one new magic spell per level of experience (two at levels 4, 7, 10 and 13). Make selections from the following list only: Armor of Ithan (10), Chameleon (6), Cloak of Darkness (6), Electric Arc (8), Energy Bolt (5), Energy Disruption (12), Energy Field (10), Escape (8), Fear (5), Fire Bolt (7), Ignite Fire (6), Impervious to Energy (20), Levitation (5), Magic Shield (6), Mystic Fulcrum (5), Negate Poison/Toxin (5), Sheltering Force (20), Superhuman Endurance (12), Superhuman Strength (10), Superhuman Speed (10), Tongues (12) and Turn Dead (6). **Note:** Unlike other practitioners of magic, the Mystic Soldier cannot be taught new spells, since the character does not have the mastery of magic to go beyond what's mentioned above, but he can use Techno-Wizard devices with excellent proficiency.

8. P.P.E.: Like other spell casters, the Mystic Soldier has the ability to hold magical energy. Base P.P.E. is 2D4x10+P.E. attribute. They get an additional 2D6 per level of experience. Like spell casters, they can draw additional P.P.E. from ley lines and nexus points. The Mystic Soldier recovers P.P.E. at a rate of four points per hour of sleep or rest. Meditation restores it at twice the rate.

9. Combat/Magic Bonuses: +2D6+5 to S.D.C., +1 on initiative, +1 melee attack when using a TW or other type of magic weapon of any kind, +2 to strike with energy beams fired from the hands or eyes, +1 to save vs all forms of mind control, +3 to save vs possession and +3 to save vs Horror Factor. **Note:** This is in addition to bonuses the character may enjoy from high attribute numbers, hand to hand combat and other skills.

Mystic Soldier O.C.C. Stats

Also Known As: TW Solider and Sorcerer Soldier.
Alignment: Any, but most are non-evil.
Attribute Requirements: I.Q. 10, M.E. 12.
Racial Requirements: None, although 90% are human (Sorcerer's Forge is a mostly human city).
O.C.C. Skills:
    Language: Native Tongue (American) at 92%.
    Language: Other: One of choice (+10%).
    General Athletics
    Climbing (+5%)
    Land Navigation (+5%)
    Mathematics: Basic (+10%)
    Military Etiquette (+10%)
    Pilot: One of choice (+10%); excluding Power Armor, Robots, or Ships.
    Radio: Basic (+10%)
    Sensory Equipment (+10%)
    Running or Weapon Systems (+10%); pick one.

    W.P. Knife (includes Vibro-Knives)
    W.P. Sword (includes Vibro-Swords)
    W.P. Energy Pistol
    W.P. Energy Rifle
    Hand to Hand: Expert, can be changed to Hand to Hand: Martial Arts (or Assassin if Evil or Anarchist) for the cost of two O.C.C. Related Skills.
O.C.C. Related Skills: Select four other skills at level one, +1 additional skill at levels 4, 8 and 12. All new skills start at level one proficiency.
    Communications: Any (+5%).
    Cowboy: None.
    Domestic: Any.
    Electrical: Basic Electronics only.
    Espionage: None.
    Horsemanship: None.
    Mechanical: Automotive and Basic Mechanics only.
    Medical: First Aid only.
    Military: Any (+10%).
    Physical: Any, except Acrobatics (+10% to Prowl only).
    Pilot: Any (+5%).
    Pilot Related: Any.
    Rogue: Tailing (+10%) only.
    Science: Math skills and Astronomy only.
    Technical: Any (+5%).
    W.P.: Any.
    Wilderness: Any.
Secondary Skills: Two at levels 1, 6 and 12, selected from the Secondary Skill list on page 300 of **Rifts® Ultimate Edition**. These are additional areas of knowledge that do not get any bonuses, other than any possible bonus for a high I.Q. All start at the base skill level.
Standard Equipment: Military fatigues, dress uniform, combat boots, suit of Mystic Soldier EBA (described later), one TW/energy weapon of choice with four P.P.E.-Clips/E-Clips for each W.P., four grenades (mix of smoke, fragmentation and TW), three flares, one Vibro-Knife, one survival knife (1D6 S.D.C.), pocket knife (1 S.D.C.), utility belt, two canteens, backpack, flashlight, walkie-talkie, compass, binoculars, and some personal items.
Money: The character starts off with 1D6x1,000 credits.
Cybernetics: None. They are avoided as they interfere with spell casting and channeling magic energy.

Techno-Wizard Robot Pilot O.C.C.

By Timothy Dorman and Kevin Siembieda

The Techno-Wizard Robot Pilot is very similar to the non-magical Robot Pilot, except they specialize in piloting the unique Techno-Wizard Power Armor/Robot Vehicles of Sorcerer's Forge. These elite individuals have an innate understanding of magic and technology like Techno-Wizards, but cannot cast any spells. Their reserve of P.P.E. is used exclusively to power Techno-Wizard devices. TW Robot Pilots are people with an aptitude for magic but who also enjoy advanced technology. They

eschew learning magic in favor of military training and the use of TW combat robots, power armor and weaponry. This means they can only use magic through TW devices. They are similar to the Mystic Soldier, in that they are living P.P.E. batteries that channel their mystic energy into and through Techno-Wizard devices. Like the Mystic Soldier, this is a rare and unusual O.C.C. developed and taught only by the mages of Sorcerer's Forge. In fact, the Techno-Wizards of the city have created TW power armor/robot vehicles with these city defenders specifically in mind.

Normal practitioners of magic would avoid using armor and vehicles that prohibit them from using their magic, but TW Robot Pilots are uniquely suited for this role. Trained and employed by the government of Sorcerer's Forge, few leave military service and most are dedicated to the defense of their city-state. Those who do leave to strike out on their own, usually become mercenary fighters, adventurers and explorers, but some choose of life of villainy, and all have a hard time teaching others how to become like them (most practitioners of magic eschew using Power Armor/Robot Vehicles, and most Robot Pilots are incapable of magic). They can also pilot conventional power armor and combat robots, but with less skill than TW versions.

Techno-Wizard Robot Pilot O.C.C. Abilities:

1. Use Techno-Wizard Device: The TW Robot Pilot can use any TW devices the same as any practitioner of magic, and prefers TW weapons and armor above all other types of magic item or conventional weapons.

2. P.P.E.: Like magic users, they have the ability to contain magical energy within their bodies and channel it through themselves into their TW body armor, power armor and robot vehicles.

Base P.P.E. is 2D4x10 +P.E. attribute number. Add 2D6 P.P.E. per each additional level of experience. The TW Robot Pilot can use ley line energy at times, but unlike other spell casters, the TW Robot Pilot can NOT draw additional P.P.E. from ley lines and nexus points to cast spells.

The character recovers P.P.E. at a rate of five points per hour of sleep or rest, double when using meditation, but can restore many times more P.P.E. when on a ley line (see #4 below).

3. Enhance Range and Damage of any TW Weapon Built into TW Armor, TW Power Armor or TW Robot Vehicle. By force of will and an additional amount of P.P.E. channeled from the TW Robot Pilot into his armor or robot vehicle, the warrior can increase the normal range and damage inflicted by it.

15 P.P.E.: The TW Robot Pilot can increase the weapon's range by 50%.

10 P.P.E.: The character can increase the damage inflicted by the TW weapon by 1D6. The latter includes damage inflicted via punches and kicks from the armor or robot vehicle.

In both cases the enhancement can only be applied ONCE per item, not many times to increase damage and range several fold.

Duration: In both cases, the increased range and damage lasts for one melee round (15 seconds).

4. Magically Heal TW Armor. For every *20 P.P.E.* points the TW Robot Pilot pumps into his TW armor/TW power armor or TW robot vehicle, he can restore 15 M.D.C. to it. Furthermore, the pilot can direct where the restored M.D.C. should be restored, such as the Main Body or a specific area like a sensor pod, head/helmet, arm, leg, etc., but the M.D.C. cannot be divided, it must all go to one specified part of the armor. Each act of restoration regardless of the amount of M.D.C. restored, counts as one melee action. When restoring lost M.D.C. to several locations (Main Body, then an arm, then a weapon system, etc.) each restorative action counts as one melee attack/action. **Note:** Only the exterior armor of TW body armor, TW power armor, TW robot vehicles and TW vehicles can be restored in this fashion, NOT normal, non-magical M.D.C. armor and vehicles, and the TW Robot Pilot must be the person piloting the armored unit being healed. This is a restorative ability, so only M.D.C. that has been lost can be *restored*. The TW Robot Pilot can NOT increase the M.D.C. above it's normal design limits. (A main body of 200 M.D.C. can not be made to have 250 M.D.C. even on a temporary basis.) **P.P.E. Recuperation Note:** Even when located on a ley line, the P.P.E. to restore the M.D.C. must come from the TW Robot Pilot, personally, not the ambient P.P.E. around him. *However,* this unique character recovers 15 P.P.E. an hour when resting or sleeping on a Ley Line and 30 P.P.E. per hour when meditating for the sole purpose of recovering spent P.P.E. at a ley line or nexus.

5. Combat/Magic Bonuses: These bonuses apply ONLY WHEN PILOTING TW Power Armor, TW Robot Vehicles, TW Vehicles and very similar things such as *Stormspire Automatons*. +1 on Perception Rolls, +1 on initiative, +1 melee attack, +1 to strike, parry and dodge, +2 to pull punch and +2 to save vs Horror Factor when piloting Techno-Wizard power armor, robots and vehicles.

6. Penalties: TW Robot Pilots are so attuned to using TW Power Armor that they are not as proficient at piloting completely tech-based (non-magical) versions; -1 attack per melee round, -1 to strike and -2 to dodge and roll with impact.

Techno-Wizard Robot Pilot O.C.C. Stats

Alignment: Any, but most are of good alignment.

Attribute Requirements: I.Q. 10, M.E. 10, P.S. 10, P.P. 12, P.E. 12 or higher. Approximately 60% are male and 40% female.

Racial Requirements: None, although 95% are human. This is due to Sorcerer's Forge being mostly a human city and few outsiders having access to TW Power Armor/Robot Vehicles.

TW Power Armor M.O.S. Skills:
Advanced Math (+15%)
Basic Mechanics (+15%) or Acrobatics.
Navigation (+15%)
Pilot: Robots & Power Armor (basic; +20%)
Pilot: Robot Combat Basic (general knowledge)
Pilot: Robot Combat Elite (select one TW power armor model to start, +1 at levels 5, 10 and 15).
Pilot: One skill of choice (+12%).
    TW Power Armor to Start: Select one model of TW Power Armor to start, usually any model made by Sorcerer's Forge.

TW Robot Pilot M.O.S. Skills:
Land Navigation (14%)
Pilot: Robots & Power Armor (basic; +10%)
Pilot: Robot Combat Basic (general knowledge)
Pilot: Robot Combat Elite (select one type of TW Robot Vehicle to start, +1 at levels 5, 10 and 15).
Pilot: One skill of choice (+12%).
Weapon Systems (+15%)
W.P. Heavy Energy Weapons (Rail Guns included)
    TW Robot to Start: Pick any one model of TW Robot to start, usually any model made by Sorcerer's Forge.

O.C.C. Skills: These are in addition to M.O.S. and reflect basic training for all Robot Pilot O.C.C.s, whether they specialize in Power Armor or Robot Vehicles.
Language: Native Tongue (American) at 94%.
Language: Other: One of choice (+20%).
Basic Mathematics: (+20%)
Body Building and Weightlifting
Climbing (+5%)
Computer Operation (+10%)
Military Etiquette (+15%)
Pilot: Combat Driving (+15%)
Pilot: One of choice (any; +15%).
Radio: Basic (+10%)
Running or Sensory Equipment (+15%).
W.P. Ancient: One of choice.
W.P. Modern: One of choice.
W.P. Energy Rifle
Hand to Hand: Expert, but it can be changed to Martial Arts at the cost of two O.C.C. Related Skills or Commando (or Assassin if evil) for the cost of three O.C.C. Related Skills.

O.C.C. Related Skills: Select three other skills, plus select one additional skill at levels 3, 6, 9 and 12. All new skills start at level one proficiency.
Communications: Any (+10%).
Cowboy: None.
Domestic: Any.
Electrical: Basic only.
Espionage: Detect Concealment and Wilderness Survival only.
Horsemanship: None.
Mechanical: Automotive, Aircraft and Basic Mechanics only (+5%).
Medical: First Aid (+5%) only.
Military: Any (+10%), except Naval History and Naval Tactics.
Physical: Any.
Pilot: Any (+10%), except Ships and Warships.
Pilot Related: Any (+10%).
Rogue: Cardsharp and Seduction only.
Science: Math (+10%) and Astronomy & Navigation (+15%) only.
Technical: Any (+5%).
W.P.: Any.
Wilderness: Any.

Secondary Skills: Two Secondary Skills at levels 3, 6, 9 and 12. These are additional areas of knowledge selected from the Secondary Skill List on page 300 of **Rifts® Ultimate Edition**. All start at the base skill level without benefit of bonuses, with the possible exception of an I.Q. bonus.

Standard Equipment: In addition to equipment in the above M.O.S. section, the character also has a suit of light M.D.C. body armor, a suit of heavy armor, one weapon per each W.P., one TW energy pistol of choice as his side arm and 1D4+2 extra E-Clips/P.P.E. Energy Clips for each, one conventional energy rifle and 1D4+1 E-Clips, a Vibro-Knife, a TW Knife or TW sword (pick one), two explosive grenades, two smoke grenades, survival knife (1D6 S.D.C.), pocket knife (1 S.D.C.), compass, first-aid medical kit, pocket computer, flashlight, utility belt, air filter & gas mask, walkie-talkie, uniform, dress uniform, combat boots, canteen, and a few personal items.

Money: The character starts off with 1D6x100 in credits and another 1D6x1,000 in other items.

Cybernetics: Usually avoid, as it impairs their P.P.E. reserve and channeling of magic energy.

Notable People of Sorcerer's Forge

Eric Walker

When travelers or traders make the journey to Sorcerer's Forge, it is Eric Walker who usually meets them on the road to the city. As is standard policy, all travelers who approach the city are stopped about 10 miles (16 km) from the Shroud by Eric's patrol. Visitors are interviewed to determine their identities and intentions. If they are expected they are escorted by his patrol to the city gates. If they are not, they are usually turned back, with force if necessary.

Lieutenant Eric Walker is, himself, a skilled, middle-aged Mystic Soldier who is enthusiastic about his job. He enjoys talking with travelers, guessing their true motives and conversing with them about the highlights and history of the Rifts North America, the Coalition States, Free Quebec, Lazlo, the Federation of Magic and other exotic places, but never about the city-state of Sorcerer's Forge. Eric's family is said to be descended from the founders of Sorcerer's Forge, and a direct descendent of one of the Seven Lords. Eric himself denies this (but it's true), often pointing out that few know anything about the identities of the Seven Lords. Eric is a loyal Mystic Soldier and though he is curious about the outside world, he considers it his home and would never willingly leave or betray it.

When travelers are spotted, Lt. Walker waits until they move to a position where his patrol would have the advantage, should things turn ugly and get rough. Once in position for an ambush or crossfire, he calls out to the strangers from afar, telling them to stop, remain where they are and not make any sudden moves. If the travelers seem reasonable, he walks out to them with one of the Psi-Stalkers and a Wilderness Scout or Psychic to conduct an interview. If not, he will keep his distance and try to communicate without showing himself. While doing so, he always keeps his Iceblast Shotgun drawn and ready, though not usually pointed at anyone.

Name: Lieutenant Eric Walker of the Sorcerer's Forge Military.
Alignment: Principled.
Attributes: I.Q. 14, M.E. 13, M.A. 18, P.S. 11, P.P. 12, P.E. 15, P.B. 11, Spd 17.
Hit Points: 26. **S.D.C.:** 25.
Size: 5 feet, 10 inches (1.77 m) tall, and weighs 170 pounds (76.5 kg).
Age: 43
P.P.E.: 81
Description: Despite being middle-aged, Eric still looks like a man in his prime. His dark brown hair is cut short and he is usually clean shaven. He maintains a friendly expression when conversing with others, but loses all expression when engaging in battle.

Disposition: Eric is friendly, outgoing and inquisitive. He is a strict follower of the laws and regulations of Sorcerer's Forge. He allows his subordinates some leeway, but insists on following regulations. Eric never makes exceptions to the rules when interviewing travelers; the risk is too great to the city. A loyal soldier first, a friend second, is the way most people would describe him. Eric is confident in his abilities but never takes risks that would endanger his mission.

Experience Level: 5th level Mystic Soldier with the rank of Lieutenant.

Combat Skills: Hand to Hand: Expert.

Skills of Note: Language: American (98%), Faerie Speak (72%), French (67%), Dragonese/Elven (67%) and Sign Language (military 50%), and Literacy: American (65%). Also, Climbing (65%), Land Navigation (57%), Mathematics (Basic; 70%), Military Etiquette (65%), Pilot: Automobile (78%), Radio: Basic (75%), Sensory Equipment (60%), Weapon Systems (70%), Wilderness Survival (50%), First Aid (65%), Trap/Mine Detection (40%), Computer Operation (50%), and General Repair & Maintenance (45%).

Weapon Proficiencies: W.P. Shotgun, W.P. Energy Pistol, W.P. Energy Rifle, W.P. Knife, and W.P. Sword, all at level 5.

Attacks per Melee: Five.

Bonuses: +1 on initiative, +4 to parry and dodge, +3 to roll with impact, +3 to pull punch, +2 to strike, +2 to disarm, and +1 to save vs Horror Factor.

Magic Knowledge: Standard for that O.C.C.

Psionic Powers: None.

Cybernetics: None.

Armor: Elite Mystic Soldier EBA (described elsewhere) with a Psi-Blocker Helmet accessory.

Weapons of Note: TW Iceblast Shotgun (described in the weapon section), TW Flaming Sword, Vibro-Knife, several normal/TW grenades, and a *Sylvan Storm pistol* (described in the weapon section). He prefers to use his Iceblast Shotgun in most situations.

Money: As a mid-ranked military officer, Eric has 2,000 credits on him and another 23,000 credits in savings at Sorcerer's Forge.

Maximilian Tyrannus

Maximilian Tyrannus is known as a frequent traveler to Sorcerer's Forge. Max, as he is known to his friends, is a learned explorer who trades information and recovered artifacts for goods and supplies when he visits the city. He has been coming to Sorcerer's Forge for decades, but seems to never get older. This has led many rumors. Some believe he is a demigod related to the Seven Lords, as he has been known to be granted frequent audiences with the Seven Lords of the city. Others claim he is a Godling, while others suspect he is a dragon who changes his shape to appear human. Others wonder if he might not be some type of D-Bee. His last name, "Tyrannus," has led some to wonder if he might not have been an "the Eighth Lord" who was banished from the city for his tyrannical ways. A few people even refer to him as the "the Exiled Lord" behind his back.

The truth is Max was, indeed, one of the original Lords of the city. When the original Lords founded Sorcerer's Forge, they all took new names to distinguish themselves from their old lives. Max took the last name "Tyrannus" from a joking nickname, earned from his forceful ways of getting things done and intolerance to ideas other than his own. He established the Sorcerer's Forge military before he left, and has encouraged an expansionist policy of action. When the other lords decided on an isolationist policy, Max was overruled. A series of incidents over the next few years created a rift between him and the Seven Lords. Max was always a loner, so when he could no longer tolerate the decisions of his comrades, he chose to leave the community he helped found. He had always believed that hiding the city was a mistake; that the world needs their knowledge and leadership. However, he accepted the majority decision and holds no ill-will toward the other Lords or the city-state of Sorcerer's Forge. In fact to this day, he considers Sorcerer's Forge to be his true home.

Eager to see what this "New Savage Earth," as he calls the world, Max left the city and has been exploring ever since. When he discovers something of significance, or learns of an imminent threat to Sorcerer's Forge, he returns to the city to inform the other Lords. He maintains several small homes, scattered across North America, including one in the shadow of Chi-Town (in an Old Town 'Burb), one at Lazlo, one in Old Bones near Free Quebec, one in the Magic Zone, a cabin in Dinosaur Swamp, and he lost his favorite home at the Kingdom of Tolkeen when the CS invaded. He has explored far and wide, including the Federation of Magic, the Chi-Town 'Burbs, and Dinosaur Swamp, and even the edges of the Vampire Kingdoms and Atlantis. Max has also found and acquired many bits of pre-Rifts technology that he trades to the Lords of the city in exchange for allowing him to visit his old friends and maintaining a secluded woodland cabin concealed within the Shroud (though he is seldom there and it contains nothing of value).

Over the years, Max and the Seven Lords have noticed they are more than just ageless. They have become some sort of *Creatures of Magic,* the very things they fear. Max views these abilities as beneficial and welcomed, while the Seven Lords are more reserved and fearful about their unnatural abilities. Which is one of the reasons they removed themselves from the public view, so as to not concern the people of the city they taught to be wary of magical and supernatural creatures. Nor did they want the people to think of them as demigods.

Max tries to keep a low profile, especially outside the city. In rare cases, he may direct travelers to Sorcerer's Forge, or lead them there himself if he is confident they can be of benefit to the place. Case in point, it was Max Tyrannus who introduced the Seven Lords to the Immaterial Hand, and helped to arrange the trade deals that have helped the city-state and the Black Market faction both prosper. Max is suspicious and cautious of others, especially demons and other supernatural beings, but is always interested in learning and knowledge, so he's been known to associate with rough customers and dangerous people of every variety. Ironically, Max has come to agree that it is probably best for Sorcerer's Forge to remain hidden to the rest of the world.

Name: Maximilian Tyrannus. (True name, unknown to all except the Seven Lords, is William Smith).

Alignment: Unprincipled.

Attributes: I.Q. 23, M.E. 19, M.A. 19, P.S. 11, P.P. 15, P.E. 18, P.B. 10, Spd 13.

M.D.C.: 154

Size: 5 feet, 8 inches (1.73 m) tall, and weighs 140 pounds (63 kg); look trim, fit and a man in his twenties.

Age: 147, but looks twenty-something.

Horror/Awe Factor: 9, but only by people who discover he is a Creature of Magic and perhaps even a demigod.

P.P.E.: 700

Description: Max appears as a man in his mid-twenties, but has the eyes and wisdom of someone much older. He has short black hair and sparkling blue eyes. He always has an expression of suspicion and scepticism when meeting strangers.

Disposition: Max is always reserved and cautious. He never reveals knowledge unless he has something to gain from it or it's a matter of importance to those he cares about. Max is friendly enough to the people he meets, and can be very charming, but he's always alert and watchful of things being said and going on around him, and is very aware that often people, places and things are not what they appear to be. He tries to be indifferent to global politics, and keep an open mind, though he still has a tendency to think his view of thing are right and his ideas better than others. He is confident, a natural leader, and always prepared to take charge. He has been known to be ruthless and sometimes struggles with doing what's best for others.

His journeys have taught him that not all Coalition soldiers or people are scoundrels, to be wary of dragons and shape-changers, and to fear the Vampire Kingdoms.

Experience Level: 12th level Ley Line Walker.

Skills of Note: All of the following at 98% skill proficiency: Literacy: American, and Language: American, Dragonese/Elven, Faerie Speak, Sign Language (military) and Techno-Can, Climbing, Computer Operation, Mathematics: Advance, Mathematics: Basic, Land Navigation, Wilderness Survival, Pilot: Jet Packs and Hovercycles, Barter, Electronic Countermeasures, Radio (Basic), Sensory Equipment, TV/Video, Basic Electronics, Intelligence, Basic Mechanics, Mechanical Engineer, Weapons Engineer, Military Etiquette, Military Fortification, and Recognize Weapon Quality.

Plus the following at 75% skill proficiency: Camouflage, First Aid, Lore: D-Bee, Lore: Demons & Monsters, Lore: Faeries & Creatures of Magic, Magic, Lore: Psychics & Psionics, General Repair and Maintenance, History: Pre-Rifts, History: Post-Apocalypse, Jury-Rig, Mythology, and Salvage.

Weapon Proficiencies: W.P. Sword (level 10), W.P. Staff (level 10), W.P. Handguns (level 12), W.P. Rifles (level 12), W.P. Energy Pistol (level 5), W.P. Energy Rifle (level 7) and W.P. Paired Weapons (level 7).

Natural Abilities: Physically ages the equivalent of one month for every 10 years. Immune to all normal poisons, toxins, and disease, super-human P.P.E., extensive Knowledge, Techno-Wizard construction knowledge, see the invisible (including spirits and Astral Beings), regenerates M.D.C. at a rate of 2D6 M.D.C. per hour and regrows lost limbs and organs in 4D6 hours, resistant to mind control, impervious to illusions, impervious to S.D.C. weapons, disease, radiation, and possession. Also see Bonuses. **Note:** All of the Seven Lords have similar abilities, P.P.E. an bonuses. Each of the Seven Lords have an affinity for magic and 1D6x100+300 P.P.E., P.E. attribute number x3 +100 M.D.C., +35 for every 100 years of life after the first 100 (obviously, they don't know that last part yet).

Vulnerabilities: Suffers double damage from Rune weapons (as well as other magic weapons that do double damage to Creatures of Magic), silver weapons do Mega-Damage, and he registers as a Creature of Magic.

Magic Knowledge: All Spell Invocations as described in Rifts® Book of Magic levels 1-9, plus Mystic Portal (60), Speed Weapon (100), Anti-Magic Cloud (140), Remove Curse (140), Re-Open Gateway (180), and Teleport: Superior (600).

Psionics: None.

Combat Skills: Hand to Hand: Expert.

Attacks per Melee: Six.

Bonuses: +4 on Perception Rolls, +2 on initiative, +3 to pull punch, +2 to roll with punch, +5 to parry or dodge, +2 to strike, +2 to disarm, Critical Strike on a Natural 18-20, +3 to save vs curses, +4 to save vs magic, +4 to spell strength, +7 to save vs possession and mind control, +4 to save vs Horror Factor, +2 to save vs psionics and insanity, +6% to save vs coma/death and +2 to save vs poison.

Weapons of Note: TK Rifle, Flaming Sword, Lightning Staff, several TW grenades, Vibro-Knife and an S.D.C. pistol (with clips for silver, TW ammo and Ramjet rounds), but has access to ANYTHING manufactured by Sorcerer's Forge, the Black Market and Northern Gun.

Armor: Techno-Wizard Armor (120 M.D.C.) with Escape (4 P.P.E. to activate) and Fly as the Eagle (20 minutes per use; 12 P.P.E. to activate) as the abilities.

Mask of the Forge Lords. This TW mask appears as a helmet with a stylized faceplate. The mask has 75 M.D.C. and functions as an air filter, gas mask and is the equivalent of a *Psi-Blocker Helmet* (**Rifts® Book of Magic**, page 332). It also has translucent lenses over the eye slits that enable the activation of the following magic spell abilities: Mask of Deceit (15), See Aura (6), See the Invisible (4), and Eyes of Thoth (8).

Cybernetics: None, as a Creature of Magic his body would reject any implants.

Money: Unknown, but given his extensive adventuring and connections, 1D6x10 million can be acquired in a matter of hours.

Weapons of Sorcerer's Forge

Sorcerer's Forge can produce many modern devices and common technological gear you'd expect in a modern city, as well as a wide range of TW items and the weapons, armor and gear described in this section. They sell these items in the city and across the eastern half of the continent via the Black Market. They acquire the raw materials, fabric and other goods also through trade via the Immaterial Hand Black Market faction.

Sylvan Storm Weapons

As Sorcerer's Forge grew, they had to defend themselves against demons, monsters, slavers, raiders and rivals, including conflicts with a rival magic community that no longer exists. During these battles, the infantry of Sorcerer's Forge found themselves overwhelmed by enemy troops, some of whom were protected by *Impervious to Energy* spells. With most of their weapons energy based, and only a few non-energy heavy weapons, they suffered heavy casualties. Eventually, Sorcerer's Forge defeated this enemy, but the conflict created a desire for a TW weapon that did not rely on energy blasts, and could be used by infantry.

After much trial and error, it was decided the weapon needed to fire physical projectiles, but be powered by magic. The ammunition was made with a fusion of wood, silver and M.D.C. materials that were magically enhanced; a side effect of which turned the rounds a silver color. The enchanted rounds are built into special ammo casings and used in TW weapons powered by magic and magical Telekinesis to fire the enchanted projectile. The use of Telekinesis as a propellant means shorter range, but there is little kick to the weapon, and even preteens can fire the weapon with excellent accuracy. (**Note:** All Sylvan Storm weapons are +1 to strike in addition to bonuses from W.P. and targeting optics.) Furthermore, Sylvan ammunition does full damage to creatures of magic and supernatural beings that are impervious to "normal" weapons and ammo. Better yet, the rounds do double damage to creatures vulnerable to *wood, silver* or *magic*.

The line of weapons were named "Sylvan Storm" because Sorcerer's Forge is surround by a vast forest wilderness and one of the designers made the comment that the use of the weapons made battles feel like a sudden "forest storm." The name, Sylvan Storm, stuck.

If there is a downside, it's that the weapons require a P.P.E. charge to fire, and the cost of a single round is not cheap, though not prohibitively expensive either. However, Sylvan Storm weapons have a P.P.E. battery that provide an impressive payload. Of course, Mystic Soldiers, TW Robot Pilots, any mage and creatures of magic can recharge the weapon with ease. In addition, leaving the weapon on a ley line, or carrying it while on a ley line, automatically recharges the P.P.E. battery at a rate of two blasts per every 15 minutes of exposure. It is a slow process, but occurs all by itself, recharging the TK firing source without direct intervention on the part the weapon's non-magical user. Of course, the physical Sylvan ammo is also required.

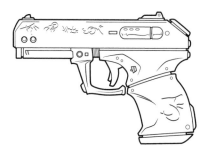

SFW-15 Sylvan Storm Pistol

This weapon is an automatic pistol; it is favored by soldiers who want a small backup weapon to use against foes resistant to energy attacks.

<u>Weight</u>: 3 pounds (1.35 kg).

<u>Range</u>: 400 feet (122 m).

<u>Mega-Damage</u>: Single shot 1D4 M.D., a burst of three rounds inflicts 2D4 M.D.; double damage to beings vulnerable to wood, silver or magic.

<u>Rate of Fire</u>: Single shot or three bullet burst.

<u>Payload of Sylvan Round</u>: 15 physical bullets per clip.

Payload of P.P.E. Energy: The P.P.E. battery can hold a maximum of 60 blasts.

Bonus: +1 to strike.

Cost: 65,000 credits for the pistol. 30 credits per bullet; both the weapon and the Sylvan ammo are super-rare outside of Sorcerer's Forge.

SFW-30 Sylvan Storm Rifle

This weapon looks like a pre-Rifts era military assault rifle; it behaves like a handheld Rail Gun without the recoil.

Weight: Rifle: 7 pounds (3.15 kg).

Range: 1,200 feet (366 m).

Mega-Damage: Single shot 1D6+2 M.D., a burst of three rounds inflicts 2D6+4 M.D.; double damage to beings vulnerable to wood, silver or magic.

Rate of Fire: Single shot or three bullet burst.

Payload of Sylvan Round: 30 physical bullets per clip.

Payload of P.P.E. Energy: The P.P.E. battery can hold a maximum of 30 blasts before requiring recharging (needs two P.P.E. per blast).

Bonus: +1 to strike.

Cost: 150,000 credits for the rifle. 40 credits per bullet; both the weapon and the Sylvan ammo are super-rare outside of Sorcerer's Forge.

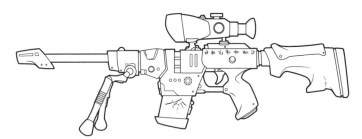

SFW-30SSR Sylvan Storm Sniper Rifle

This sniper rifle is a single shot weapon used for sniping and precision hunting. The weapon comes equipped with a bi-pod and an scope with telescopic scope, laser targeting and passive nightvision capabilities.

Weight: 10 pounds (4.5 kg).

Range: 2,200 feet (670.5 m).

Mega-Damage: 2D6+2 M.D.; double damage to beings vulnerable to wood, silver or magic.

Rate of Fire: Single shot only.

Payload of Sylvan Round: 30 physical bullets per clip.

Payload of P.P.E. Energy: The P.P.E. battery can hold a maximum of 15 shots before requiring recharging (needs three P.P.E. per blast).

Bonus: +1 to strike or disarm. +3 to strike when used in a prone position or with the weapon braced against a solid surface.

Cost: 175,000 credits for the rifle. 40 credits per bullet; both the weapon and the Sylvan ammo are super-rare outside of Sorcerer's Forge.

SFW-17 Sylvan Storm Heavy Gun

This is a larger, heavier, rapid-fire version of the Sylvan Storm Rifle that is deployed as a light machine-gun. It can be used by a single individual, provided he has a P.S. of 20 or greater. Due to its large size and weight, the weapon is meant to be used in a prone position or braced against a solid surface; if it is not used as such, the shooter suffers a penalty of -4 to strike, unless he has a P.S. of 30 or greater, in which case the penalty is -2. Sorcerer's Forge light infantry squads usually have a single soldier equipped with one of these as a squad support weapon.

Weight: Gun: 12 pounds (5.4 kg), clip: 1.5 pounds (0.67 kg), belt: 3 pounds (1.35 kg), drum: 10 pounds (4.5 kg).

Range: 1,200 feet (366 m).

Mega-Damage: Single shot 1D6+2 M.D., a burst of five rounds inflicts 4D6 M.D., and a burst of 10 rounds does 6D6 M.D.; double damage to beings vulnerable to wood, silver or magic.

Rate of Fire: Single shot or bursts firing.

Payload of Sylvan Round: 30 physical bullets per standard clip, 60 round belt, or 120 round drum (12 long bursts).

Payload of P.P.E. Energy: A pair of large P.P.E. batteries can hold a maximum of 60 single shot blasts, 10 short bursts or 5 long bursts before requiring recharging.

Bonus: None.

Cost: 300,000 credits for the light machine-gun. 40 credits per bullet; both the weapon and the Sylvan ammo are super-rare outside of Sorcerer's Forge.

TW Firestorm Rifle

This weapon looks like a heavy plasma rifle but it fires bolts of magical fire. It also has a long tube below the main barrel that is capable of firing short streams of flames like a flamethrower. Both functions are powered by the same power source. This weapon was originally designed by Sorcerer's Forge, but the schematics were sold to Stormspire in exchange for a discount on a large order of magic components purchased using the Immaterial Hand Black Market Faction as the go-between.

Weight: 8 pounds (3.6 kg).

Range: 1,200 feet (366 m) firing fire bolts. 100 foot (30.5 m) range firing a stream of magic fire.

Mega-Damage: 3D6 M.D. per bolt of fire or 6D6 M.D. per stream of fire.

Rate of Fire: Single shot or single stream of flame.

Payload: 15 shots per 30 P.P.E. or 60 I.S.P. pumped into the weapon to charge/recharge it. Remember, a fire stream counts as two blasts.

Cost: Gun: 200,000 credits; very rare.

TW Iceblast Shotgun

This weapon looks like a typical shotgun with crystals and wires built into the stock and a coil around the barrel. When fired, it unleashes a blast of cold and ice to a two foot (0.6 m) blast radius.

Weight: 8 pounds (3.6 kg).

Range: 800 feet (244 m).

Mega-Damage: 5D6 M.D. per bolt of cold and ice fragments.

Rate of Fire: Single shot.

Payload: 8 shots per 30 P.P.E. or 60 I.S.P. pumped into the weapon to charge/recharge it.

Cost: 250,000 credits; rare.

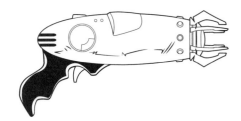

TW Nova Pistol

This pistol version of the *Nova Rifle* (Federation of Magic) was created by Stormspire to be a more versatile and portable model. It is favored by Special Forces and mercenaries.

Weight: 6 pounds (2.7).

Range: 400 feet (122 m).

Mega-Damage: 3D6 M.D. to all targets in a 4 foot (1.2 m) radius.

Rate of Fire: Single shot only.

Payload: Four shots per P.P.E.-Clip.

Note: The Tolkeen version of this does not use P.P.E.-Clips and requires 12 P.P.E. or 24 I.S.P. to reload/recharge the weapon with 2 energy blasts.

Cost: Gun: 95,000 credits, P.P.E.-Clip: 40,000 credits; rare.

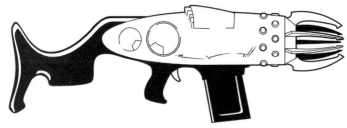

TW Nova Cannon

This is a larger version of the *Nova Rifle* developed by Stormspire (see page 114 of **Rifts® Federation of Magic**). It fires swirling red globes of energy that explode on impact. This is the Sorcerer's Forge version of the weapon, though Stormspire has

a similar cannon. The weapon is normally mounted on a vehicle or power armor, but a character with an Augmented P.S. of 28 or greater (or Robot P.S. 20+) can use it as a two-handed rifle.

Weight: 50 pounds (22.5 kg).

Range: 1,500 feet (457.2 m).

Mega-Damage: 1D6x10 M.D. to all targets in a 6 foot (1.8 m) radius.

Rate of Fire: Single shot only.

Payload: 50 P.P.E. or 100 I.S.P. to reload/recharge the weapon with four energy blasts. **Note:** The Stormspire version has four shots per P.P.E.-Clip, but holds four clips for 16 blasts.

Cost: Gun: 300,000 credits, P.P.E.-Clip: 40,000 credits; very rare.

Body Armor of Sorcerer's Forge

These unique suits of EBA are mostly exclusive to Mystic Soldiers; normal people can use them but would be unable to use the TW abilities, and magic users could use them but it would impair their spell casting. They are made of a combination of natural and synthetic materials, and enhanced by Techno-Wizardry. All of these suits of armor are camouflaged to blend into the surrounding terrain (forest and snow are most common). Mystic Soldiers are trained to use their magic while wearing these specific designs. They have all the standard features of EBA and some TW abilities.

Accessories: The following accessories may be added as Techno-Wizard abilities to any of these suits of body armor for an additional price. Normal accessories for EBA may also be added.

Flaming Dagger: A Flaming Dagger (Book of Magic) may be added to either forearm; costs an additional 40,000 credits.

Magic Optic System: As the standard TW item (see Rifts Ultimate Edition), except it is a visor-like attachment to the helmet; costs an additional 30,000 credits.

Night Goggles: Night Goggles (Book of Magic) may be added as a visor-like attachment to the helmet (cannot have both Night Goggles and Magic Optic System), and cost an additional 50,000 credits.

Psi-Blocker Helmet: A Psi-Blocker Helmet (Book of Magic) may be added as a replacement for the standard helmet (50 M.D.C. regardless of EBA model), and costs an additional 250,000 credits (due to the extreme expense, usually only high-ranking officers have them).

SFMA-5 Mystic Soldier EBA

M.D.C. by Location:
    Head/Helmet –50
    Arms – 25 each
    Legs – 35 each
    Main Body – 50

Weight: 10 pounds (4.5 kg); fair mobility, -5% to Prowl, Gymnastics, Acrobatics, and other such Physical skills.

TW Abilities: Superhuman Endurance (12) and Chameleon (6); each lasts for 10 minutes per activation. The cost to activate the spell is in parenthesis.

Black Market Cost: 65,000 credits, rare.

Note: A non-TW version of this is made for Sorcerer's Forge's non-magic using soldiers (or customers); it has identical stats except no TW/magic abilities and costs 30,000 credits.

SFMA-8 Elite Mystic Soldier EBA

M.D.C. by Location:
- Head/Helmet – 70
- Arms – 35 each
- Legs – 50 each
- Main Body – 80

Weight: 15 pounds (6.75 kg); fair mobility, -5% to climb; -10% to Prowl, Gymnastics, Acrobatics, and other such Physical skills.

TW Abilities: Superhuman Endurance (12), Chameleon (6) and Superhuman Strength (10; only gains strength bonus); each lasts for 10 minutes per activation. The cost to activate the spell is in parenthesis.

Black Market Cost: 120,000 credits, very rare.

Note: A non-TW version of this is made for Sorcerer's Forge's non-magic using soldiers (or customers); it has identical stats except no TW abilities and costs 50,000 credits.

Power Armor of Sorcerer's Forge

Sorcerer's Forge uses several types of Power Armor, both technological and Techno-Wizard. They buy many Northern Gun models, and produce their own TW Power Armor. The unique models created by Sorcerer's Forge have the standard Power Armor features (see page 271 of **Rifts® Ultimate Edition**), with the additional abilities listed below. Individual models have additional features as listed in their specific descriptions.

All TW Power Armor of Sorcerer's Forge have the following features:

1. Powered by a Magical Reactor: The TW equivalent of a nuclear reactor, it powers all the basic functions of the armor. This includes any attached TW weapons and limited other TW abilities (see specific model for descriptions). Average life: One year, but the reactor can be recharged in a secret process known only to Sorcerer's Forge (it involves magical energy being absorbed from a ley line at a special facility for one week), and costs one million credits.

2. TW Armor of Ithan: All TW Power Armor produced by the Sorcerer's Forge are built with a self-generating *Armor of Ithan* effect built onto them. This magic feature gives power armor an additional 50 M.D.C. (75 M.D.C. when on a ley line or at a nexus point), and any damage is subtracted from this number first, before damage is inflicted to the armor itself. Once the Armor of Ithan M.D.C. is reduced to zero, it regenerates back to full strength (50 M.D.C.) after one hour, and automatically goes back in place. Likewise, if the magic armor is damaged/reduced, but not completely, the reduced armor remains in place and does not regenerate to the full 50 M.D.C. until one hour after the last bit of damage was inflicted. The pilot may "turn off" the armor if there is some reason to do so. In the alternative, the pilot may channel 15 P.P.E. or 30 I.S.P. to reactivate the armor to full strength at any time. It costs more I.S.P. than the typical Armor of Ithan spell, but it can be worthwhile.

3. Optical Systems: All Sorcerer's Forge Power Armor have the following optical systems: Full optical systems, including laser targeting, telescopic, passive night vision (light amplification), thermal-imaging, infrared, ultraviolet, and polarization. In addition, the power armor has a *See the Invisible* magic effect (as per the spell) that can be activated at any time for the cost of one P.P.E. It has a range of 200 feet (61 m) and the effect lasts for 20 minutes.

4. Optical Systems: All Sorcerer's Forge Power Armor have a magic language translator that is, in effect, the same as the *Tongues* spell. It can be activated at any time for the cost of 12 P.P.E., has a range of 200 feet (61 m), and the effect lasts for 15 minutes per 12 P.P.E. pumped into it.

5. Self-Destruct Mechanism: Each has a built-in self-destruct mechanism to prevent the armor and its technology from falling into enemy hands. It is initiated by overloading the Magical Reactor. Since it is magic, there is no radiation and the damage is self-contained, destroying most of the internal systems, TW gemstones, and the TW Magic Reactor, doing 2D6x10 M.D. and turning the armor scrap metal. It is activated via voice command.

SFPA-500 Exoskeleton Armor

The Five-Hundred Exoskeleton, as it is known, is, in effect, a heavy suit of body armor with power armor type augmentation and superior M.D.C. and magic features. It is a favorite among heavy infantry troops and can be used by the Mystic Soldier as well as the TW Robot Pilot.

Model Type: SFPA-500 Exoskeleton.
Class: TW Armored Infantry Assault Suit.
Crew: One.
M.D.C. by Location:
- *Helmet – 80
- *Hands – 20 each
- Arms – 40 each
- Legs – 65 each
- **Main Body – 135

* A single asterisk indicates a small and difficult target to strike, requiring the attacker to make a "Called Shot," and even then the assailant is -3 to strike.

Destroying the head of the power armor eliminates all forms of optical enhancement and sensory systems. The pilot must now rely on his own vision and senses; no power armor combat bonuses to strike, parry, and dodge.

** Depleting the M.D.C. of the main body shuts the power armor down completely, making it useless.

Speed: See TW Exoskeleton features.

Statistical Data:
Weight: 50 pounds (22.5 kg); fair mobility, -10% to Prowl, Gymnastics, Acrobatics and other such Physical skills.

Size: Man-sized and resembles body armor.

TW Exoskeleton Features: To activate the "exoskeleton" abilities the wearer must channel 30 P.P.E. or 60 I.S.P. into the power armor. The bonuses remain in effect for three hours per charge to the exoskeleton features. Exo-Bonuses: +5 to P.S. and P.S. becomes the equivalent of Robot Strength, +10 to Spd, +10 feet (3 m) to leaping, and reduces the rate of fatigue by 50%. The improved strength can allow a wearer with a high P.S. to wield heavy weapons, such as rail guns, the Nova Cannon and Sylvan Storm Heavy Gun.

TW Abilities: Superhuman Endurance (12), Chameleon (6), See the Invisible (4), Float in Air (5), and Breathe Without Air (5). Each lasts for 10 minutes per activation. The cost to activate the spell is in parenthesis.

Underwater Capabilities: Swimming: The power armor can swim at a speed equal to its running speeding, on the surface of water or half that underwater. It can also walk along the bottom of the water at 20% of its normal running speed up to a depth of 800 feet (244 m).

Black Market Cost: 1.8 to 2.5 million credits, rare.

SFPA-800
Nexus Guardian

The Nexus Guardian is the most common and popular of the handful of power armors manufactured by the Sorcerer's Forge. When the Techno-Wizards of Sorcerer's Forge began designing their own Power Armor, the Seven Lords instructed them to draw inspiration from the designs of the Glitter Boy and Triax Predator. Though the Nexus Guardian lacks the armor and firepower of a Glitter Boy, it is more mobile and versatile.

When on reconnaissance or guard duty in the field, it is typically concealed by the Chameleon Cloaking System, so if an enemy is spotted and the power armor prepares to attack, it becomes visible. However, if it wishes to remain unseen and observe, the Chameleon enchantment remains in place and the power armor remains concealed, as per the parameters of the spell, i.e. does not move. Operations near or on ley lines augment the TW features of the Nexus Guardian (via the Ley Line Booster), increasing the damage of its weapons 25%, increasing its magic M.D.C. and doubling the duration of sensors and special features.

The main weapon of the Power Armor is either a Starfire Pulse Cannon (Federation of Magic), or a Sylvan Storm Cannon (a larger version of the Sylvan Storm Heavy Gun). These large weapons are attached to the back and shoulder of the Power Armor, and when not in use, the weapon is flipped back and stored in an upward position. When needed for combat, the pilot simply reaches back, grasps the handle and pulls forward. A special version of the Nexus Guardian called the "Nexus Grenadier," replaces the big gun with a second shoulder rack of missiles or a TW Nova Cannon (described previously; connected to Magical Reactor to give almost unlimited payload). A non-magic user can pilot the Nexus Guardian, but is unable to activate any of the Techno-Wizard (TW) weapons or special armor features. Only about 75 Nexus Guardians have been manufactured due to manpower limitations and extreme cost.

Model Type: SFPA-800 Nexus Guardian.
Class: TW Armored Infantry Assault Suit.
Crew: One.
M.D.C. by Location:
    Main Weapon (Sylvan Storm Cannon or Starfire Pulse Cannon) – 100
    *Head – 130
    *Hands (2) – 35 each
    Arms (2) – 120 each

Legs (2) – 180 each
Retractable Flaming Sword – 70
Missile Launcher Pod (1; left shoulder) – 25
Forearm Blaster (1; right arm) – 30
Ammo-Canister (1; rear, back) – 50
**Main Body – 325

Note: The TW Armor of Ithan adds +50 to M.D.C. (75 M.D.C. at a ley line or ley line nexus).

* A single asterisk indicates a small and difficult target to strike, requiring the attacker to make a "Called Shot," and even then the assailant is -3 to strike.

Destroying the head of the Power Armor eliminates all forms of optical enhancement and sensory systems. The pilot must now rely on his own vision and senses; no Power Armor combat bonuses to strike, parry, and dodge.

** Depleting the M.D.C. of the main body will shut the Power Armor down completely, making it useless.

Speed:

Running: 100 mph (160 km) maximum, but the Ley Line Booster system improves the speed by 50% when on a ley line. The act of running does tire out its operator, but at 20% of the usual fatigue rate.

Leaping: The robot legs can leap up to 10 feet (3 m) high or across unassisted by the boosters built into the legs and feet. A jet booster assisted leap can propel the unit up to 50 feet (15.2 m) up and across. This is NOT flight.

Underwater Capabilities: Swimming: The power armor can swim or use its jet booster at a sluggish speed of 10 mph (16 km), on the surface of water or underwater. It can also walk along the bottom of the water at 20% of its normal running speed.

Statistical Data:

Height: 10 feet (3 m).

Width: 4 feet (1.2 m).

Length: 3.5 feet (1 m).

Weight: 1,100 pounds (495 kg) for a suit of Power Armor without the main weapon. One ton with a Sylvan Storm Cannon and ammo canister or Starfire Pulse Cannon.

Physical Strength: Equal to Robot P.S. of 30.

Cargo: Small storage area for extra supplies and personal weapons.

Power System: Magical Reactor; average life is 1 year (can be recharged at Sorcerer's Forge).

Black Market Cost: 5-10 million credits, rarely sold and very few lost/stolen.

Weapon Systems:

1. SFW-48 Sylvan Storm Cannon: This larger version of the Sylvan Storm Heavy Gun is modeled on the Glitter Boy's Boom Gun. It fires a single large, telekinetically-accelerated round that releases 50 Sylvan Storm flechette rounds that strike the target simultaneously. The six foot (1.83 m) long weapon is attached to a swivel unit on the shoulder and is stored, locked into place, behind the shoulder.

Primary Purpose: Assault, Anti-Armor and Anti-Aircraft.

Weight: Gun: 225 pounds (101.25 kg), ammo canister: 500 pounds (225 kg).

Range: 1,200 feet (366 m).

Mega-Damage: 6D6 M.D. per blast; double damage to beings vulnerable to wood, silver or magic.

Rate of Fire: Single shots only.

Payload: 100 round ammo canister. A second canister can be carried attached to the hip, but it must be manually removed by another suit of Power Armor (or a character under the effects of Superhuman Strength) to replace the canister. Reloading the canister will take about 5 minutes for those not trained, but 1 minute by someone trained in the use of Nexus Guardian Power Armor.

2. Starfire Pulse Cannon (alternative weapon): This weapon is used alternatively to the Sylvan Storm Cannon by half of all Nexus Guardians. It is effectively the normal Starfire Pulse Cannon attached to a swivel unit on the shoulder of the Power Armor. When not in use, it is stored, locked into place, behind the shoulder. It is powered by the Magical Reactor rather than P.P.E.-Clips, giving it nearly unlimited ammo. Although this weapon is almost twice as powerful and needs no ammo compared to the Sylvan Storm Cannon, it also has less than half the range and is reliant on energy blasts.

Primary Purpose: Assault & Anti-Armor.

Weight: 124 pounds (55.8 kg).

Range: 2,000 feet (610 m).

Mega-Damage: 2D6x10 M.D.

Rate of Fire: Single shots only.

Payload: Effectively unlimited; connected to Magical Reactor power supply.

3. Flaming Retractable Sword: Inside of a forearm housing on the left arm is a retractable Flaming Sword. Since it is connected to the Magical Reactor it takes no magical energy from the pilot to activate it.

Primary Purpose: Anti-Personnel & Defense.

Mega-Damage: 4D6 M.D.

Rate of Fire: Equal to the number of combined hand to hand attacks of the pilot and his Power Armor.

Effective Range: 4 foot blade (1.2 m).

Note: Some models have an Ice Blade (Book of Magic) instead of a Flaming Sword.

4. Starfire Blaster: Effectively a version of the Starfire pistol built directly under the left arm (to the side of the Flaming Sword), added as a backup for the main weapon.

Primary Purpose: Anti-Personnel.

Mega-Damage: 3D6 M.D. per blast.

Rate of Fire: Single shots only.

Effective Range: 1000 feet (305 m).

Payload: Effectively unlimited; tied to Magical Reactor power supply.

5. Shoulder Missile Launcher: To the top and side of the shoulder opposite the main weapon is a large pod that can hold short-range missiles or mini-missiles. These are used for long-range or area attacks.

Primary Purpose: Anti-Aircraft & Anti-Armor.

Mega-Damage: Varies with missile type.

Rate of Fire: May be fired one missile at a time or in volleys of two, three, or four.

Effective Range: Varies by missile type.

Payload: Total of 4 short-range missiles or 12 mini-missiles.

6. Alternative Weapons: In rare circumstances, the Nexus Guardian may pick up and use any large, handheld heavy weapons meant for Cyborgs or Power Armor. It cannot use man-sized weapons.

7. **Hand to Hand Combat:** Rather than use a weapon, the pilot can engage in Mega-Damage hand to hand combat.
8. **TW Abilities:** These abilities require P.P.E. /I.S.P. to activate and are in addition to the above listed abilities. The first four abilities are identical to the TW Vehicular Features (Book of Magic) of the same name. The caster level for spell effects are at 5th level.

Chameleon Cloaking System: Costs 5 P.P.E. or 10 I.S.P.

Super-Stealth Mode (Invisibility: Superior): Costs 20 P.P.E. or 40 I.S.P.

Impervious to Energy: Costs 20 P.P.E. or 40 I.S.P.

Ley Line Booster: Continuous when applicable.

Sense Evil: Costs 2 P.P.E. or 4 I.S.P.

Sense Magic: Costs 2 P.P.E. or 4 I.S.P.

Detect Concealment: Costs 3 P.P.E. or 6 I.S.P.

Ley Line Transmission (Book of Magic): Costs 10 P.P.E. or 20 I.S.P.

Dispel Magic Barriers: Costs 10 P.P.E. or 20 I.S.P.

Ley Line Fade (Book of Magic): Costs 10 P.P.E. or 20 I.S.P.

9. **Sensor Systems of Note:** Standard for Sorcerer's Forge Power Armor (see above).

SFPA-880 Avenger

The Avenger is a smaller version of the Nexus Guardian that was built with a special TW flight pack. This Power Armor was developed to give the military of Sorcerer's Forge a stealthy, flight-capable unit that could respond quickly to a threat. The flight pack is a set of foldable wings and a set of jet boosters attached to the back of the armor. This model is effectively the Techno-Wizard equivalent of the SAMAS. It lacks the firepower and armor of the Nexus Guardian, but can fly almost completely silently. Most Avengers are kept within the Shroud, and are usually only used for reconnaissance or in response to a large enemy presence. Only about 50 Avengers have been produced, and are exclusively used by skilled TW Robot Pilots.

Model Type: SFPA-880 Avenger.
Class: Strategic TW Armor Assault Suit.
Crew: One.

M.D.C. by Location:
    *Head – 65
    *Hands (2) – 25 each
    Arms (2) – 60 each
    Legs (2) – 120 each
    Shoulder Wings (2) – 30 each
    Main Rear Jets (2) – 55 each
    *Lower Maneuvering Jets (2) – 20 each
    Ammo Canister (rear) – 30
    Main Weapon – 75
    Forearm Blaster – 45
    Retractable Flaming Sword – 45
    *Shoulder Mini-Missile Launchers (2) – 20 each
    **Main Body – 220
    Note: The TW Armor of Ithan adds +50 to M.D.C. (see above).

    * A single asterisk indicates a small and difficult target to strike, requiring the attacker to make a *Called Shot*, and even then the assailant is -3 to strike. Destroying the head of the Power Armor will eliminate all forms of optical enhancement

and sensory systems. The pilot must now rely on his own vision and senses. No Power Armor combat bonuses to strike, parry, and dodge.

    ** Depleting the M.D.C. of the main body will shut the Power Armor down completely, making it useless. **Note:** Destroying a wing will make flight impossible. However, even with no wing(s), the Avenger can make jet powered leaps and hover stationary above the ground.

Speed:
Running: 60 mph (96 km) maximum (the Ley Line Booster can increase the speed by 50% when on a ley line). Note that the act

of running does tires out its operator, but at 10% of the usual fatigue rate.

Leaping: The robot legs can leap up to 15 feet (4.6 m) high or across unassisted by the thrusters. A jet thruster assisted leap can propel the unit up to 100 feet (30.5 m) high and 200 feet (61 m) across without actually attaining flight.

Flying: The TW flight system enables it to hover stationary up to 5,000 feet (1524 m) or fly. Maximum flying speed is 300 mph (480 km), but cruising speed is considered to be 150 mph (240 km). Maximum altitude is limited to about 10,000 feet (3,048 m). The TW flight system is almost completely quiet, only the normal sounds of the Power Armor and the rush of the wind is heard. Note: The Ley Line Booster allows all the given speeds and altitudes to be increased by 50% when on a ley line; additionally, when off the ley line, the pilot may expend 10 P.P.E. or 20 I.S.P. to maintain these bonuses for 30 minutes.

Flying Range: The Magical Reactor gives the Avenger indefinite power, but the engines get hot and need to cool after a maximum of ten hours of flight when traveling at speeds above cruising, and twenty hours of cruising speed, can fly indefinitely with rest stops. The Ley Line Booster allows the engines to never overheat when traveling on a ley line (if cruising on and off ley lines, treat as if you stopped to rest when on a ley line).

Statistical Data:

Height: 8 feet (2.4 m).

Width: Wings down: 3.5 feet (1.06 m). Wings extended: 9 feet (2.7 m).

Length: 4 feet, 3 inches (1.3 m).

Weight: 850 pounds (382.5 kg) fully loaded.

Physical Strength: Robotic P.S. of 25.

Cargo: None.

Power System: Magical Reactor, average life is 1 year (can be recharged at Sorcerer's Forge).

Black Market Cost: 5 to 10 million credits, rarely sold and very few lost/stolen.

Weapon Systems:

1. SFW-18 Sylvan Storm Heavy Gun: This is the main weapon for 50% of Avengers; it has a large ammo canister installed on the back above the flight system. Other Avengers are equipped with TW Force Cannons (Book of Magic) or TK Heavy Machine-Guns (Book of Magic), and either one is connected to the Magical reactor, giving it a nearly unlimited payload (also lowers total weight by 300 pounds/135 kg).

Primary Purpose: Assault & Defense.

Weight: Gun: 12 pounds (5.4 kg), clip: 1.5 pounds (.67 kg), belt: 3 pounds (1.35 kg), drum: 10 pounds (4.5 kg).

Range: 1,200 feet (366 m).

Mega-Damage: Single shot 1D6+2 M.D., a burst of five rounds inflicts 4D6 M.D., and a burst of 10 rounds does 6D6 M.D.; double damage to beings vulnerable to wood, silver or magic.

Rate of Fire: Single shot or via burst.

Payload: 1,000 round canister, that's 100 long bursts. A second canister can be carried under the flight system, but must be manually removed by another suit of Power Armor (or a character under the effects of Superhuman Strength) to replace the canister. Reloading the canister will take about 5 minutes for those not trained, but 1 minute by someone trained in the use of Avenger Power Armor.

2. Flaming Retractable Sword: Inside of a forearm housing on the left arm is a retractable Flaming Sword. Since it is connected to the Magical Reactor, it takes no magical energy from the pilot to activate it.

Primary Purpose: Anti-Personnel & Defense.

Range: 4 foot blade (1.2 m).

Mega-Damage: 4D6 M.D.

Rate of Fire: Equal to the number of combined hand to hand attacks of the pilot and his Power Armor.

Note: Some models have an Ice Blade (Book of Magic) instead of a Flaming Sword.

3. Mini-Missile Launchers (2): On top of each shoulder is a small missile pod that can fit four Mini-Missiles. These are normally used for long-range or area attacks.

Primary Purpose: Anti-Aircraft & Defense.

Range: Varies with missile type.

Mega-Damage: Varies with missile type.

Rate of Fire: May be fired one missile at a time or in volleys of two, three, or four.

Payload: A pod of 4 mini-missiles on each shoulder for a total of 8 missiles.

4. Starfire Blaster: Effectively a version of the Starfire pistol built directly under the left arm (to the side of the Flaming Sword). It is meant as a backup in case the main weapon runs out of ammo or is disabled.

Primary Purpose: Anti-Personnel.

Range: 1,000 feet (305 m).

Mega-Damage: 3D6 M.D. per blast.

Rate of Fire: Single shots only.

Payload: Effectively unlimited; tied to Magical Reactor power supply.

5. Alternative Handheld Weapons: Any weapons can be substituted in an emergency or as a back-up weapon; typically a heavy weapon when the pilot has his choice.

6. Hand to Hand Combat: Rather than use a weapon, the pilot can engage in Mega-Damage hand to hand combat.

7. TW Abilities: These abilities require P.P.E./I.S.P. to activate and are in addition to the above listed abilities. The first three abilities are identical to the TW Vehicular Features (Book of Magic) of the same name. The caster level for spell effects are at 5th level.

Super-Stealth Mode (Invisibility: Superior): Costs 20 P.P.E. or 40 I.S.P.

Impervious to Energy: Costs 20 P.P.E. or 40 I.S.P.

Ley Line Booster: Continuous when applicable, with above-mentioned differences (for flying speed).

Sense Evil: Costs 2 P.P.E. or 4 I.S.P.

Sense Magic: Costs 2 P.P.E. or 4 I.S.P.

Detect Concealment: 3 P.P.E. or 6 I.S.P.

Ley Line Transmission (Book of Magic): Costs 10 P.P.E. or 20 I.S.P.

Dispel Magic Barriers: Costs 10 P.P.E. or 20 I.S.P.

8. Sensor Systems of Note: Standard for Sorcerer's Forge Power Armor (see above).

Sorcerer's Forge Samson

The NG-X9 Samson is the most commonly purchased Power Armor in the Sorcerer's Forge military. Around a total of 100 are in use by the city, some of which are TW converted. The Samson's TW conversion has all the standard Sorcerer's Forge power armor features (described earlier), but has different weapons. Instead of the Rail Gun, they are fitted with either a TW Force Cannon or a TK Heavy Machine-Gun (see **Rifts® Book of Magic** for the description of both) or a Sylvan weapon. The TW Samsons that are armed with TW energy weapons have them connected to their Magical Reactors so they have nearly unlimited ammo.

Robot Vehicles of Sorcerer's Forge

Sorcerer's Forge uses several types of Robot Vehicles, both technological and Techno-Wizard. They buy many Northern Gun models, and produce their own TW Robot Vehicles. The unique models created by Sorcerer's Forge have the standard Robot Vehicle features (see page 273 of **Rifts Ultimate Edition**), with the additional abilities listed below. Individual models have additional features listed in their descriptions.

All TW Robot Vehicles of Sorcerer's Forge have the following features:

1. Powered by Magical Reactor: The TW equivalent of a nuclear reactor, it powers all the basic functions of the vehicle. This includes any attached TW weapons and limited other TW abilities (see specific model for descriptions). Average life: 1 year; the reactor can be recharged in a secret process known only to Sorcerer's Forge (it involves magical energy being absorbed from a ley line at a special facility for one week).

2. TW Armor of Ithan: All of Sorcerer's Forge's TW Robot Vehicles are built with a continuous Armor of Ithan effect built onto them. This armor gives the Robot Vehicle an additional 50 M.D.C. (this armor is damaged first), as well as reducing all magical fire, cold and electricity damage by half (while it is in effect). This effect is always active while the Robot Vehicle is activated. If the M.D.C. from this is depleted, the energy resistance is disabled. The armor regenerates to full strength after one hour (if the armor is damaged at all in that hour, the pilot must wait an additional hour to regenerate the M.D.C.; the pilot may "turn off" the armor to recharge it without interruption). Alternatively, the pilot may channel 10 P.P.E. or 20 I.S.P. to reactivate the armor to full strength.

3. Self-Destruct Mechanism: A self-destruct mechanism to prevent the robot and its technology from falling into enemy hands. It is initiated by overloading the Magical Reactor (since it is magic, there is no radiation). The damage is largely self-contained, destroying most of the internal systems with 2D6x10 M.D.

4. Optical Systems: All Sorcerer's Forge Robot Vehicles have the following optical systems: Full optical systems, including laser targeting, telescopic, passive nightvision (light amplification), thermal-imaging, infrared, ultraviolet, and polarization. In addition, they have a *See the Invisible* effect (as per the spell) that is continuous, with a range of 200 feet (61 m). They are also equipped with a language translator. This is in addition to all normal Robot Vehicle optical systems.

SFRV-8089 Dreadnaught

The Dreadnaught is the most powerful Robot Vehicle in the Sorcerer's Forge military. It was created to fill the role of a heavily armed and armored vehicle that was mobile and versatile. Since most of the terrain around Sorcerer's Forge is heavily forested and mountainous, it was decided to make it a Robot Vehicle. For weaponry, it was decided to give it as much long- and short-range firepower as possible. The resulting robot was named Dreadnaught because of its heavy firepower and armor. Because of their size, Dreadnaughts are mostly used within the Shroud. If a large enemy force is located, Dreadnaughts are called in to annihilate them. Most are camouflaged, but some of the ones stationed at the city are colored black. Only about 25 Dreadnaughts have been produced so far, with only 1 lost in battle.

Model Type: SFRV-8089 Dreadnaught.
Class: Ground Infantry Assault Robot with multiple weapon systems.
Crew: Two: One pilot and one co-pilot/gunner; can be fully operated by one if necessary.

M.D.C. by Location:
    Sylvan Storm Cannon – 100
    Medium-Range Missile Launcher Pod – 100
    Shoulder Missile Launchers (2) – 100 each
    TW Heavy Force Cannon/Nova Cannon – 200
    Retractable TW Blade – 100
    Arm Laser Blaster – 100
    Leg Missile Launchers (2) – 100 each
    **Head & Sensors – 200
    Arms (2) – 200 each
    *Shoulder Spotlights (2) – 10 each
    *Hands (2) – 100 each
    *Leg Spotlights (2; at knees) – 10 each
    Legs (2) – 250 each
    Feet (2) – 200 each
    ***Main Body – 412
    Reinforced Pilot's Compartment – 100
    Note: The TW Armor of Ithan adds +50 to M.D.C. (see above).

    * A single asterisk indicates a small and difficult target to strike, requiring the attacker to make a *Called Shot*, but even then the attacker is -3 to strike.

    ** Destroying the sensor head of the robot will eliminate all forms of optical enhancement and sensory systems. The pilot must then rely on his own vision and senses.

    *** Depleting the M.D.C. of the main body will shut the robot down completely, rendering it useless.

Speed:
Running: 60 mph (96 km) maximum (Ley Line Booster allows 50% increase on ley lines).
Leaping: The powerful robot legs can leap up to 15 feet (4.6 m) high or across. Add 10 feet (3 m) with a running start.

Statistical Data:
Height: 30 feet (9.1 m).
Width: 12.5 feet (3.8 m).
Length: 12 feet (3.65 m).
Weight: 30 tons fully loaded.
Physical Strength: Robotic P.S. 45.

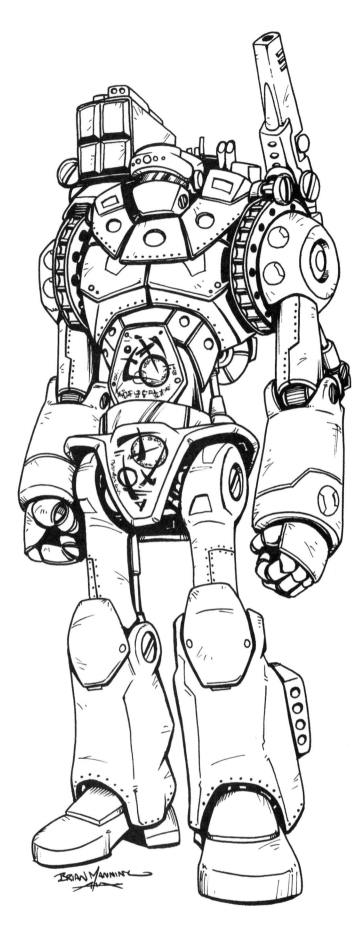

Cargo: Minimal storage space; about 4 feet (1.2 m) for extra clothing, weapons, and personal items.

Power System: Magical Reactor, average life is 1 year (can be recharged at Sorcerer's Forge).

Black Market Cost: Never sold, but if it was it would go for 50-100 million credits.

Weapon Systems:

1. SFW-48 Sylvan Storm Cannon: This weapon fires a single large, telekinetically-accelerated round that releases 50 Sylvan Storm flechette rounds that strike the target simultaneously. It is mounted on the back; it swings down over the left shoulder to fire. This is considered the main weapon.

Primary Purpose: Assault, Anti-Armor and Anti-Aircraft.

Weight: Gun: 225 pounds (101.25 kg), ammo canister: 1,200 pounds (540 kg).

Range: 1,200 feet (366 m).

Mega-Damage: 6D6 M.D. per blast; double damage to beings vulnerable to wood, silver or magic.

Rate of Fire: Single shots only.

Payload: 250 round ammo canister. Reloading the Dreadnaught's cannon requires special equipment or another giant-sized robot. It will take about 10 minutes for those not trained, but 5 minutes by someone trained in Robot Mechanics (or an Operator).

2. TW Nova Cannon: This large cannon is held by the right arm of the Dreadnaught, and is used for area fire support at medium range. It is connected to the Magical Reactor, giving it an almost unlimited payload.

Primary Purpose: Anti-Personnel & Defensive Cover.

Range: 1,500 feet (457.2 m).

Mega-Damage: 1D6x10 M.D. to all targets in a 6 foot (1.8 m) radius.

Rate of Fire: Single shot only.

Payload: Effectively unlimited; tied to Magical Reactor power supply.

3. Medium-Range Missile Launcher: A pod of four medium-range missiles is attached above the right shoulder. They are primarily used for long-range attacks.

Primary Purpose: Anti-Aircraft & Anti-Armor.

Range: Varies by missile type.

Mega-Damage: Varies by missile type.

Rate of Fire: May be fired one missile at a time or in volleys of two, three, or all four.

Payload: Total of four.

4. Short-Range Missile Launcher (2): Each shoulder has a short-range missile launcher built into it.

Primary Purpose: Anti-Aircraft & Anti-Personnel.

Range: Varies by missile type.

Mega-Damage: Varies by missile type.

Rate of Fire: May be fired one missile at a time or in volleys of two, three, or all four.

Payload: Four total, two in each shoulder.

5. Retractable TW Blade: A large, retractable TW blade is attached to the left forearm. When needed, the blade is extended to be used for close-quarters combat.

Primary Purpose: Anti-Personnel & Defense.

Range: Hand to hand combat; 7 foot (2.1 m) long blade, 18 foot (5.5 m) reach.

Mega-Damage: 3D6 M.D.

Rate of Fire: Equal to the number of combined hand to hand attacks of the pilot and his Robot Vehicle.

6. Arm Laser Blaster: A magically powered laser is built directly under the left forearm (to the side of the TW Blade). It is meant as a backup in case the main weapons are destroyed or run out of ammo.

Primary Purpose: Anti-Personnel.

Mega-Damage: 3D6 M.D.

Rate of Fire: Single shot only.

Range: 2,000 feet (609.6 m).

Payload: Effectively unlimited; tied to Magical Reactor power supply.

7. Leg Mini-Missile Launchers (2): A missile launcher box is attached to the outside of each of the Dreadnaught's legs (just below the knee); each holds 8 mini-missiles.

Primary Purpose: Anti-Aircraft & Anti-Personnel.

Mega-Damage: Varies by missile type.

Rate of Fire: May be fired one missile at a time or in volleys of two, three, or four.

Range: Varies by missile type; typically one mile (1.6 km).

Payload: 16 total, 8 mini-missiles per launchers.

8. Hand to Hand Combat: Rather than use a weapon, the pilot can engage in Mega-Damage hand to hand combat.

9. TW Abilities: These abilities require P.P.E. or I.S.P. to activate and are in addition to the above listed abilities. The first four abilities are identical to the TW Vehicular Features (Book of Magic) of the same name. The potency of each spell is 5th level.

Chameleon Cloaking System: Costs 5 P.P.E. or 10 I.S.P.

Super-Stealth Mode (Invisibility: Superior): Costs 20 P.P.E. or 40 I.S.P.

Impervious to Energy: Costs 20 P.P.E. or 40 I.S.P.

Ley Line Booster: Continuous when applicable.

Sense Evil: Costs 2 P.P.E. or 4 I.S.P.

Sense Magic: Costs 2 P.P.E. or 4 I.S.P.

Detect Concealment: 3 P.P.E. or 6 I.S.P.

Ley Line Transmission (costs Book of Magic): Costs 10 P.P.E. or 20 I.S.P.

Ley Line Fade (Book of Magic): Costs 30 P.P.E. or 60 I.S.P.

10. Sensor Systems of Note: Standard for Sorcerer's Forge Robot Vehicles (see above).

Vehicles of Sorcerer's Forge

Sorcerer's Forge uses a mix of technological and TW vehicles. They produce many of their own, as well as buying many from Stormspire and Northern Gun. The below listed vehicles are produced and used by the city.

Raptor Wing Board

The Raptor Wing Board is Sorcerer's Forge's version of the Turbo-Wing Board (Book of Magic). It has a built-in hover and micro-jet propulsion system that enables it to fly on and off of ley lines. It is designed to be flown while standing, kneeling or in a crouched position. Like the Turbo-Wing Board, magic keeps the pilot attached to the board, and by moving his feet, legs or body, the pilot can maneuver the device. The Raptor is modified to be powered by a small Magical Reactor, and is armed with missiles and a small laser. The weapons are built onto the front and under the wings of the Wing Board; they are controlled by a special helmet the pilot wears and a forearm-attached control interface. The pilot's helmet (50 M.D.C.) has a targeting display on the see-through visor that automatically tracks all human-sized or larger, moving targets within 1 mile (1.6 km). The small control interface the pilot wears on his arm can select targets, fire the weapons and display a detailed map. Both the helmet and arm control interface are interchangeable with different Raptors, and they activate when the pilot steps onto the Wing Board, and deactivate when they step off. The helmet/control interface may be added as an accessory for the Mystic Soldier EBA (see above). The Raptor was designed to provide close air support for troops in the field; the pilots also typically carry handheld weapons and grenades. With minimal training, most Men of Arms and Practitioner of Magic O.C.C.s can learn to pilot these devices, but without benefit of the bonuses listed below. Only *RPA Power Armor Pilots*, *Aces*, *Crazies* and *Operators* enjoy the vehicle bonuses listed below. Also, practitioners of magic schooled as a *Conjurer*, *Battle Magus*, *Techno-Wizard* or *Mystic Soldier* (see above) O.C.C. have a natural affinity for all types of Wing Boards and get both sets of bonuses when piloting the Raptor Wing Board. They may also cast spells while flying.

Model Type: SFV-2039 Raptor Wing Board.

Class: Motorized, hover TW Wing Board; the TW equivalent of an exotic hovercycle. Use the Hovercycle Piloting skill.

Vehicle Bonuses: +1 on initiative, +1 to strike, +2 to dodge, +5% to piloting skill.

O.C.C. Bonuses: +2 on initiative, +2 to dodge, +1 physical attack or action per melee round when riding the board and +10% to piloting skill.

Crew: One humanoid rider with one additional rider possible in emergencies, with the second rider having to cling to the main rider to stay on. The increased weight, encumbrance and unbalance causes the following penalties: reduce speed by 20%, reduce combat bonuses by half, and -1 attack per melee round.

M.D.C. by Location:

* Small Hover Jets (4, undercarriage) – 10 each

* Rear Hover Jets (2, rear base platform) – 15 each

** Wings (2) – 120 each

*** Main Body – 150

* A single asterisk indicates a small and difficult target to strike, requiring the attacker to make a *Called Shot*, but even then the attacker is -4 to strike.

** Destroying one of the wings will prevent flight, causing the rider and what's left of the board to spiral down to the ground, but land safely.

*** Destroying the main body will destroy the device and send its rider falling to the ground.

Speed:

Flying: Hover stationary to rocketing along at a maximum speed of 120 mph (192 km); double when riding on ley lines. Maximum altitude is 10,000 feet (3,048 m); double on ley lines. VTOL capable. The pilot can also expend 10 P.P.E. or 20 I.S.P. to keep the speed/altitude bonuses from ley lines when off ley lines for 30 minutes.

Statistical Data:

Height: 2 feet, 5 inches (0.76 m).

Width: 15 foot (4.6 m) wingspan.

Length: Approximately 5 feet (1.5 m).

Weight: 50 pounds (22.5 kg).

Cargo: Can carry one pilot and one companion (if both are human-sized) with a maximum weight tolerance (in addition to pilot's weight) of 300 pounds (135 kg). Anything heavier will reduce maximum altitude by half, speed by 30% and bonuses by half, and inflicts a -15% piloting penalty. The device has straps on the top, near the pilot's feet, for carrying additional gear.

Power System: Magical Reactor, average life is 1 year (can be recharged at Sorcerer's Forge).

Black Market Cost: 500,000 credits; rare.

Weapon Systems:

1. **Laser Blaster:** A magically powered laser is built onto the front of the Wing Board; it is targeted and fired by the pilot's helmet and arm control interface. It is capable of 90 degree rotation side to side and up and down, and the pilot "points" the Wing Board at the target. Mystic Soldiers can use their *Enhance Energy Weapon Damage* (see above) on this weapon while flying the Raptor.

Primary Purpose: Anti-Personnel.

Mega-Damage: 3D6 M.D.

Rate of Fire: Single shots only.

Effective Range: 2,000 feet (609.6 m).

Payload: Effectively unlimited; tied to Magical Reactor power supply.

2. **Wing Missiles:** Two mini-missiles or 1 short-range missile can be mounted below each wing. They are targeted and fired by the pilot's helmet and arm control interface.

Primary Purpose: Anti-Aircraft/Armored Vehicle.

Mega-Damage: Varies by missile type.

Rate of Fire: May be fired one missile at a time or in volleys of two, three, or four.

Effective Range: Varies by missile type.

Payload: 2 short-range missiles or 4 mini-missiles.

3. **Optional Sensor Systems:** Can potentially be equipped with a small radar system, and the pilot's helmet can be equipped with other optical systems.

Sorcerer's Forge Armored Transport

This eight-wheeled armored transport is created and sold by Sorcerer's Forge. It is a cheap, light, armored, all-terrain transport that can carry a squad of infantry into battle. It is effectively an armored box on eight wheels with a large hatch on the back for entering and exiting. It also has, above and behind the pilot's seat, an armored roof hatch with a weapon station that can equip any common heavy weapon (like a Rail Gun or Sylvan Storm Heavy Gun). If all the hatches are closed the vehicle can be sealed from the outside environment like the complete environmental crew compartment feature of Robot Vehicles (see Robot Vehicle features). The vehicle can alternatively be used to transport cargo. Additional technological systems or TW abilities may also

be added. The version used by the Sorcerer's Forge military has several TW abilities.

Model Type: SFV-1070 Armored Transport.

Class: Infantry Armored Transport Vehicle.

Crew: Two; pilot and gunner/commander.

Troop Transport Capabilities: Can carry up to 12 infantry, or 4 Power Armors.

M.D.C. by Location:

   *Main Body – 250

   Wheels (8) – 40 each

   Forward Headlights (2) – 10 each

   Reinforced Crew Compartment – 80

      * Depleting the M.D.C. of the main body will shut the APC down completely, rendering it useless.

Speed: 100 mph (160 km) maximum on land. In water, speed is about 30 mph (48 km).

Maximum Range: Gasoline/electric: 500 miles (800 km), Magical Reactor: effectively unlimited.

Statistical Data:

Height: 14 feet (4.26 m).

Width: 8 feet (2.4 m).

Length: 22 feet (6.7 m).

Weight: 10 tons.

Cargo: Minimal storage space; about four feet (1.2 m) for extra clothing, weapons, and personal items; also has twelve small, overhead weapon compartments (can fit a single rifle and a few other small items).

Power System: Combustion or electric or Magical Reactor (average life 1 year; can be recharged at Sorcerer's Forge).

Cost: 400,000 credits gasoline engine, 420,000 credits electric engine, or 700,000 credits Magical Reactor.

Ley Line Cargo Transport

This large Techno-Wizard aircraft was designed to carry large amounts of cargo. It primarily moves along ley lines, but is capable of flying off them for short durations. The aircraft is similar to the Ley Streaker (Federation of Magic) but is larger, longer and designed to carry a large cargo load in an internal cargo bay. The pilot's compartment is located at the front of the aircraft. The cargo is loaded and unloaded via a rear door that doubles as a ramp. Typically, the aircraft must land to unload its cargo, but it can, in some cases, airdrop its cargo, or allow flying characters/vehicles to fly out the back. Combat models of the Ley Line Cargo Transport typically have defensive abilities, and fly troops/vehicles into battle. This aircraft was originally built by Dweomer, but has been copied by many other TW communities.

Model Type: Ley Line Cargo Transport.

Class: TW Transport Aircraft.

Crew: Three: one pilot, one copilot, and a cargo deck chief.

Cargo Capabilities: Can carry up to 70 tons in a cargo bay 20 feet (6.1 m) wide, 40 feet (12.2 m) long, and 20 feet (6.1 m) high.

M.D.C. by Location:

   **Wings (2) – 250 each

   *Forward Section/Cockpit – 250

   *Cargo Bay – 250

      * Depleting the M.D.C. of the Forward Section/Cockpit or Cargo Bay will effectively destroy the transport; if the front section/cockpit is destroyed, the cargo bay will slowly spiral down to the ground and gently settle onto the surface. No crash but all vehicle systems shut down and the crew is vulnerable to further to attack.

** Destroying one wing rear section will knock out the propulsion systems, causing the transport to crash to the ground.

Speed:

Flying/Floating: The Ley Line Cargo Transport can fly at speeds of 500 mph (800 km) on a ley line, as well as float, glide and hover. Maximum altitude is 10,000 feet (3,048 m). Away from a ley line it can only move at about 50 mph (80 km) and best altitude is 250 feet (76.2). It is also completely silent (the propulsion system is silent, not any other aspect of the vehicle).

Statistical Data:

Height: 25 feet (7.62 m).

Width: Wingspan: 70 feet (21.3 m); cargo bay/cockpit: 22 feet (6.7 m).

Length: 70 feet (21.3 m).

Weight: 20 tons (not counting any cargo).

Cargo: There is minimal storage space for the crew's equipment; a 4 foot (1.2 m) space for extra clothing, weapons, and personal items.

Power System: Magic. Runs on ley line energy. In the absence of a ley line, the vehicle can run for 4 hours before running out of energy.

Cost: 15-20 million credits.

Weapon Systems: None.

Additions: Weapons, TW Vehicular Features, and equipment such as computer control systems, radar, sensors, radios, etc. (both conventional and TW), may be added at the owner's expense.

Other TW Vehicles of Sorcerer's Forge

Sorcerer's Forge uses many conventional and TW vehicles, and conventional vehicles that break down are sometimes converted to TW vehicles. Military TW vehicles typically have the following additions applied to them (most of the abilities are the same as Robot Vehicles/Power Armor versions mentioned above): Magical Reactor, TW Armor of Ithan, optical systems, self-destruct mechanism, and the following TW Vehicle Features: Chameleon Cloaking System, with more elite versions having Ley Line Booster, Impervious to Energy and Super Stealth Mode (Invisibility: Superior). Sorcerer's Forge's Battle Streakers and Ley Line Cargo Transports have a modified flight system like that of the Avenger, allowing them to fly near continuously. The Sorcerer's Forge Ley Line Cargo Transport is capable of carrying 2 Dreadnaughts (must be loaded in a "kneeling" position), or 1-2 large vehicles, or 14 suits of Power Armor, or 42 infantry soldiers (most common load is 1 Dreadnaught or heavy vehicle, 4 suits of Power Armor and 9 infantry).

D-Bees of the Northeast

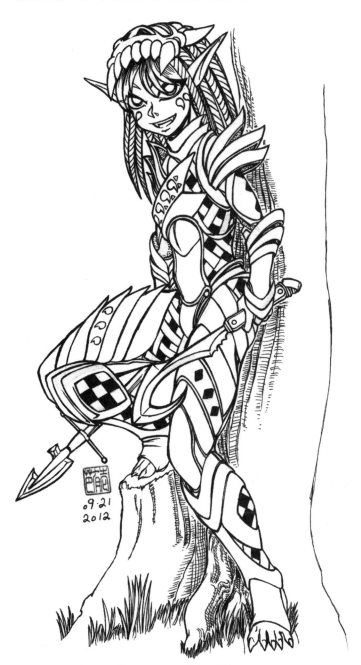

Faeriekin R.C.C.

By Timothy Dorman and Kevin Siembieda

Faeriekin are said to have been, at one time, true Faeries, but due to an unknown event, lost their powers and became a mortal race. Some stories say they were stripped of their powers by other Faeries as punishment for consorting with demons, others say they are relatives of Faeries with less magical aptitude, like Goblins. Outwardly, Faeriekin resemble small, young, attractive humans with pale skin, long dark hair, and long, narrow, pointed ears. They stand 4-5 feet (1.2 to 1.5 m) tall, and tend to grow long fingernails and have pointed, canine teeth and fangs.

The menacing smile and claw-like fingers can deceive those unfamiliar with them into believing they are a more menacing creature than they really are. Indeed, their teeth and claws are adapted for the ripping and tearing of raw meat, but usually small animals and tough plants, not humanoids. Faeriekin tend to fight only to defend themselves and when angry. They have dark colored hair they grow long and keep loose. They wear ragged clothing that often resembles strange and exotic, fanciful armor.

Like their Faerie cousins, most Faeriekin are playful, free-wheeling and friendly among themselves, but more reserved and cautious when in the presence of larger beings. Faeriekin love to sing and dance, and many a traveler recounts stories of hearing the beautiful singing of a Faeriekin in the midst of a forest. They are also talented though limited in the use of magic. Faeriekin live deep in secluded forests, where they enjoy and live among nature, and prefer the isolation. While they happily associate with other Faerie Folk, they are wary of humans and most outsiders. This means most tend to avoiding contact with large numbers of humans but may make contact with a small group of 10 or fewer. They have been known to help lost children and people in trouble in the wilderness, but seldom get seriously involved with them nor travel with them long distances. If the trespassers (as they see outsiders) persist in areas they consider their homes, or are destructive, Faeriekin may use magic, trickery and sabotage to lure or chase them away. When necessary, they will resort to violence, and may enlist other magical or supernatural beings to help, or lead interlopers into the clutches of monsters (or vice versa). Faeriekin communities are seldom larger than 4D6+4 and they live in a few wooden huts reminiscent to Native Americans of old. Faeriekin usually avoid technology, preferring nature, psionics and magic.

On Rifts Earth, Faeriekin are a rarity. They are most common in the areas where True Faeries are found, or strangely enough, demons, Entities and lesser supernatural beings. For reasons unknown, such monsters leave them alone and allow them to co-exist without trouble or incident. The two forces may not even cooperate or associate with one another, but they leave each other alone. This, and their fangs, is what has earned Faeriekin the nickname "Demon Faeries." As a result, they are found in and around the demon haunted ruins of old Detroit and Windsor, Calgary and other parts of Canada, as well as England and other Faerie habitats. They usually live in communities less than a hundred, far from any other intelligent creatures. An exception to this is in the hidden city of Sorcerer's Forge, where a few hundred Faeriekin have settled.

The unusual civility and alliance between Faeriekin and Sorcerer's Forge is the result of a mutually beneficial alliance. Early in Sorcerer's Forge's history, a small force of demon slayers who were hoping to establish themselves in the area began to assault the demons living in the region. Among those they struck were a multitude of Faeriekin villages, forcing hundreds of them to flee. The demon slayers, in turn, stirred up considerable chaos and retaliation on the part of demons, which caused the monsters to strike back in a series of skirmishes that turned the region into a battle ground. As it turned out, these self-styled demon slayers turned out to be "Slavers" with ties to the Splugorth's Atlantis. Slavers out to capture Faerie Folk and demons alike. As fate would have it, some of the fleeing Faeriekin found themselves inadvertently herded to Sorcerer's Forge. Caught between two forces of big people, they expected annihilation, so they were dumbfounded when the leaders of Sorcerer's Forge welcomed them with open arms and sanctuary from the warring forces. When the small army of Slavers arrived on the doorstep of Sorcerer's Forge, demanding they turn over the Faeriekin refugees and any other Faerie Folk in their company, (the Splugorth lobotomize and use such creatures as living generators in many of their dark Bio-Wizard creations), the people of Sorcerer's Forge refused. More than that, they stood steadfast to protect their new friends. When the Slavers, many of them monstrous beings themselves, threatened death and destruction lest they hand over the Faeriekin, the defenders of Sorcerer's Forge went to battle with the Slavers to protect their new arrivals. Needles to say, this heroic defense has forever endeared the Faeriekin refugees to the town of Sorcerer's Forge. Impressed by the integrity and heroism of its people, the Faeriekin accepted their offer of citizenship and struck a lasting alliance with them. The Faeriekin of Sorcerer's Forge serve the city as healers, scouts, musicians, singers, and tinkerers. Most live on the outskirts of the community or in the neighboring woodland, but they visit the city regularly and will stand to protect it, fighting to the death.

Like many of the Faerie races, Faeriekin dislike routine, rules, laws, hard labor and the trappings of civilization. The latter includes the dirt, grime, garbage and noise that comes with towns and cities, as well as their paved roads, large building and a general obliteration of nature. Faeriekin, prefer a simple life of hunting and living off the land, dancing, singing, games and pranks. Yes, like their Faerie cousins, Faeriekin enjoy practical jokes, puns, slapstick and all manner of jokes, good humor and comedy. The only thing they enjoy more than living among nature and singing is laughing. Nice as this may sound, Faeriekin jokes, goofing around and pranks can become annoying and/or distracting. And some people find Faeriekin to never be serious – this is not true, but that's how some people feel.

Also Known As: Fallen Faeries or Demon Faeries.

Alignment: Any, usually Unprincipled or Scrupulous.

Attributes: I.Q. 2D6+5, M.E. 2D6+5, M.A. 2D6, P.S. 2D6+5, P.P. 3D6+3, P.E. 2D6+5, P.B. 3D6+5, Spd 3D6+3.

Hit Points: P.E. attribute number, +1D6 per level of experience.

S.D.C.: 10, plus those gained from O.C.C.s and Physical skills.

Natural Armor Rating: None.

M.D.C.: 2D6+16 as per M.D.C. clothing or armor, non-environmental. (On S.D.C. worlds their armored clothing incorporate animal hides, bone and scrap metal creating protective garments with an A.R. of 14 and 2D6+16 S.D.C.

Height: 4-5 feet (1.2 to 1.5 m).

Weight: 70-90 pounds (31.5 to 40.5 kg).

P.P.E.: P.E. attribute number, +2D4 P.P.E. per level of experience.

Horror Factor: None.

Average Life Span: 100 years. They reach maturity at 15 and always maintain a youthful appearance.

Disposition: Faeriekin are wary of outsiders, typically avoiding them. However, they generally get along with non-evil creatures, and can be especially friendly with those they consider friends. When interacting with friends, they like to sing, dance, and play various physical activities (like games and sports).

Experience: Non-Player Characters may range from levels 1-4 (1D4) or as the Game Master desires. Player characters should start at first level and advance in experience as per their chosen O.C.C.

Natural Abilities: Nightvision 100 feet (30.5 m; can see in total darkness), magically understand and speak all languages and are able to fashion clothing and light armor out of M.D.C. scrap metal and materials via a sort of natural magic even they don't fully understand.

R.C.C. Skills of Note: Dance, Gardening, Sing and Wilderness Survival all with a +30% skill bonus and all at a professional level.

O.C.C.s: Body Fixer (Holistic in nature), Vagabond, Wilderness Scout or similar "nature" based O.C.C.s only. **Note:** All Wilderness skills get an additional +5% bonus regardless of O.C.C.

Attacks per Melee: As per O.C.C., combat training and skills.

Magic: P.P.E. is the P.E. attribute number +2D4 P.P.E. per level of experience.

All Faeriekin have an innate magic ability and start with the following spells: Death Trance (1), Cleanse (6), and Lantern Light (1). As they advance in level, they intuitively know one new Magic Spell Invocation per each new level of experience starting at level two; treat like a Mystic in this regard, but limit spell selections to level 1-3 of Magic Invocations. Faeriekin cannot learn any more spells via any other means, and cannot select a magic O.C.C.

Psionics: Major Psychics with the abilities of Deaden Senses (4), Healing Touch (6), Impervious to Cold (2), Impervious to Fire (4), Induce Sleep (4) and See the Invisible (4). I.S.P. is M.E. attribute number x2 plus 1D6+1 I.S.P. per level of experience. They do NOT acquire additional psionic abilities with experience.

Habitat: Any area Faeries are common, especially in the northeastern portions of North America. They usually live in secluded forests and wilderness areas.

Allies: Their own kind and humans, D-Bees and trustworthy beings, usually of good alignments.

Enemies: Evil destructive beings. Though demons don't usually molest or bother them, they are not friends nor allies of demons or supernatural creatures.

Equipment of Note: Faeriekin usually wear a ragged or piecemeal set of clothing or armor made out of animal hides, bone and Mega-Damage scrap materials (2D6+16 M.D.C.), but the exact process they use to make this clothing is unknown. They also will have one or two water skins, a knife, walking stick or spear and many like bow weapons. Though Faeriekin tend to avoid guns, vehicles and technology, they love Techno-Wizard devices and magic items, including magic weapons. Faeriekin that live in Sorcerer's Forge are more tolerant of technology, but even they are resistant toward using technology, living in town and hanging around too much with outsiders.

Cybernetics: Usually avoided.

Money: As per O.C.C.

09-16-2012

Ashen Hunters

By Timothy Dorman and Kevin Siembieda

Ashen Hunters are a race of D-Bees that loosely resemble humans, except they are larger, hairless, have dark grey skin, a muscular body, claw-like hands, sharp teeth, golden eyes, and no outside ears or nose (have two small nostrils for a nose and an ear hole on the side of head). The skin of their face is stretched tight, giving them skull-like facial features. Their home world is said to be a primeval forest with many fierce predators. There they lived as nomadic hunters, while battling creatures that would hunt them.

With the coming of the Rifts, seven of their tribes were transported to Earth. They found this world alien and dangerous, but with no way home, they have adapted to hunting the "native" creatures. All of the current tribes are descended from the original seven tribes, who now are divided into two dozen tribes. Each tribe has 50-200 members, and when a tribe gets over 200 they divide into smaller camps. Ashen Hunters gain their name from their grey skin and their method of cooking their meat until burnt, since they prefer the ash flavor. Ashen Hunters wander across the northeast and Canada, and they occasionally trade hides/skins and other goods for advanced tools. They prefer well-crafted knives, bows and spears. In recent years, they have begun using advanced weapons such as M.D. rifles and modern M.D.C. armor (prefer Mega-Damage bows and spears, but occasionally acquire other heavy weapons). They also use their hunting skills to hunt Creatures of Magic for bounties or exotic materials. Aside from trading, the Ashen Hunters usually avoid other sentient beings, and feel most comfortable trading with Native Americans, Psi-Stalkers and Simvan.

A couple of tribes of Ashen Hunters are friends of the people at Sorcerer's Forge. A relationship that spans years and that continues today. The Ashen Hunters trade their goods and services for tech and magical items. Some Ashen Hunters also serve as scouts for the Sorcerer's Forge military, with some earning citizenship in the city. There are several hundred Ashen Hunters that live permanently in the city; they are descended from scouts that obtained citizenship. These "City Hunters" are seen as pampered by "Wild" Ashen Hunters. The Ashen Hunters who serve in the Sorcerer's Forge military are prized as scouts or heavy weapon users. Their great strength allows them to use heavy weapons (machine-guns, grenade launchers, missile launchers) as two-handed weapons.

Also Known As: Death Stalkers and Ash Eaters.

Alignment: Any, but tend towards Scrupulous (35%) and Unprincipled (30%); varies by tribe.

Attributes: I.Q. 3D6, M.E. 3D6+2, M.A. 3D6, P.S. 3D6+14 (equivalent to Augmented P.S.), P.P. 2D6+8, P.E. 3D6+4, P.B. 2D6, Spd 3D6+6.

Hit Points: P.E. attribute number x10, +1D6 per level of experience.

S.D.C.: 2D4x10+12, plus those gained from O.C.C.s and Physical skills.

M.D.C.: Via armor or magic only.

Natural Armor Rating: 8

Height: 7-7.5 feet (2.13 to 2.28 m) tall.

Weight: 200-300 pounds (90 to 135 kg).

P.P.E.: 3D6 (if a practitioner of magic, this number is added to the usual P.P.E. base).

Horror Factor: 11

Average Life Span: 3D6+60 years, reaching maturity at 16.

Disposition: Ashen Hunters are seemingly unemotional and harsh, but can be helpful to those in need. They despise weakness, believing every hardship is an obstacle to be overcome. The Ashen Hunters are honorable creatures that always keep their word. They see hunting as the ultimate sport, relishing the excitement of the hunt. They usually avoid other creatures, except to trade.

Experience: 1D4+1 for Non-Player Characters or as the Game Master desires. Player characters should start at first level and advance in experience as per their chosen O.C.C.

Natural Abilities: Sharp vision, Nightvision 120 feet (36.6 m), Presence Sense (like the psionic ability, always active as an in-

nate sense), need half as much sleep as humans, great strength, tough constitution, and heals five times as fast as humans.

R.C.C. Skills of Note: Speak American and Native Language at 90%, plus Hunting, and Land Navigation and Wilderness Survival at +20%.

O.C.C.s: Potentially any (except CS military), but favor Wilderness Scout, hunting and Men-at-Arms O.C.C.s.

Attacks per Melee: As per O.C.C., combat training and skills.

R.C.C. Bonuses: +1 to initiative, +1 attack per melee, +2 to strike, parry and dodge, +2 to saves vs disease, poisons and toxins, and +2 on saves vs Horror Factor.

Magic: Only if a magic O.C.C. is selected. Most choose O.C.C.s that relate to nature, and those who pursue magic are usually Mystics.

Psionics: None.

Habitat: They are typically found in areas with ample game animals and large animals to hunt. Ashen Hunters are only found in North America, particularly Canada.

Allies: They get along reasonably well with others who are close to nature and live with honor, including Native Americans, Psi-Stalkers and Simvan. They are also on good terms with communities willing to trade with them for animal hides, meat and herbs.

Enemies: Any evil or deceitful creatures, especially supernatural beings; Ashen Hunters hate the supernatural and shape changers (hunt and kill them) and distrust people with psionic abilities.

Cybernetics: They usually avoid cybernetics, seeing them as tools of the weak.

Money: As per O.C.C.

Hook, Line and Sinker™ Adventures

A New Home

Hook: A small group of Tolkeen refugees, who are tired of war, are searching for a peaceful place to live. They have heard of a TW city that is hidden beyond the Magic Zone, and wish to settle there.

Line: The refugees are spreading word of their offer to pay a large amount to know the location of the city and to be escorted there. Meanwhile, a mysterious merchant offers the player characters a map to Sorcerer's Forge, but in exchange, he wants all the up-front money they would get from the refugees (he does not have time or resources to escort the refugees).

Sinker: The mysterious merchant acquired the map from a group of mercenaries who were hired to find Sorcerer's Forge. They only have a general idea where it is, so they made a fake map (they just guessed a location) and sold it to the merchant in hopes he would sell it to the Tolkeen refugees. The mercenaries would then follow them, hoping they would find it, or make contact with people from the city. Along the way, the player characters and the refugees encounter Eric Walker's patrol (see above). As he questions them as to how they knew of Sorcerer's Forge, the mercenaries decide to attack and capture the patrol from the city. Depending on how the player characters resolve this, they could succeed in allowing the refugees to settle in Sorcerer's Forge. They could also be hired to find out who was employing the mercenaries.

Stolen Super-Weapon

Hook: The Techno-Wizards of Sorcerer's Forge have created a TW missile that duplicates the magical effect of the invocation *Annihilate* (Book of Magic). One of the Techno-Wizards who helped create it has stolen it and the schematics. He was last seen heading to the Federation of Magic to sell it.

Line: The Seven Lords have put a large bounty out for the capture of the rogue Techno-Wizard, the weapon and the schematics; this offer is spread all over the region (the player characters only know middlemen who offer the bounty).

Sinker: When the player characters track down the rogue Techno-Wizard, they find he has hired mercenaries to protect him (he used the up-front money sent to him by the buyer). The player characters must fight their way past them to get to the meeting place for the deal. Once there, they must fight both the remaining mercenaries and whatever bodyguards the buyer has.

False Accusation

Hook: The player characters are visiting Sorcerer's Forge (assuming they know where the city is and have the permission to do so), and while there, one of them is accused of selling maps of the city's location.

Line: The player character was set-up by a traveling merchant, who will use the incident as cover to quickly sell a limited number of his maps to the city to outsiders.

Sinker: The other player characters must prove their friend's innocence before he is executed. The traveling merchant is the witness who claims to have seen the player character selling the maps. He has boasted he will soon depart the city to make a fortune. If the player characters search his vehicle they will find the maps in a secret compartment in the floor.

Steal Artifact

Hook: Maximilian Tyrannus (see above) has discovered the location of a unique magical artifact. It is being held by a small, militant, technological human-supremacist city. The city will soon send it to the Coalition States to be studied and then destroyed.

Line: Max approaches the player characters to help him retrieve the artifact before the Coalition acquires it. He does not have time to request help from Sorcerer's Forge, and can't do it himself.

Sinker: Max's strategy to steal the artifact will depend on the player characters' abilities. If they are battle oriented, they will fight their way in; if they are magical or technical oriented, they will sneak in. If the player characters can successfully retrieve the artifact without bringing the wrath of the city down on them, Max will pay them well.

CSV New Hope

An Adventure and *Optional* Source Material for Heroes Unlimited™

By Thomas Morrison

Introduction

I'm the type of Game Master who normally lets the players roll up what they want and then tailor my campaign to them, instead of trying to get the players to fit into a campaign I wrote up before they made their characters. Well, I was Game Mastering a Heroes Unlimited campaign a few months ago and all four players rolled – you guessed it – aliens. Needless to say, everyone had questions: How and why did they go to Earth? Was there any way they could contact other aliens? How much high-tech stuff could they get? How did they all know each other? Could they make more alien-equivalent stuff from materials they could get on Earth, or could they call a nearby spaceship and trade some back issues of *The Rifter®* for another plasma ejector?

These were all good questions. I decided to give the players a hand in answering them by starting the campaign in space, before they arrived on Earth.

Overview

The players were all of different races and from different planets, so in order to know each other, they all came from a galaxy far, far away, where everyone lived as one big, happy group in the multicultural Galactic Republic. Or, perhaps not so happy: some aliens were more successful than others, which caused envy, discord, and disunity. One day, a trio of unscrupulous (or Aberrant?) politicians took advantage of an external threat and internal divisions to dissolve the Republic and proclaimed themselves the Imperial Triumvirate. The players were all part of the rebel Confederate Systems and began with basic alien military gear. The players were all first level: they just graduated from rebel basic training and were assigned as cadets to the same spaceship.

To keep the players from fighting for freedom in their own galaxy and never going to Earth, the story went like this: The rebels lost. The players' ship – an old troop transport – was almost all that's left of the Confederate fleet. They needed to evacuate their families from the last rebel outpost and flee before the vastly superior Imperial fleet caught them and executed them all. The rebels knew where Earth is and the Empire didn't. The rebels had a ship that could reach Earth and the Empire didn't. Easy, right?

Unfortunately for the players, lead elements of the Imperial fleet were closer than they thought. Even worse, there was also a saboteur aboard the ship: Someone who belonged to something more evil than the Empire...

Background

Give the players the schematic of the *CSV New Hope*. Let them ooh and aah over it. Then give them the below background notes and let them pore over them. If they have questions, direct them to the list of key terms at the end as you set up your dice and your G.M. Screen of Unutterable Fear. Do not laugh maniacally. Yet.

Yes, it's cruel. With all this back story, it makes the players think there's a chance that they will keep their nice, super-powerful spaceship when they cruise unmolested to Earth. But read the Aliens section of the Heroes Unlimited book again: letting aliens have too much alien stuff – especially a spaceship – would unbalance the game (see Heroes Unlimited, page 100).

So, players, here's your spaceship. Better have fun with it now, because after one or two gaming sessions, it's going bye-bye.

A Little History

"Why are we going to Earth in this old spaceship and why is an evil empire trying to kill us?"

Confederate Systems Vessel *New Hope* is an old, pre-Republic hull that has been refurbished and modernized several times. The ship was first christened in 1876 (equivalent Earth year) as the *Demolisher*, the third of the Xijian Union's *Dominator*-class, sub-light armored monitors. The vessel saw regular action against rival merchant princes and pirate freeholds until the House of Ri consolidated power and brought the Xijian Union into the Galactic Republic in 1896.

Upgraded with rudimentary shields and re-christened *GRS Steadfast* in 1898, the ship performed mainly second-line duties until the mobilization of the Galactic Republic Home Fleet during the First Sipathian Incursion in 1910, where the ship's fa-

mously resilient armor and powerful armament proved useful in reducing the fanatical Sipathians' hardened bases. The vessel was re-mobilized twice more in response to Sipathian incursions, in 1915 and 1921, proving its worth each time. However, the Galactic Republic's Second Separatist Crisis of 1923 led to the permanent demobilization of its member states' fleets; the *GRS Steadfast* became an exhibit in the Xijian Union's Museum of Military History.

Troubles with the Republic's *Admiral Klod*-class fire support vessels during the Fourth Sipathian Incursion of 1964 led to the *GRS Steadfast* being re-activated and modernized; the end of that conflict in 1967 saw the ship return to the museum. Again in 1986, the ship was re-activated and used as a technology demonstrator and training vessel for the development of the fleet's new planetary assault doctrine. It was during this time that the ship's heavy weapons were removed from the side bays and replaced with assault pods. (Oddly, the *Steadfast* received new fusion engines capable of only 50% light speed, instead of the fleet standard, faster than light, matter-antimatter reactor drives.) The *Steadfast* continued in this role throughout the Fifth Sipathian Incursion of 1989-1990.

In early 2008, scandals involving alleged government corruption combined with long-simmering discontent over perceived Xijian economic dominance led to widespread rioting in many less-developed systems. These riots were led by militant, grass-roots nationalist groups, which by mid-2008, began toppling the first of several regional governments. The nationalist factions precipitated the Third Separatist Crisis by expelling Xijians, seizing their property, and declaring varying degrees of autonomy from the Republic. Within days, the Sipathian Hive launched its sixth incursion, initially targeting only those areas still under Republican control. The *Steadfast* was recalled to Republican service, where the ship received its final upgrades in fire control, electronics, and shields.

The collapse of the Republic in 2010 led to the outbreak of civil war, which only accelerated the pace of Sipathian territorial expansion. In mid-2011, three demagogues (a governor, an admiral, and an evangelist) united the various nationalist systems to establish the despotic Peoples' Empire, which prompted the Xijian Union to go over to the rebel Confederate Systems. The *Steadfast* went with them. Re-christened the *CSV New Hope*, this vessel and her crew have participated in almost every battle in this side of the galaxy, from the heady Happy Times to the hard-fought Operation Riposte to the Long Retreat.

The Peoples' Empire and the Sipathian Hive are locked in mortal combat, with the Empire appearing to have gained the upper hand. However, the rebels have clearly lost: The Empire was simply too ruthless and unified; the rebels too indecisive and fragmented. The rebel fleets have been scattered and their bases have been overrun. Many former Confederate systems have gone over to the side of Eivel.

Resistance is futile at this point. The majority of the survivors accepted the Empire's offer of amnesty and surrendered. They and their families disappeared: The Empire claims that they were re-educated and settled elsewhere; the rumor is that they were executed. The Xijian home world was taken without a fight and all its inhabitants are even now being deported as slaves.

The last orders you received was for all who could save themselves to do so. Even now, an Imperial punitive squadron approaches the last rebel outpost, the former Xijian colonies of the Wuwu system. Your mission is to assist in the evacuation of Wuwu-3, where your family has taken refuge.

Unbeknownst to all but a handful of well-connected Xijians, the Wuwu system contains a unique space-time anomaly that enables intergalactic travel to a system that the Sipathians and the Empire do not know and cannot reach, a place that was discovered by the House of Ri and kept secret for over a hundred years.

The dominant people in that system call it Earth.

Mandatory Disclaimer: RiCorp discovered Earth and the Wuwu space-time anomaly prior to the Xijian Union's admission into the Galactic Republic and, under the laws of the time, was not required to disclose its unique and proprietary trade secret to any other government, syndicate, or scientific entity. Over the past 120 years, a select few RiCorp scientists have visited the Earth to conduct various studies. Unfortunately, the highly confidential nature of these intergalactic visits meant that the normal corporate and governmental oversight processes were non-applicable, leading to an environment where insufficient enforcement of the RiCorp Code of Ethics may have occurred. However, there is no conclusive evidence that any RiCorp employee engaged in unprofessional conduct, nor was any RiCorp employee ever detained or formally charged with a crime by any of the indigenous governments of Earth. RiCorp assures the passengers and crew of the *CSV New Hope* that the company has done its due diligence to maintain appropriate scientific detachment from the indigenous people of Earth in keeping with the spirit of appropriate non-interact/non-interfere statutes and regulations of the Confederate Systems and the former Galactic Republic. RiCorp's extensive sociological studies of Earth indicate that its dominant species will react favorably to the passengers and crew of the *CSV New Hope* based on their own merits as saviors, teachers, and protectors. However, past success in the field of sociology is no guarantee of future behavior and initial individual interactions with Earth's dominant species may greatly influence later group dynamics; therefore, RiCorp accepts no responsibility should the people of Earth react unfavorably to any individual or group of individuals at this time or in the future.

Key Terms:

Fusion Reactor: Colliding two deuterium (heavy hydrogen) atoms together causes a nuclear reaction that partially destroys the matter, fusing them into one helium atom and unleashing a substantial amount of energy. Much of that energy is used to maintain the intense magnetic containment grid that keeps the reaction from consuming the reactor itself. A fusion reactor that suffers catastrophic damage will explode, which is why they all have multiple hardened automatic safeties that will (93% chance) eject the reactor core into space should the containment grid start to fail. Fusion reactors are more economical than matter-antimatter reactors for short-haul distances (.02 light years or less), meaning that they are generally used only for vessels designed

to travel between starports in the same system (e.g., the seven planets orbiting the star Wuwu).

Happy Times: The Empire at first concentrated its fleets on the Sipathians, which enabled it to win two major victories, temporarily halting their advance. However, it also allowed the Confederate Systems almost free rein in raiding Imperial systems, depots, and supply convoys. Many trillions of credits' worth of expropriated property was retaken, for which the Confederate Systems' ship crews received 10% "finder's fees" from the Xijian Union. Even junior personnel got rich. The Happy Times were followed by the Empire's Operation Riposte.

Light Speed: Sustained speed equal to, or greater than, the speed of light. Matter pushed to the speed of light becomes energy (i.e., it disintegrates in a nuclear reaction). Light speed can only be achieved by modern (post-1922) matter-antimatter reactors, which alone can create the intense energy needed to tear a spacecraft from the fabric of space-time, creating the paradox of stationary matter encapsulated in a hyper-velocity field of energy. (Matter-antimatter engines enable light speed and above by creating a patch of null space-time – a.k.a. a "pocket dimension" – around a vessel. The paradox of faster-than-light travel is that within that patch, the vessel cannot move, as all movement is relative, and there is nothing in the patch but the vessel itself. It is the energy encapsulating the null area in space-time that moves relative to the rest of the universe.) Movement at light speed or above must be through empty space: any impact with a physical object heavier than 2.2 pounds (1 kg) will cause every atom in the vessel instantly to split into sub-atomic particles. Current technology restricts light speed travel to relativistic straight lines (i.e., straight compared to space-time; if space-time is bent, the line of travel will be equally bent), but scientists believe it may be possible to build faster-than-light engines capable of turning. It is notable that the Galactic Republic achieved light speed in 1922, but the Sipathians did not field a light speed vessel until 1959. (This may have been the reason there was no Sipathian incursion between 1922 and 1964.)

Long Retreat: With its main battle fleet destroyed, a powerful Imperial fleet driving the survivors before it, and a surge in Sipathian raids in Confederate space, people lost faith in the Confederate cause. Individual systems began breaking with the Confederacy and suing for peace. Far from home, out of supplies, and pursued by a relentless enemy, the remnants of the Confederate Fleet fought a months-long running battle, falling back on the Xijian Union, the last member of the Confederate Systems. The few that made it back were no match for the Imperial Fleet, which declared its intent to enslave the entire Xijian race and to incinerate any Xijian planet that offered resistance. What remained of the rebel civil and military authorities gave the order that all who could save themselves should do so.

Matter-Antimatter Reactor: Antimatter reacts with matter, completely converting both into pure energy, far greater than even the biggest fusion reaction. To contain this reaction safely, much of this energy is used to create an artificial, self-contained patch of null space-time. Should a matter-antimatter reactor suffer catastrophic damage, its core would (98% chance) safely disappear into the null space-time. All modern military vessels have matter-antimatter reactors, as do all civilian inter-system vessels such as passenger spacecraft, long-haul freighters, etc. (Note: Although matter-antimatter reactors are incredibly expensive, they are more economical than fusion reactors for any distance greater than .02 light years.)

Operation Riposte: Having thrown back the Sipathians, the Empire turned its combined fleets against the Confederate Systems. The rebel ships were divided among factions that variously sought to continue raiding the Empire, to defend against the Sipathians (who were still advancing in the Confederate sector), or to meet the Imperial fleet head-on. Although the rebels fought hard and brilliantly, the end result was an Imperial victory. The Confederate Systems Fleet began the Long Retreat.

Sipath, Sipathian: These aliens are from a thermo world in an adjoining part of the same galaxy as the former Galactic Republic. Sipathians are handsome, 6.5 to 8 feet (2-2.4 m) tall, and have small horns, non-prehensile tails, cloven hooves, and red or bronze skin. Most have membranous wings and are left-handed; others have two pairs of full-sized arms and are ambidextrous. Males are stocky and broad; females are double-jointed and are quite attractive. Comparison to almost every sentient race's description of mythical demons is simply hate-mongering propaganda on the part of the Empire. Sipathans are devoted to their religion, which guides every facet of their lives. They worship Sipath, a deity that naturally is depicted as a member of their race and who is known as the Prince of Alternate Lightness and Situational Ethics. Sipathians insist that their various incursions were not a series of unprovoked wars of aggression against the Republic, but creative re-interpretations of perceived ambiguities in the various peace treaties between the Sipathian Hive and the Galactic Republic, which afforded the Sipathians legitimate grounds to propagate their peaceful faith, a faith which commands its adherents to engage in constant religious struggle until sentient beings everywhere submit to the will of Sipath. (Note: The former Galactic Republic agreed in several peace treaties that hate-mongering and/or inflammatory speech regarding Sipath and/or Sipathians will not be tolerated. Republic schools were obliged to teach children that there are no such things as demons, that Sipathians are peaceful, and that the various incursions were not wars but tragic misunderstandings between the Republic and the Sipathian Hive. *The Devil's greatest accomplishment was convincing the world he didn't exist.* – Jim Carroll.)

Space-Time Anomalies: It is known that gravity bends both space and time; other forces that do not manifest themselves until light speed is approached also affect space and time. In theory, such forces can bend the space-time fabric over on itself so that two points anywhere in the universe merge into one, in effect making the same point exist in two different places simultaneously. Although scientists have debated the nature and existence of so-called "wormholes" for centuries, none have been found. Should one be found or created, no null point of space-time would be able to cross it. (Thus, a matter/antimatter-powered vessel would not be able to cross a "wormhole" at all at light speed or faster, and if it managed to cross at less than light speed, would emerge on the other side without its reactor.)

Sub-Light: Sustained speed of 1-50% light speed (Speed Class 39 to 42). Ten percent light speed (Speed Class 41) was the maximum velocity of the old-style (pre-1980) fusion reactors. Fusion reactors built after 1980 can attain 50% light speed (Speed Class 42).

Xijian: These humanoids come from a low-gravity world and have the "classic alien" appearance: short, thin bodies; bald, bulbous heads; black, oval eyes; and gray, hairless skin. They are known as insular, highly competitive, and highly successful merchants – the proverbial 1% of the galactic population that owned over 50% of the former Galactic Republic's wealth. The government of the Xijian Union is a council of mega-corporations known as the Syndicate. The largest of these corporations is RiCorp, the ultra-profitable conglomerate owned for generations by the merchant "princes" of the Ri family (formally referred to as "the House of Ri"). The idea that Xijians are aloof, ruthless, money-grubbing, domineering, nepotistic capitalists is simply hate-mongering propaganda on the part of the Peoples' Empire and is punishable by a steep fine. Pay here, please...

CSV New Hope

Type: Armored Troopship.
Speed Class: 42 with both ion drives, 41 with one.
S.D.C.: 25,000
Shields: A.R. 26, S.D.C. 50,000. Cover the entire vessel.
Armor (Assault Bays): A.R. 20, S.D.C. 5,000 each.
Armor (Bridge): A.R. 20, S.D.C. 5,000.
Armor (Engine Room): A.R. 20, S.D.C. 5,000.
Armor (Fuel Compartment): Not applicable, fusion engine.
Armor (Main Hull): A.R. 22, S.D.C. 75,000.
Armor (4 Turrets): A.R. 18, S.D.C. 3,500 each.
Weapons: (12) Type 55 dual-purpose guns: Range and damage: 0-20 miles (0-32 km), 2D10x100, 21-40 miles (33-64 km), 1D10x100; capacity: Not applicable; rate of fire: semi-automatic only; length: 20 feet (6 m); weight: 2,200 pounds (990 kg) per gun. Bonus to strike: +5.

(8) Medium missile pods: (Plasma warheads) Range: 400 miles (640 km); damage: 4D6x100; capacity: 19 tubes per missile pod, automatic reload, storage for 1,900 missiles; rate of fire: volleys of up to two pods (38 missiles) per turret; length: 6.5 feet (2 m); weight: 5,500 pounds (2,475 kg) per pod when fully loaded. Bonus to strike: +5.

Crew: 4 officers, 44 enlisted.

Designed to transport 240 fully-loaded combat troops and two assault landing craft.

Currently carrying 400 refugees; expecting another 400 to arrive from Wuwu-3.

Sensors: Fleet standard radar, IR/UV search and track, electro-optical, and magnetic anomaly. The chief engineer has field-modified these systems to provide a +10% bonus to Surveillance Systems checks.

Lock-On: A successful Surveillance Systems skill check will provide a sensor lock-on to a given target. No guided missiles may be launched without lock-on. A lock-on also enables the ship's combat computer to provide a +1 bonus to all gunnery strike rolls. Roll once to establish (or to re-establish) lock-on to all targets in range; one roll per action. A successful lock-on remains in effect until jammed.

ECM/ECCM: Fleet standard radar detector, laser detector, magnetic dampener, signals intercept and jamming suite. The chief engineer has field-modified these systems to provide a +10% bonus to Radio: Scramblers checks. (Note: If none of the players have the Radio: Scramblers skill, a non-player character is present with 35% proficiency.)

Electronic Counter-Measures (ECM): A successful Radio: Scramblers skill check can jam enemy sensors. A ship with jammed sensors cannot launch guided missiles (no lock-on) and treats all gunnery as shooting wild. A missile with jammed sensors will miss. Roll once to establish (or to re-establish) ECM on each target; one target per action. Once jammed, a target will remain jammed until the jamming is turned off or countered.

Electronic Counter-Counter Measures (ECCM): A successful Radio: Scramblers skill check can counter enemy jamming of one's own ship's sensors; it cannot counter a jam on a missile that is already launched. Roll once per action to counter enemy jamming.

Deck Plan

Each square on the map represents a 5 foot x 5 foot area (1.5 m x 1.5 m).

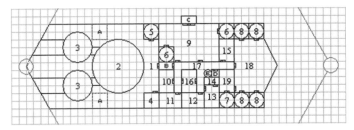

Top Level

1. Engine Room. This area spans all three decks due to the huge size of the fusion reactor (Area #2), and the twin ion drives (Area #3). The floor is non-conductive ceramic grating, so the engineers can see and talk to everyone on all three decks as well as spray firefighting foam as needed without a solid floor getting in the way. This room contains multiple hardened and redundant automatic and manual controls and readouts for the reactor and drives: A successful Computer Operation or Read Sensory Equipment skill check will provide a +5% to all Mechanical Engineering skill checks to operate or troubleshoot them. Wall racks for damage control equipment are exceptionally well-stocked: +5% to all Mechanical Engineering skill checks for repairs, fire suppression, or emergency shutdowns. Two power lifts (A) provide access to the lower engineering levels. The entire roof of this room is a blow-out panel – a section of the hull that will separate from the ship in the event of an internal explosion, so that if the fusion reactor blew up, the force of the blast would be vented into space instead of destroying the ship. Should the hull be breached in this area, damage control crews could still access the room via the adjacent airlock (B); two firefighting suits are stored in that location (see Area #4 for a description of the firefighting suits). *It is standard procedure for all engineers to wear their space suits in this area.*

2. Fusion Reactor. The chief engineer keeps the ship's power plant in exceptional operating condition: +5% to all Mechanical Engineering skill checks to operate the system. In addition, the automatic safeties have a 98% chance of ejecting the reactor core in case of system failure.

3. Ion Drives. The ship has two drives, each supplied with power by the fusion reactor. The chief engineer keeps them in tip-top shape: +5% to all Pilot: Spacecraft skill checks. If one drive is inoperative, the ship's speed will be reduced to 10% light speed (Speed Class 41) and all Pilot: Spacecraft skill checks will suffer a -10% penalty.

4. Firefighting Station. This top deck of this reinforced locker contains six firefighting suits and two extendible hoses; the middle and bottom decks hold 2,000 cubic feet (56.6 cubic meters) of advanced firefighting foam. The foam contains nano-robots that are capable of sealing cracks in the reactor containment structure and repairing simple electrical circuits (like the fusion reactor's magnetic containment grid). The firefighting suits are designed to be worn over the standard GSM-26 space suit and provide additional protection from heat and radiation. Each suit has two helmet-mounted spotlights (infra-red, ultraviolet, and white light), a computerized heads-up display (useful for schematics, etc.), 1.5-200x microscopic vision, and infrared and ultraviolet sensors (820 foot/250 m range). While not designed as armor, their heavy construction provides some degree of protection from weapons: A.R. 10, S.D.C. 132, immune to the first 100 points of heat and radiation damage per melee round and half damage thereafter.

5. Engine Room Life Pod: The standard model of life pod can hold six creatures of up to 8 feet (2.4 m) tall and 300 pounds (135 kg), each in its own sealed cocoon. It has a built-in, automated medical robot (Paramedic 90%), two weeks of food and water, an ion drive (Speed Class 39) with eight hours of thrust, a basic electronics suite (communications, distress signal, navigation), and a parasail system for planetfall. The pod's computer automatically steers it toward the closest habitable planet in range. The chief engineer stores the equivalent of a spaceship trunk toolkit in this pod and has modified this pod's ion engine to last for ten hours versus eight.

6. Medical Bay Life Pods: This is the standard model of life pod (see #5, above), except that the individual cocoons have additional life support functions for transporting injured personnel (First Aid 90%). Each of the two medical life pods has had one of its standard cocoons removed to accommodate the surgical robots for the evacuation of critically ill or injured patients (see #9, below). The ship's doctor keeps an extra fully-stocked medical bag in each of these pods.

7. Ship's Signals Exploitation Space Life Pod: This is the standard model of life pod (see #5, above). Launching this pod, however, sets off the self-destruct mechanisms for all the sensitive electronic gear in the SSES (see #19, below).

8. Bridge Life Pods: These four pods are the standard models (see #5, above). When abandoning ship, all personnel on this deck who do not have a dedicated life pod are assigned to these.

9. Medical Bay: This 24-bed mini-hospital has full facilities for all kinds of medical procedures to include surgery on all species found in the former Galactic Republic. Two surgical robots (self-contained gurneys with Biology, Chemistry, Botany, Pathology, and Medical Doctor, all at 90%) assist the ship's doctor. These robots can be fit into the medical bay life pods in case of evacuation (see #6, above). There is a power lift (©) leading from the port side troop walkway (Area #27) to expedite the care of wounded troops.

10. Leading Petty Officers' Quarters: Two columns of three slightly less-cramped "coffin racks" are in this room, as are six lockers and a holographic video monitor. The senior enlisted members of the crew live here, including the chief engineer. (Note: A "coffin rack" is just what it sounds like: a military bed with 18 inches (46 cm) of vertical space. The bed part can lift up to reveal a storage space 6 inches (15 cm) deep for the storage of uniforms and a few personal items.)

11. **Visiting Officers' Quarters:** Two columns of two fairly comfortable "sit-up racks" are in this room, as are four roomy lockers and a holographic video monitor. This room is reserved for the parents and sisters of the ship's captain, who are expected to arrive on the first SpaceBus. (Note: "Sit-up rack" is another descriptive term: This military bed has 36 inches (91 cm) of vertical space by the headboard, allowing its occupant to sit up to read, use a personal computer, etc. The foot of the bed has 18 inches (46 cm) of vertical space and 18 inches (46 cm) of storage area. The bed can still lift like a "coffin rack" for more storage space.)

12. **Officers' Quarters:** Two columns of two "sit-up racks," four double-sized lockers, a small table, and a holographic entertainment center are in this room. Rank has its privileges. The executive officer (a lieutenant) and two junior officers (ensigns) live here. (Note: If any of the players is a pilot, then let him or her be one of the ensigns.)

13. **Captain's Quarters:** The ship's captain, Lieutenant Commander Ri, lives here. (Yes, a member of the House of Ri, but not a "prince.") This room has a computerized lock; it contains a bed, an armoire, a table, four chairs, a holographic entertainment center, and a display case. The display case, emblazoned at the top with the phrase, "We Serve With Honor," contains relics of the ship's 136 years of service, each one donated and dedicated by a previous captain for the campaigns served and victories won. The relics include dozens of holographic mini-videos of battles won, a small fragment (2-6 inches/5-15 cm in length) from each of the 14 spaceships, 22 bases, and three Sipathian space dragons the ship destroyed, a RiCorp Earth-type mini-laser, and a still holograph of a half-dozen jubilant Xijians entitled, "ROSWELL RESCUE: Thanks for the assist, 'Curator'!" A plaque on the wall holds a RiCorp Earth-Compatible submachine-gun that looks exactly like a World War II German MP40. It is labeled in German, "With great appreciation to our little friends, March 24, 1943," and is signed by the Chancellor of Germany.

14. **Captain's Head:** A slightly fancier zero-gravity toilet and shower are here.

15. **Administrative Space:** This is a simple office for administrative matters such as pay, personnel records, etc. There are two desks with computer consoles and six chairs.

16. **Head:** In space, a zero-gravity shower and a zero-gravity toilet are combined into one pod-like contraption. There are four of them here.

17. **Passageway:** The bulkheads are a dreary institutional gray with patches of motivational posters. There is a floor hatch with a power lift (E) leading to the mess hall (Area #37) next to a storage locker (D) that contains damage control material and cleaning gear. All rooms have external signs with both room number and description. All hatches are airtight and can maintain their seal in case of hull breach.

18. **Bridge:** This is the brain and nervous system of the ship. There are two rows of seats and consoles for the various ship functions: navigation, weapons control, combat information center (ship's sensors), command, control, and communication. The ship's weapons turrets can be controlled from here, but at -1 to strike. Normally, one officer and five crew members work here.

19. **Ship's Signals Exploitation Space (SSES):** This is the only other room that has a computerized thief-proof lock (-35% to Pick Locks). This section is kept separate from the rest of the bridge to provide the required security for sensitive functions (e.g., intelligence, ECM/ECCM, encrypted communications

servers, etc.). The computerized workstations are on their own separate network and cannot be accessed by other computers on the ship. Each workstation has a small incendiary device attached for self-destruct purposes to keep them from falling into the hands of the enemy. Should the SSES life pod be launched, all self-destruct devices not already activated are supposed to ignite (90% chance), but the operators are trained to ensure destruction by activating them before they abandon ship. Axes and sledgehammers are also stored here for manual destruction, if all else fails. Because this is the ship's most secure room, its heavy safes hold not only cryptographic materials but most of the crew's allotted Earth wealth (gems and gold). Normally, two crew members work here. A player character with the Intelligence and/or Radio: Scramblers skill can be assigned here.

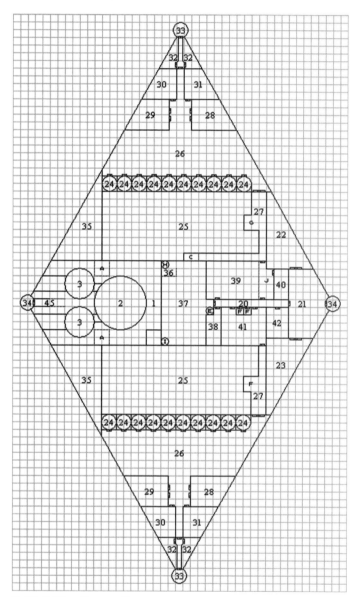

Middle Level

20. **Passageway:** This area is the same institutional gray as Area #17 (above), but it has more motivational posters because it is a higher-traffic area. There are two single-person, zero-gravity heads (F). Some of the motivational posters show signs of defeatist graffiti. For example, on a poster emblazoned, "The 7th War Bond Drive. For Victory. For Us All," someone scrawled, "SCREW YOU LOSERS I WANT MY MONEY BACK!" An-

other poster has been defaced to read, "The Confederate Systems Fleet: ~~Fighting for Freedom~~ TOOLS OF THE SYNDICATE!"

21. Forward Torpedo Room: This reinforced area originally held the loading, servicing, and launching mechanisms for the long-range, multi-warhead missiles for the planetary bombardments that were this ship's hallmark. When the ship was converted to a troop transport, this room was used for meetings and recreational activities. Now it is used as refugee berthing. Eight temporary zero-gravity shower/port-a-potties are in the middle of the room. Even though there are no more missiles here, this room retains its original blow-out panels.

22. Port Torpedo Storage: This bunker-like room originally held half of the ship's heavy missiles; the large double doors linked this room's automatic feed to the forward torpedo room (Area #21, above). Now all the missile storage and feeding mechanisms are gone and the room is used as additional refugee berthing. Four temporary zero-gravity shower/port-a-potties are in the back of the room. This area also kept its original blow-out panels.

23. Starboard Torpedo Storage: This area was once the mirror image of the port torpedo storage (Area #22, above). Now it is used as storage for emergency rations, shelters, tools, seeds, etc., just in case the ship doesn't make it to Earth and lands on an uninhabited planet. The double doors are kept locked. Like the other torpedo storage area, this room retains its original blow-out panels.

24. Life Pods: These models are twice as long as the standard model and can hold twelve creatures of up to 8 feet (2.4 m) tall and 300 pounds (135 kg), each in its own sealed cocoon. They are otherwise identical to the standard model (see Top Level, #5, above).

25. Assault Bays: Each assault bay has a large sliding door at the bottom for the launching and docking of a single combat landing craft; each craft was designed to hold 120 fully-loaded assault troops. In the interest of saving as many people as possible, however, the assault craft have been jettisoned in order to take on civilian, short-haul, SpaceBus 550s, which are 1% light speed craft designed to hold 200 people each for two weeks. Each bay has gantries mounted in the ceiling for the docking, servicing, and repair of a standard combat landing craft. Although the gantries can handle the docking of the SpaceBus 550s, no spare parts are on board to fix them. (Note: The passengers of the SpaceBuses are to remain aboard their craft after docking because there is no more room aboard the *New Hope*.)

26. Troop Quarters: Normally, these hold assault troops. Now they are full of refugees (120 each). Each room has thirty stacks of four "coffin racks" and little else.

27. Loading Ramp/Troop Walkway: The double-wide hatches leading to Areas #26 and #39 slide in place and automatically lock when the air pressure in the troop and crew quarters is higher than in the assault bay (e.g., when the assault bay is docking or launching craft). Standard combat landing craft load from the nose; this room had an extensible, enclosed loading ramp (G) so the troops could enter the landing craft swiftly. It has been field-modified to enable it to hook up to one of the side emergency exits for the civilian SpaceBus 550s the ship is expecting to receive. The port side walkway has an extension to a power lift Ⓒ) that leads directly to the medical bay (Area #9) in order to expedite patient handling.

28. Troop Head: The zero-privacy, zero-gravity group shower/toilet can accommodate eighteen people at a time.

29. Troop Storage: This is normally where troops would store their extra military gear. Now it's full of refugee belongings.

30. Armory: This is normally where the troops would stow their heavy weaponry and hazardous ammunition. Now the weapons racks and storage lockers are used as overflow space for refugees' baggage.

31. Troop Office: This is normally where the troops' leaders would conduct their administrative tasks. Now it is used for refugees with special needs. The port side office is set up to house those from high-temperature worlds; the starboard side office is for those from low-temperature worlds. Each office has two zero-gravity port-a-potties specially designed for their intended users.

32. Missile Bay: The medium missiles fired from the port and starboard weapons turrets are normally stored here. Unfortunately, the collapse of the Confederacy meant that the expected resupply of missiles never happened. These bays are empty, save for the machinery for storing, feeding, and loading 1,900 medium missiles into their respective gun/missile turrets. There is a narrow (2.4 feet/0.76 m wide) walkway to provide access to the gun/missile turret. Each bay is equipped with blow-out panels.

33. Port and Starboard Gun/Missile Turrets: As advertised, each turret has two Type 55, long-range, medium-caliber guns in a single under-over mount, plus four 19-tube, auto-loading mini-missile pods. These weapons are meant primarily for point defense (i.e., shooting at enemy missiles and fighters), but the guns are capable of inflicting moderate damage in ship-to-ship combat. Each turret has room for a single operator and is equipped with a targeting computer, heads-up display, independent sensor array, and hardened communications links with the bridge and the other turrets. Normally, two missile pods are in firing position at a time while the other two are automatically reloading; the reloading process takes one full melee round. However, the ship has not been resupplied with missiles in the last six months of fighting. The port turret has six medium missiles; the starboard one has five; all have plasma warheads. Each turret is sealed during operation and can detach from the ship in case of catastrophic damage (such as an ammunition explosion). Although the turrets have enough independent life support for 48 hours, they have no means of independent locomotion; they will simply drift until picked up by another vessel. It is standard procedure for gunners to wear their GSM-26 space suits.

34. Fore and Aft Gun Turrets: Each turret has four Type 55 long-range, medium-caliber guns in a box mount for point defense and limited ship-to-ship engagements. There is no provision for launching missiles from these positions. They are otherwise identical to the port and starboard turrets.

35. Ship's Storage: These areas contain the spare parts and other sundries needed for the maintenance of the ship. Somehow, the chief engineer manages to keep them well-stocked. Allegedly, the chief engineer also keeps a secret stash of high-potency intoxicants in the port side storage area, which is secured with a thief-proof electronic lock (-35% to Pick Locks).

36. Galley: Food is prepared and served here and is consumed in the main part of the room (Area #37). Actual cooking in zero gravity is extremely difficult, so the food preparation consists of heating and/or chilling sealed bags of bland processed foods and beverages. There is a floor hatch in the location marked H that leads to the food storage area (area #43); it is equipped with a power lift.

37. Mess Hall: This is where food is eaten. It can seat 96 people at tables at a time, so when troops are embarked, they eat in three shifts. The tables can fold away into the floor so the room can be used as an auditorium for 144 people. The mess crew keeps the entire area spotless. A garbage receptacle and compactor in the corner (I) feeds into the waste storage tank (area #44). There is a vertical shaft and a power lift (E) leading up to the passageway on the top deck (Area #17) and down to the passageway on the bottom deck (Area #45).

38. Auxiliary Life support: This is where the back-up devices are for the purification and recirculation of the ship's air supply. Should these devices fail, additional oxygen is kept here in liquid form, sufficient for 288 persons for six months. This door is kept locked due to the hazardous nature of liquid oxygen.

39. Crew Quarters: This area has six rows of four cramped "coffin racks" for junior personnel, six rows of three less-cramped "coffin racks" for junior petty officers, and forty-two lockers for extra storage. There are thirty-eight crew members and four additional military personnel living here. (Note: These four military personnel could be the players, if they have no skills suitable for use on the ship.) The crew has a small lounge (J) with a holographic video monitor, but it is also a high-traffic area for refugees assigned to the port-side troop berthing (Area #26).

40. Crew Head: This room has a six-person, zero-privacy, zero-gravity shower/toilet, plus a single private model.

41. Gym: Troops need to exercise. This is where they would normally do it, using zero-gravity equipment like torsion bars and aerobic resistance machines. Now, however, the exercise gear is lashed to the side bulkhead to make room for additional food and water.

42. Library/Recreation Room: The ship's chief petty officer has made extra effort to stock the ship's library with electronic copies of almost every piece of literature (fiction, non-fiction, poetry, music, etc.) known to the former Galactic Republic; hundreds of extra computer data storage devices line the walls. Many of the computer files are "how to" self-learning programs about every Heroes Unlimited skill. The self-learning programs enable a character to learn any non-physical secondary skill in one week; non-physical primary skills can be learned in 25% of the time it would take to study the same skill at a prestigious Earth university. RiCorp's extensive sociological studies on Earth are also available to the crew; however, for security purposes, Earth's location is not. These self-learning programs enable any member of the crew to gain +20% on his or her "Familiarity with Earth" roll and to learn three additional secondary skills as if taught by a friendly human (see Heroes Unlimited, page 97).

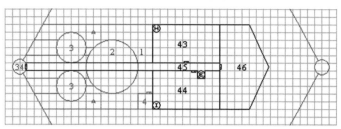

Bottom Deck

43. Food storage: This is actually a detachable pod enclosed within the thick armor of the ship's hull. This pod has enormous walk-in cold storage units as well as many shelves to hold dry and liquid foodstuffs. There is a roof hatch and power lift (H) leading to the galley (Area #36). The use of detachable pods for food, waste, and life support means that a full resupply that normally would take 24 hours of crew work can be completed in less than 20 minutes by a space tug. The hatch to this area has a computerized lock and provides maintenance access to the refrigeration units.

44. Waste storage: This detachable pod contains a garbage bin and a septic tank, which has a built-in water reclamation system. Like the other pods, it is accessible via armored hatches built into the hull. All the ship's waste (sewage and compacted garbage) is collected here. There is a roof hatch and power lift (I) leading from the mess hall (Area #37) to the garbage bin. Port-a-potty waste is manually collected via a wet-vac and then flushed down the nearest ship's toilet. The hatch to this area has a computerized lock and provides maintenance access to the water reclamation system.

45. Passageway: This one is the same institutional gray as Area #17, but has no motivational posters. It extends underneath the bottom deck of the engine room (Area #1) to a ramp that leads up between the ion drives (Area #3) to the aft gun turret (Area #34). There is a roof hatch with a power lift (E) that leads to the mess hall (Area # 37).

46. Primary Life support: This is another detachable pod accessible behind armored hatches. It contains an air recycling system (carbon dioxide to oxygen), plus enough air and water for 288 people for two years. Between the air recycling system and the water recycling system (Area #44), the two-year supply of air and water can last up to ten years. The hatch to this area has a computerized lock and provides maintenance access to the air recycling system.

Alien Skills

My players had plenty of questions regarding skills. What's their native language? Can they learn Earth languages as secondary skills? Do they get Pilot: Automobile as an automatic skill? Then, too, the players needed skills that would put them in good stead on a spaceship, but the basic military program was more tailored to Earth foot soldiers than to alien starship sailors. Below are the skills I gave my players:

<u>Automatic Skills:</u>
Read/Write Native Language (+20%)
Speak Native Language (+25%)
Basic Mathematics
Pilot: Hovercraft (+10%)

<u>Basic Alien Fleet Program:</u> (Bonus skill program for all players.)
  Basic Electronics
  Basic Mechanics
  Computer Operation
  Military Etiquette
  Pilot: Jet Pack
  Weapon Systems
  W.P. Energy Pistol

Alien Weapons and Equipment

Ah, yes. What do the players have that can blow things up? I thought that too many of the weapons listed in the Heroes Unlimited book were out-ranged and out-classed by modern Earth weapons, so I made some improvements. Note that none of the below items are available on Earth. Feel free to drool over the following:

Standard Issue

All characters are issued the following items:

GSH-67 Plasma Grenade: Range: Thrown, 10 feet (3 m) per point of P.S.; damage: 6D6x10 at 0-5 feet (0-1.5 m) from detonation, 3D6x10 at 6-50 feet (1.8-15.2 m); capacity: single use explosive; length: 2 inches (5 cm); weight: 2 ounces (56 g); W.P.: none. This grenade is the size of a golf ball, except that each dimple is a port for the venting of an intense stream of super-hot, ionized gas (plasma), a process that consumes the body of the grenade itself. Each grenade is equipped with a pin safety, a grip safety, and a dual-action three-second-or-impact fuse. The impact fuse is disabled until one full second after the grip safety is released to preclude accidental death from dropping an armed grenade. A hand grenade takes one action to pull the pin and another to throw it. This is the standard explosive grenade of the former Galactic Republic. Every member of the crew was issued one; most think that they will be dead long before an Imperial space marine comes within throwing range. For $20 of cheap booze,

a crewmate might be persuaded to give you his (or hers). Bulk orders require a successful Find Contraband and Illegal Weapons check (one try per character): $30 per grenade.

GSM-26 Space Suit: Required skill: Pilot: Jet Pack. This standard-issue, antigravity space suit (see Heroes Unlimited, page 99) looks like a white, full-body Spandex jumpsuit with a bubble helmet. It has a helmet-mounted spotlight, a communications link (50 mile/80 km range), and 72 hours of full life support. The antigravity system is thought-controlled with a verbal override, making it very easy to use: +10% to all Pilot: Jet Pack skill checks. Every crew station and rack has a receptacle where a crew member in a GSM-26 can plug in and live off the ship's life support system. It is a sturdy piece of gear, designed to protect against the explosive decompression of the crew space and being blown out of a jagged metal hole into the hard vacuum of space. While not actually armor, it provides A.R. 8, S.D.C. 45, and immunity to the first 10 points of heat and radiation damage per round. Armor or a heavy environmental suit can easily be worn on top of the thin GSM-26, but only specially-made helmets will fit over the bubble. *All crew are to don their space suits for battle stations.* Price: Not otherwise available. Millions of desperate refugees have already bought, begged, borrowed, or stolen every available space suit in Confederate space. Civilian space suits have no antigravity system, provide only 24 hours of life support, and cannot plug into military life support systems (incompatible plug).

GSP-9 Laser Pistol: Range and damage: 0-400 feet (0-122 m), 2D6x5 per shot; 401-800 feet (122-244 m), 5D6 per shot; capacity: 30 shots per "L-type" E-Clip; rate of fire: semi-automatic only; length: 6 inches (15.2 cm), weight: 1.1 pounds (0.5 kg) fully loaded; W.P.: Energy Pistol. The weapon comes standard with a "dumb" (non-computerized), fixed 1.5x magnification combat optic, a blue-dot laser sight, and a detachable white-light flashlight (illumination to 800 feet/244 m). Bonus to strike: +2 (+1 for the non-computerized sight, +1 for the non-computerized laser). Like most energy weapons, the GSP-9 does less damage at long range. This weapon uses only the light "L-type" E-Clip and is the standard issue for space crew. The ship's chief engineer can computerize the weapon sight for a bottle of high-quality intoxicant and $30,000 (Heroes Unlimited, page 205), which will provide an additional +2 to strike. Price: Every member of the crew was issued a GSP-9 with two fully-charged "L-type" E-Clips. Additional GSP-9s are so widely available from deserters as to be an open market item: $650.

RiCorp Earth-Compatible Submachine-Gun: Range: 800 feet (244 m); damage: 6D6 per bullet; capacity: 60 round clear drum magazine; rate of fire: semi-automatic, three-round burst, or full automatic; length: 1.5 feet (46 cm); weight: 7.5 pounds (3.4 kg) fully loaded; W.P.: Submachine-Gun. This bullpup Xijian weapon is designed for long-term use on Earth and accepts standard Earth 9mm Parabellum rounds. It employs a Kisentite squeeze bore coated with a frictionless ceramic to increase the range and velocity of the Earth ammunition, doubling its kinetic impact. It comes standard with a flash suppressor, a "dumb" (non-computerized), fixed 1.5x magnification combat optic, a blue-dot laser sight, and a detachable white-light flashlight (illumination to 800 feet/244 m). Bonus to strike: +2 (+1 for the non-computerized sight, +1 for the non-computerized laser). A three-round burst will strike with two bullets and takes one action. A proficient shooter can fire single shots or three-round bursts from this weapon one-handed without penalty, but full automatic fire requires two hands or else the character is firing wild. Price: Every member of the crew was issued one of these and four full drum magazines; crew members are strongly encouraged to visit the library to learn how to use them. Not otherwise available.

Universal Translator (U.T.): Required skill: None. See Heroes Unlimited, page 97. This two-part device consists of a microfilm corneal implant and an audio device the size of a grain of rice that is normally implanted under the skin, by the ear. A U.T. translates any spoken or written, former Galactic Republic or Sipathian language or dialect at 98% proficiency. The weakness of the U.T. is that it only allows one to *understand* spoken or written languages, not to *speak* them. After all, that's why other people have *their* U.T.s. Price: $20 open market for one still in the box (i.e., not yet implanted). Everyone has one, military and civilian alike; that's how so many races of aliens have been able to communicate all these years. The crew's U.T.s have been loaded with Earth data and thus can also translate Earth languages at 88% proficiency. Uploading Earth data to a U.T. requires a successful Computer Operation skill check at the ship's library.

Optional Gear

The items listed below may or may not be available to your character, depending on your character's money, education, race, and skill at working the black market. All weapons acquisitions are assumed to have been made pre-game.

Standard issue: The character gets the weapon for free from what's left of the Confederate Systems Fleet. Although this is in theory a loan of government property, everyone knows that the Confederate Systems will cease to exist in a few days, so no one will be left to ask for it back.

Robots: The price listed does not include the weapon sights but does include the cost of integrating the weapon with the robot's targeting systems, armor, and power source. No E-Clips are necessary if integrated with the robot's power source.

Open market: Anyone can purchase items available on the open market.

Black market: The collapse of the Confederacy has created a buyer's market in military weapons as millions of deserting soldiers sell their arms and corrupt quartermasters try to liquidate depots full of military assets before the Empire arrives to seize them. Characters attempting to buy "never fired and only dropped once" weapons must succeed on a Find Contraband & Illegal Weapons skill check (one check per character per weapon) and pay the black market price. Due to the glut of weapons and the sellers' willingness to part with the weapons quickly, the check is made with a +30% bonus; even unskilled characters have a flat 30% chance.

E-Clips: Although they are police and military items, the market is flooded with them. Price: $30 open market for "L-type" E-Clips, $50 black market for "H-type" E-Clips.

GSH-41 Ion Blaster: Range and damage: 0-800 feet (0-244 m), 4D6x10 plus knockdown; 801-1,600 feet (244-488 m), 2D6x10 plus knockdown; capacity: 30 shots per "H-type" E-Clip; rate of fire: semi-automatic only; length: 4 feet (1.22 m); weight: 33 pounds (15 kg) fully loaded; W.P.: Heavy Energy Weapons & Rail Guns. Using the same principle as a spaceship's ion drives, the cone-faced ion blaster shoots a shotgun-like blast of lightspeed subatomic particles, potentially hitting everything in a 5

feet (1.5 m) wide line, centered on the intended target. Despite a high-grade, antigravity-based recoil dampener, the weapon packs an extraordinary kick, requiring a P.S. of 30 or superhuman strength to handle. Those shot do not get the benefit of the recoil system and may get knocked down (see Heroes Unlimited, page 73). The weapon comes standard with a "dumb" (non-computerized), fixed 1.5x magnification combat optic and an infrared laser sight. Bonus to strike: +4 (+2 for shotgun spread, +1 for the non-computerized sight, +1 for the non-computerized laser). This weapon uses only the heavy "H-type" E-Clip. Price: $350,000 for robots, $90,000 black market.

GSH-70 Mini-Missile: Range: 31,680 feet (9.6 km); damage: by warhead type; capacity: single use explosive; length: 20 inches (51 cm); weight: 4.4 pounds (2 kg); speed: Mach 2; W.P.: Heavy Energy Weapons & Rail Guns. Bonus to strike: +5. These guided missiles have computerized digital cameras that "see" the designated target via passive IR, UV, and visible light and then seek that target at high speed. The GSH-70 is propelled by antigravity and thus has zero launch signature (i.e., no flash of light or smoke trail to betray the location of the firer). If the missileer keeps a laser designator on the intended target, the missile gains an additional +3 to strike. Once locked on to a target, the missile will continue to home in on it, even if the laser designator should move off the target. (Note: Only plasma warheads are available at this time. They cause the same damage as the GSH-67 Plasma Grenade.) Price: $4,000 each for robots, $1,000 each black market.

GSH-72 Particle Beam Rifle/Plasma Ejector: Range: 16,000 feet (4,877 m); damage: 6D6x10+20; capacity: 20 shots per "H-type" E-Clip; rate of fire: semi-automatic, three-round burst, or full automatic; length: 6.5 feet (2 m); weight: 22 pounds (10 kg) fully loaded; W.P.: Heavy Energy Weapons & Rail Guns. The weapon comes standard with a "smart" (computerized), 1.5-20x magnification combat optic, ultraviolet laser sight, and a gyrostabilized floating barrel that is datalinked to the weapon sight. Bonus to strike: +5 on aimed shots only (+3 for laser targeting system, +1 for targeting sight, and +1 for the sight's combat computer; see Heroes Unlimited, pages 205-206). Unlike most energy weapons, this weapon does not lose effectiveness at long range. It uses only the heavy "H-type" E-Clip. This two-stage weapon uses a cylindrical pulse of electromagnetically charged particle beams to create a Birkeland current to the target for the follow-on payload of plasma. It essentially throws perfectly straight lightning bolts. It has zero recoil; however, it makes a distinctive flash and thunderclap, advertising the shooter's location. Thus, its ability to deal massive damage at long range is tempered by its ability to attract enemy fire. Price: $500,000 for robots, $125,000 black market.

GSH-205 Grenade/Mini-Missile Launcher: Range: 2,000 feet (610 m) for grenades fired directly, 8,000 feet (2,438 m) for grenades fired indirectly, or by missile type; damage: by grenade or missile type; capacity: 10 grenades in clear tubular magazine plus one in the chamber, or 1 mini-missile muzzle-loaded, with 120 grenades launched per "H-type" E-Clip; rate of fire: semi-automatic or full automatic (grenades), single shot (minimissile); length: 19 inches (0.5 m); weight: 5.5 pounds (2.5 kg) fully loaded; W.P.: Heavy Energy Weapons & Rail Guns. This multi-use weapon comes with a "dumb" (non-computerized), 1.5x magnification combat optic and a laser rangefinder. Bonus to strike: +1 for direct fire, +2 for indirect fire (i.e., over an obstacle rather than through it). It uses a rail-gun system to launch hand grenades (such as the GSH-67) and can launch GSH-70 mini-missiles via their integral antigravity motors. Fortunately for the user, it comes standard with an antigravity recoil system to deal with its hefty "kick," but a full-automatic burst of grenades still requires a P.S. of 17 or else it is considered shooting wild. It can be used as a stand-alone weapon, but it is normally attached to the underside of the GSR-16 series laser rifles, where it taps into the rifle's "H-type" E-Clip. Its combat optic can be slaved to the GSR-16's combat computer, providing another +1 to strike. As a safety feature, a missile cannot be loaded while a grenade is in the weapon's chamber; once loaded, a missile will not fall out of the tube if it is pointed down. It takes one action to muzzle-load one mini-missile and two actions to load a standard hand grenade into a tubular magazine (one to pull the pin, the other to load the grenade; the launcher does not toggle the grip safety until the grenade is launched). Multiple magazines are normally carried. The laser rangefinder doubles as a target designator for guided missiles and "smart" grenades. (Note: The rebels are out of "smart" grenades.) Price: Standard issue for combat specialists with W.P. Heavy Weapons (plus four magazines and 40 plasma grenades), $40,000 for robots, $10,000 black market.

GSO-7A Special Forces Bayonet: Range: melee or thrown; damage: 2D6 plus P.S. bonus (blade), plus 5D6 (energy jolt); capacity: 60 jolts per "L-type" E-Clip; rate of fire: Not applicable; length: 1.5 feet (45 cm); weight: 1 pound (0.45 kg); W.P.: Knife. Bonuses: +1 to strike, parry, and throw. This is the masterwork-quality bayonet of the former Republic's special forces soldiers. It is balanced for throwing. An "L-type" E-Clip plugs into the handle, allowing the wielder to transmit an energy jolt to anyone touched by the blade. Price: $200 open market.

GSR-16F Laser Rifle: Range and damage: 0-4,000 feet (1,219 m), 2D6x10 per shot; 4,001-8,000 feet (1,219-2,438 m), 2D6x5 per shot; capacity: 120 shots per "H-type" E-Clip; rate of fire: semi-automatic only; length: 30 inches (76 cm); weight: 4.5 pounds (2 kg) fully loaded; W.P.: Energy Rifle. The weapon comes standard with a "smart" (computerized), 1.5-20x magnification combat optic, infrared laser sight, and a gyrostabilized floating barrel that is datalinked to the weapon sight. Bonus to strike: +5 on aimed shots only (+3 for laser targeting system, +1 for targeting sight, and +1 for the sight's combat computer; see Heroes Unlimited, pages 205-206). Like most energy weapons, this laser rifle loses effectiveness at long range. This weapon uses only the heavy "H-type" E-Clip. A bayonet lug is optional; give the chief engineer a $250 bottle of high-quality intoxicant and he'll hook you up. Converting the weapon to full automatic (in essence, turning it into the ruggedized, Kisentite-frame GSR-16M space marine version) will cost $5,000 and adds another 4.5 pounds (2 kg) to the weapon's weight; a bayonet lug will be added free. Price: Standard issue to fleet cadets who are military specialists or combat specialists (plus four "H-type" E-Clips), $300,000 for robots, $75,000 black market. (Note: GSR-16M price: $350,000 for robots, $90,000 black market.)

RiCorp Earth-Type Mini-Laser: Range: 400 feet (122 m); damage: 5D6; capacity: 10 shots on internal rechargeable capacitor; rate of fire: semi-automatic; length: 4 inches (10 cm); weight: 0.5 ounces (14 g); W.P.: Energy Pistol. This Xijian mini-laser looks and writes like a fancy Earth ball-point pen. It recharges 1 shot every 10 minutes from an Earth wall outlet or car battery. (Note: The existence of such an obvious espionage weapon

is evidence that RiCorp may have conducted covert operations on Earth in violation of the non-interact/non-interfere statutes of galactic law.) Price: *Special.* Standard issue to Xijian characters with RiCorp affiliation and rogue/smuggler or science specialist education, $2,000 open market for Xijians with RiCorp affiliation and other than rogue/smuggler or science specialist education. It is otherwise not available.

Valiant Stun Pistol: Range: 165 feet (50 m); damage: save vs toxin or be stunned for 1D4+1 rounds; capacity: 30 shots per "L-type" E-Clip; rate of fire: semi-automatic only; length: 6 inches (15.2 cm); weight: 1.65 pounds (0.74 kg) fully loaded; W.P.: Energy Pistol. The Valiant comes standard with a "dumb" (non-computerized), fixed 1.5x magnification combat optic, a blue-dot laser sight, and a detachable white-light flashlight (illumination to 800 feet/244 m). Bonus to strike: +2 (+1 for the non-computerized sight, +1 for the non-computerized laser). The stun effect is caused by an invisible electromagnetic field and not an actual toxin. A stunned person is -8 to strike, parry, dodge, and roll with impact; -40% on all skills; and loses initiative and half (fractions round up) of all attacks per melee. The Valiant uses only the light "L-type" E-Clip and is the standard issue for police forces. Price: $24,000 for robots, $6,000 black market.

VLEB (Variable Length Energy Blade): Range: melee or thrown for the weapon itself, 1,000 feet (305 m) for the energy blast; damage: 3D6 (knife), 5D6 (sword), 5D6 (energy blast) or 2D6x5 (double-strength energy blast); capacity: internal rechargeable capacitor with 144 charges, with one charge able to energize the knife for one minute, or energize the sword for 30 seconds, or shoot one normal-strength energy blast, and three charges required for a double-strength energy blast; length: 8 inches (20 cm) for the handle, 1-5 feet (0.3-1.5 m) for the variable-length energy blade; weight: 2.2 pounds (1 kg); W.P.: *Special* (see below). Combat bonuses: The weightless blade provides +1 to strike and parry; the sai-like hilt guard gives a +2 bonus to disarm an opponent; the thought-controlled command ring provides a +1 bonus to strike with the energy blasts. This novelty is a favorite unofficial piece of survival gear for space crews; the handle and hilt guard are made of Kisentite and the hollow hilt holds a survival kit with a survival blanket, a multi-tool (like a Kisentite Swiss Army knife), fire-making materials, water purifier, navigation device, distress beacon/emergency radio, and a universal translator. The "nano-smart" survival blanket is as thin as plastic wrap but absorbs low levels of radiation and can increase or decrease the temperature of its user by up to 90 degrees Fahrenheit (32° C). It also doubles as a recharger for the VLEB, with one hour of bright sunlight or ambient radiation restoring one charge. Each VLEB is uniquely coded and comes with a matching, thought-powered command ring; only the wearer of the ring can open or activate the VLEB. With a thought, the ring's wearer can sense the location of the matching VLEB within 1,000 feet (305 m), even through water, rock, etc. In addition, the ring's wearer can even make the VLEB fly an equal distance into his or her hand via the VLEB's built-in mini-antigravity device. Thus, the wielder can throw the weapon and have it return almost instantly. However, the VLEB cannot move if held by more than 11 pounds (5 kg) of force, nor can the VLEB be wielded at a distance. Having the VLEB return when thrown does not count as an action, but otherwise commanding the weapon to come to one's hand does. As a safety feature, the VLEB will not extend its blade unless it is in the hand wearing the matching ring and will automatically cancel the blade if it is out of its wielder's hand for more than one action. The VLEB requires W.P. Knife to wield a knife-sized energy blade proficiently, W.P. Sword to wield a sword-sized energy blade proficiently, and W.P. Energy Pistol to shoot energy bolts proficiently. Price: $2,000 open market. An extra $500 buys the deluxe model, which features a basket-style, Kisentite hand guard with small, retractable spikes (+2D4 punch damage, +2 to avoid being disarmed).

G.M. Section

Introduction:

Hello, This Is Your Captain

What fun would it be if you blew up the ship too soon? None! So as the introductory mini-adventure, have the players get into an altercation with some refugees prior to the big battle scene. Explain to the players that the *New Hope* and a sub-light freighter are in the process of evacuating 30,400 refugees from a few mining colonies on the second moon of Wuwu-4 (the fourth planet orbiting Wuwu) prior to the ships' arrival at Wuwu-3 (the third planet orbiting Wuwu), which is where the players' families are. The freighter is taking on the two main colonies' 30,000 miners and family members, while the *New Hope* is bringing in a smaller colony's 400 residents, among whom are members of the cap-

tain's family. Stress to the players that for security purposes, the refugees are not to know about Earth or the wormhole.

What happens next should be tailored to the players' skills and abilities. Maybe a few loudmouths from among the first 400 refugees are in a panic to leave and try to take over the ship. Maybe a crew member wigs out because he/she got a message that his/her family was supposed to be on Wuwu-4 but wasn't. Maybe someone entices a player to try to break into the chief engineer's stash of intoxicants, or someone steals something belonging to the player. Maybe one of the refugees is an old flame who throws herself/himself at a character, but she/he is not "yet" divorced from her/his current spouse, an abusive and unfaithful martial artist.

In any event, fisticuffs ensue and the responsible parties are brought before the ship's captain for disciplinary action. Whether the players' characters are there as witnesses or the accused, they get a good look at the captain's quarters and some sense of the history of the ship. If they're smart, they'll also get a sense that not all will be well when they get to Earth. (**Note:** The mini-laser, the Roswell rescue plaque, and the submachine-gun are irrefutable evidence that the ship violated galactic non-interact/ non-interfere statutes during its alleged "museum time;" see Area #13 for details.)

Captain Vochiyu Ri

Alias: None.
Power Category/O.C.C.: Alien, no super abilities.
Alignment: Scrupulous.
Attributes: I.Q. 17, M.E. 14, M.A. 13, P.S. 9, P.P. 16, P.E. 9, P.B. 11, Spd 6 (12).
Experience Points: 17,250
Level: 5
Race: Xijian.
Education: Alien Pilot.
Sex: Male
Age: 35
Height: 4 feet, 5 inches (1.35 m).
Weight: 66 pounds (30 kg).
H.P.: 27. S.D.C.: 25.
Armor A.R.: 10. Armor S.D.C.: 98.
P.P.E.: 8
Attacks per Melee: 5
Strike: +2
Parry: +4
Initiative: +1
Dodge: +4
Roll: +3
Pull Punch: +2
Kick (Karate): 2D4
Kick (Snap): 1D6
Natural/Mutant/Power Category/O.C.C. Abilities:
· Classic alien appearance (modified): Xijians have three fingers and an opposable thumb on their hands and have four toes on their feet. They gain +2 to I.Q., and +2 to M.E. They also gain -1 on M.A. due to a mild sense of superiority and arrogance.
· Low gravity (modified): Xijians are smaller and lighter than other low-gravity races. They gain no weight or S.D.C. bonuses, but gain a bonus of +1D6 to P.P. and retain the normal low gravity penalty to Speed.

Primary Skills: Computer Operation 68%, Language: Xijian 98%, Literacy: Xijian 98%, Mathematics: Advanced 73%, Mathematics: Basic 73%, Military Etiquette 63%, Navigation 88%, Navigation: Space 78%, Pilot: Hovercraft 98%, Pilot: Jet Fighter 74%, Pilot: Jet Packs 86% (includes GSM-26 bonus), Pilot: Race Car 85%, Pilot: Warships & Patrol Boats 74%, Radio: Basic 73%, Read Sensory Equipment 68%, and Weapon Systems 78%.

Secondary Skills: Astronomy 38% (gained at third level), Athletics (general), Basic Mechanics 53%, First Aid 68%, Hand to Hand: Basic, Language: English 73%, Pilot: Automobile 73%, W.P. Energy Pistol, and W.P. Submachine-Gun (gained at third level).

Equipment/Power Armor/Bionics/Robotics:

GSH-67 plasma grenade.

GSM-26 space suit with built-in concealed armor (A.R. 12, S.D.C. 98).

Personal communicator (encrypted).

RiCorp Earth-compatible submachine-gun with four full, 60-round drum magazines.

RiCorp Earth-type mini-laser.

Universal translator.

Valiant stun pistol (modified to look like a GSP-9 laser pistol) with three "L-type" E-Clips.

Wedding band (platinum with small diamonds, worth $40,000).

Character Background: Captain Ri is a good-natured and knowledgeable ship's captain, running his ship with an even hand. Before the civil war, he was a RiCorp pilot, specializing in shuttling scientists to and from Earth. Although Captain Ri never personally took part in the abduction of, or experimentation on, Earth humans, he was aware of the activity and kept his mouth shut. He is not as ambitious as other members of the House of Ri, being content to be a well-paid ship's captain instead of a merchant prince. He loves his wife and daughters and would risk his life to save them. His sense of duty is such that he would also risk his life to save the families of the other members of his crew.

Leading Petty Officer Dragoman-he' Valikashnikopitkai

Alias: The Chief Engineer, "Drinky-Man."
Power Category/O.C.C.: Alien, no super abilities.
Alignment: Scrupulous.
Attributes: I.Q. 24, M.E. 10, M.A. 9, P.S. 14, P.P. 8, P.E. 11, P.B. 8, Spd 11.
Experience Points: 22,000
Level: 5
Race: Turkohindi.
Education: Alien Engineer.
Sex: Male.
Age: 41
Height: 5 feet (1.5 m). Weight: 99 pounds (45 kg).
H.P.: 33. S.D.C.: 25.
Armor A.R.: 8. Armor S.D.C.: 45.
P.P.E.: 4
Attacks per Melee: 5
Strike: +1
Parry: +3
Initiative: +1
Dodge: +3
Roll: +3
Pull Punch: +2
Kick (Karate): 2D4
Kick (Snap): 1D6

Natural/Mutant/Power Category/O.C.C. Abilities

· Alien humanoid: Turkohindis have green skin, no hair, pointy ears, black eyes, and delicate hands. Their base height is four feet, five inches + 2D6 inches (1.35 m + 5D6 cm); their base weight is 77 pounds + 4D10 pounds (35 kg + 2D8+2 kg).

· Normal Earth environment: Turkohindis can live on Earth without artificial life support.

Primary Skills: Aircraft Mechanics 80%, Astrophysics 60%, Automotive Mechanics 80%, Chemistry 65%, Computer Operation 75%, Computer Repair 80%, Electrical Engineer 85%, Language: Turkohindi 98%, Literacy: Turkohindi 98%, Mathematics: Advanced 98%, Mathematics: Basic 98%, Mechanical Engineer 80%, Optic Systems 65%, Pilot: Hovercraft 90%, Radio: Basic 80%, Read Sensory Equipment 65%, and Weapons Engineer 80%.

Secondary Skills: Athletics (general), Dance 60%, First Aid 75%, Hand to Hand: Basic, Language: English 80% (gained at third level), Pilot: Jet Pack 78% (includes GSM-26 bonus), Streetwise 46%, W.P. Energy Pistol (+8 aimed shot, +2 burst; includes computerized sight bonuses), W.P. Sword (+3 to strike with blade, +4 to strike with blast, +3 to parry, +1 to throw; includes VLEB bonuses), and W.P. Submachine-Gun (gained at third level; +6 aimed shot, +2 burst; includes weapon-sight bonuses).

Equipment/Power Armor/Bionics/Robotics

GSH-67 plasma grenade.

GSM-26 space suit.

GSP-9 laser pistol with computerized weapon sight and two "L-type" E-Clips.

Hip flask with 10 ounces (0.3 L) of high-potency intoxicant.

Optics band.

Personal communicator (encrypted).

RiCorp Earth-compatible submachine-gun with four full, 60-round drum magazines.

Universal translator.

VLEB

Character Background: Leading Petty Officer Valikashnikopitkai is a highly intelligent and diligent chief engineer who cares deeply for his ship and his subordinates. He is also a party animal who has earned the nickname "Drinky-Man" many times over. Over the past six months, he traded his prize possession, his vast collection of rare and high-potency intoxicants, for the supplies the ship needed to remain operational. All he has left is his hip flask, which he is trying to make last until the ship lands safely on Earth. He maintains a deep and abiding hatred of Sipathians, as the Turkohindi home world sits by the border of the former Republic and the Sipathian Hive, and was brutally attacked during each and every one of the six Sipathian incursions. For all the chief engineer knows, he is the only one of his race still alive and free; the thought that he never settled down and had a family weighs on his soul.

First Adventure: Know Your Enemy

The first real adventure should be done en route to Wuwu-3 (the third planet orbiting the star Wuwu). Explain to the players that the *New Hope* and a sub-light freighter have just evacuated 30,400 refugees (400 of whom are aboard the *New Hope*) from a mining colony on the second moon of Wuwu-4 (the fourth planet orbiting Wuwu). The freighter captain estimates that she can hold another 20,000 refugees in her cargo hold, so instead of making a break for the wormhole, she'll follow the *New Hope* to Wuwu-3 to assist in the evacuation of its over one billion inhabitants. A pair of Imperial GF-312 fighters (see below), advance scouts for the main Imperial fleet, will intercept the *New Hope* and the freighter as the ships are en route. The *CSV New Hope* will go to battle stations.

Enemy actions: The Imperial fighters know well the range of the *New Hope*'s Type 55 guns but do not know that the ship is desperately low on missiles. They will *not* close within gun range of the *New Hope*, but will call in the contact to the rest of the Imperial fleet. The fighters will hope to score an easy kill by massed missile fire against the freighter at maximum range. Once their missiles are expended, the fighters will shadow the *New Hope* all the way to Wuwu-3. Once the good guys approach the defenses of Wuwu-3, the Imperial fighters will break off and return to the Imperial fleet to rearm.

Friendly actions: The captain of the *New Hope* will order his vessel to remain between the fighters and the freighter at all times and will order that no missiles be fired except as necessary to shoot down enemy missiles. See below for the statistics for freighters; this one is speed class 42. The freighter's captain is third level and has Pilot: Spacecraft 45%; she commands a dozen civilian crew members with no combat ability.

Second Adventure: Getting Away from Wuwu-3

The players' second mission is to get their families and loved ones away from Wuwu-3 before the Imperial punitive expedition arrives to enslave/kill the populace. Unfortunately, Imperial destroyers and fighters show up just as the first SpaceBus 550 is approaching for docking. The ship cannot take evasive maneuvers while it is docking with the SpaceBus, so it is a sitting duck unless the gun turrets can fend off the enemy fighters for a full minute (4 melee rounds). Worse, all of the players' families are on the second SpaceBus, which won't be able to dock until another full minute after the first SpaceBus docks.

The players' saving grace here is that the Imperial fleet's vanguard is only 12 destroyers and 540 fighters, while there are literally thousands of Confederate craft; however, almost all the rebel spacecraft are unarmed civilian vessels (freighters, cruise liners, pleasure yachts, etc.) – anything that one billion desperate people could use to evacuate the planet. The Confederates have three armed but puny vessels – a privateer (armed, fast freighter), a guided missile patrol ship and an anti-missile corvette – plus 180 fighters orbiting on the other side of the planet, where the richest continent is. The players' families are not rich, so the *CSV New Hope* is orbiting over the poor continent with six civilian craft. Initially, the Imperial fleet will concentrate on the VIPs and armed vessels on the far side of the planet, with only 2-6 fighters circling around to probe and harass the players' group and to get some easy pickings from among the helpless and slow civilian vessels there. Once the Imperial fighters get shot up by an armored troopship, however, they will call for destroyer backup.

Remember, you're not trying to kill off the players; the point here is both to show the power and the brutality of the Imperial Fleet and to give the players' ship a good pounding before it gets to Earth. You're taking away their spaceship, right? Having it crash-land on Earth due to battle damage is a good way to do it. Sabotage is another. Sabotage *and* battle damage are a good combination, too. Just remember that the players' ship should be the *only* ship to make it through the wormhole.

So feel free to roll huge handfuls of dice and announce, "Golly! Those poor rebel fighters were no match against three-to-one odds... Ooh, there goes another unarmed cruise ship! Scratch off another 15,000 refugees... Direct hit on the hospital ship! You know, your sister volunteered to serve as a nurse there..." There are millions of tragic deaths happening *right now*, and a billion more to come. Remind the players of that and personalize these deaths as you see fit.

In case the players are getting pounded *too* hard, don't forget that there are plenty of other Confederate vessels engaged in the main battle on the other side of the planet. Maybe a pair of Confederate fighters flies out to help the *CSV New Hope*. Maybe a tug pulls up alongside and offloads a few dozen medium missiles – all that's left of the Confederate arsenal. Maybe the privateer is actually on the players' side of the planet (looks like just another freighter). Maybe a luxury cruise liner with thousands of Confederate VIPs makes a break for the wormhole, attracting Imperial fire for a few actions until it and its escort(s) are overtaken and overwhelmed. Maybe a yacht's captain is driven to suicidal fury by the death of her family and tries to ram a destroyer, or self-destructs her ship to take out a swarm of fighters or a wave of missiles. Some of these tragic deaths can be heroic.

As the damaged Imperial fighters break off to attack easier targets, the lone responding destroyer will launch volleys of long-range nuclear missiles at the *New Hope*. Meanwhile, the second SpaceBus should be able to dock, allowing the *CSV New Hope* to head straight for the wormhole with the destroyer in hot pursuit. The destroyer will attempt to close with and tractor beam the *New Hope* to prevent its escape. Although the destroyer has a matter-antimatter reactor and could theoretically just jump to light speed to cut off the *New Hope*, it doesn't know that there even *is* a wormhole. Besides, every other surviving Confederate vessel will also be making a break for the wormhole and the destroyer can't chance getting vaporized by a missile while in light speed. (See the notes above for the strengths and weaknesses of light speed and matter-antimatter reactors.) The fight becomes a stern chase with the destroyer catching up by moving *just under* light speed. The two ships should slug it out at close range briefly just before the *New Hope* gets away by transiting the wormhole.

Indomitable-class Imperial (ex-Republic) Destroyer

Type: Guided Missile Destroyer.

Speed Class: 43 with matter-antimatter drive.

S.D.C.: 15,000

Shields: A.R. 25, S.D.C. 35,000. Cover the entire vessel.

Armor (Bridge): A.R. 15, S.D.C. 1,100.

Armor (Engine Room): A.R. 14, S.D.C. 800.

Armor (Fuel Compartment): Not applicable, matter-antimatter reactor.

Armor (Main Hull): A.R. 12, S.D.C. 1,800.

Armor (Missile Bay): A.R. 14, S.D.C. 800.

Armor (4 Turrets): A.R. 14, S.D.C. 800 each.

Weapons: (4) Type 55 Dual-Purpose Guns: Range and Damage: 0-20 miles (0-32 km), 2D10x100, 21-40 miles (33-64 km), 1D10x100; Capacity: Not applicable; Rate of Fire: Semi-automatic only; Length: 20 feet (6 m); Weight: 2,200 pounds (990 kg) per gun. Bonus to Strike: +5. The guns are mounted two per turret with one turret on the top of the vessel and the other on the belly.

(4) Type 20 Rapid-Fire Guns: Range and Damage: 0-25,000 feet (7,620 m), 4D6x10 +20, 25,001-50,000 feet (7,620-15,240 m), 2D6x10+10; Capacity: Not applicable; Rate of Fire: Automatic, up to 300 shots per melee round; Length: 8 feet (2.4 m); Weight: 500 pounds (225 kg) per gun. Bonus to Strike: +5. The guns are mounted two per turret with one turret on the ship's port side and the other on the starboard side. These weapons use the rules for machine-gun fire (see Heroes Unlimited, page 76).

(6) Long-Range Missile Launchers: (Nuclear multi-warhead) Range: 18,000 miles (28,800 km); Damage: 2D4x1,000; Capacity: Automatic reload, storage for 120 missiles; Rate of Fire: Volleys of up to six missiles every action; Length: 80 feet (24 m); Weight: 80,000 pounds (36,000 kg) per missile; Speed: *Special:* 99% light speed (effectively 43). Bonus to Strike: +5.

(1) Tractor Beam: Range: 5 miles (8 km); Damage: None; Capacity: One vessel or item not exceeding the size of the destroyer; Rate of Fire: One attack per melee; Length: 40 foot by 40 foot (12 m by 12 m) panel; Weight: 20 tons. Bonus to Strike: +3. The tractor beam holds a vessel or item in place relative to itself. Once a tractor beam "strikes" a target, a push/pull contest begins, with both vessels rolling 1D20 and adding their speed class to their results. The vessel that is at least 50% larger than the other gains a bonus of +2 for every size multiple it is (e.g., a vessel that is twice as big gets a +4 bonus, one that is three times bigger gets a +6 bonus, etc.). A vessel may "push" its power plant for another +4 bonus, but must succeed on a Mechanical Engineering skill check or lose 1D6 speed class. If the vessel that initiated the tractor beam gets the higher result, the other vessel cannot move away from it. If the target of the tractor beam gets the higher result, it can move normally. The defender wins ties.

Crew: 7 officers, 129 enlisted.

Notes: The gunners in the turrets are first level and have four actions per melee; the missile control officer is fourth level and has five actions per melee. The sensor operators have Surveillance Systems: 30% and the ECM/ECCM operators have Radio: Scramblers: 35%.

The *Indomitable*-class destroyer is a very maneuverable craft: +2 to dodge.

Characters with a successful Military Etiquette or Intelligence roll will know that the *Indomitable*-class destroyer is designed for speed, maneuverability, and long-range firepower. It lacks the heavy armor and defensive weaponry for close-in battle.

Characters with a successful Intelligence roll will know that the destroyer pursuing the *CSV New Hope* is the *PES Retribution*, commanded by Lieutenant Commander Biggie Goh, an unusually aggressive (i.e., risk-taking glory hound) captain. They will also know that the other destroyers will most likely follow their standard doctrine of keeping their distance and shooting missiles at extreme range at their primary targets, the concentration of VIPs on the other side of Wuwu-3.

Sensors: Fleet standard radar, IR/UV search and track, electro-optical, and magnetic anomaly.

ECM/ECCM: Fleet standard radar detector, laser detector, magnetic dampener, signals intercept and jamming suite.

GF-312 Imperial and Confederate (ex-Republic) Space Fighter

Type: Fighter.

Speed Class: 43 with matter-antimatter drive.

S.D.C.: 2,500

Shields: A.R. 19, S.D.C. 3,500. Cover the entire vessel.

Armor (Cockpit): A.R. 15, S.D.C. 550.

Armor (Engine): A.R. 12, S.D.C. 200.

Armor (Fuel Compartment): Not applicable, matter-antimatter reactor.

Armor (Vehicle): A.R. 8, S.D.C. 300.

Weapons: (2) Type 20 Rapid-Fire Guns: Range and Damage: 0-25,000 feet (7,620 m), 4D6x10 +20, 25,001-50,000 feet (7,620-15,240 m), 2D6x10+10; Capacity: Not applicable; Rate of fire: Automatic, up to 300 shots per melee round; Length: 8 feet (2.4 m); Weight: 500 pounds (225 kg) per gun. Bonus to Strike: +5. The guns are both in fixed mounts, facing forward. These weapons use the rules for machine-gun fire (see Heroes Unlimited, page 76).

(2) Medium-Range Missiles: (Nuclear multi-warhead) Range: 800 miles (1,280 km); Damage: 5D6x100; Capacity: One single-rail hard point each; Rate of Fire: Singly or both simultaneously; Length: 6.5 feet (2 m); Weight: 110 pounds (50 kg); Speed: *Special:* 99% light speed (effectively 43). Bonus to Strike: +5.

(6) Short-Range Missiles: (Plasma warheads) Range: 30 miles (48 km); Damage: 2D6x100; Capacity: Up to six may be fired simultaneously at a single target; Length: 5 feet (1.5 m); Weight: 55 pounds (25 kg); Speed: *Special:* 99% light speed (effectively 43). Bonus to Strike: +5.

Crew: 1

Notes: Both the Confederates and the Empire use the same ex-Republic fighters. Gunners relying on their eyeballs will not be able to tell them apart, but electronic systems can do so easily (98% chance) via IFF (Identification Friend or Foe).

The pilots are all second level, with four attacks per melee, Pilot: Jet Fighter: 59%, Weapon Systems: 60%, and Surveillance Systems: 50%. The GF-312 has a small but automatic ECM/ECCM suite equivalent to Radio: Scramblers: 20%.

The Imperial fighters will launch their medium missiles at maximum range at the first likely targets, then press the attack with short-range missiles and guns. They will back off if their sensors are jammed.

The Confederate fighters carry 12 short-range missiles vice two medium and six short. They will attempt to take out as many Imperial fighters as possible before dying.

The GF-312 is a nimble craft and has a +6 to dodge.

Sensors: Semi-automated, forward-facing radar, IR/UV search and track, and electro-optical.

ECM/ECCM: Automated radar detector, laser detector, magnetic dampener, and electro-optical mask.

Typical Short-Haul Space Freighter

Type: Civilian Freighter.
Speed Class: Usually 41, but some are 42. Fusion reactor.
S.D.C.: 10,000
Shields: None.
Armor: None.
Weapons: None.
Crew: 12 civilians.
Notes: This vessel maneuvers like a bus: -2 to dodge and -10% to all Pilot: Spacecraft skill checks. When full of cargo (living or otherwise), it maneuvers like an overloaded bus: -4 to dodge and -20% to all Pilot: Spacecraft skill checks. The vessel's five cavernous cargo holds can hold up to 10,000 people each for short periods of time, albeit in horribly crowded conditions.
Sensors: Navigation radar, and basic civilian electro-optical.
ECM/ECCM: None.

Third Adventure: Welcome to Earth, Comrade!

This is where you take away the players' spaceship. There are many ways to do this. The one I used was to have a terrible engine fire due to battle damage (and I honestly did roll engine damage during the fight with the Imperial destroyer). Most of the engine room crew are badly hurt and so additional damage control personnel are needed; a dozen members of the ship's crew (including the players) are volunteered (or, in military parlance, volun-told). Almost as soon as the fire is put out, the ship enters Earth's atmosphere and the crew is told to "brace for impact." The ship rocks violently for a few minutes, then smacks against a giant iceberg, breaks into a thousand pieces, and sinks in deep water. Of course, the fusion reactor core was ejected during the crash, so the equivalent of a multi-megaton hydrogen bomb detonated in low Earth orbit (as designed, the core was ejected far enough so that its blast radius would not affect the crash site).

The players should be given the opportunity to jump into a life pod before the crash; those that don't (or can't) should still be wearing their heavy firefighting suits, so they may be able to survive a crash outside a life pod. The refugees, however, have no space suits (although you may rule as the G.M. that the SpaceBus refugees have non-antigravity space suits). Those that could not get to a life pod are almost certain to die – if not in the crash, then in the below-freezing salt water of the Arctic Ocean. Remember, the refugees in the troop bays have access to life pods, but the ones in the forward torpedo spaces do not, nor do the ones still

in the SpaceBuses. Give the players a little time to gather themselves and any survivors there may be. In my game, only 27 total aliens survived the crash and the icy water (one of whom was the saboteur).

However, the crash site is in *Russian territorial waters*, off the northern coast of Siberia, 600 miles from Alaska. And the nearby Russian military forces are very interested in killing or capturing the "American stealth bomber crew" for their unprovoked nuclear attack on the Russian motherland. If the Russians realize that they are dealing with aliens, they will only redouble their efforts to capture the "intergalactic criminals" so they can be tortured into revealing all their advanced technological secrets – er, properly tried and imprisoned for their crimes.

Russian jets, attack helicopters, and even an icebreaker ship and a guided missile destroyer respond to the crash of the *New Hope*, albeit in piecemeal fashion. (G.M.s, feel free to determine the order; I led off with the icebreaker and guided missile destroyer.) They will generally shoot first and ask questions later.

Meanwhile, the Russian nuclear weapons arsenal is put on high alert, a hair-trigger away from launching a full nuclear strike against the United States...

Resolution: Obviously, the aliens do not want to be captured by the Russians and should flee to the United States or Canada. However, that will only "confirm" to the Russians that America was indeed behind this nuclear incident. At the very least, there will be saber-rattling and nuclear brinkmanship not seen since the 1962 Cuban Missile Crisis. At worst, Russia will attack the United States and Canada with nuclear missiles; the United States will respond in kind. Meanwhile, the first side to realize that this was an alien crash-landing will be very keen to retrieve any survivors, wreckage, and corpses for study.

What comes next? Why, the rest of your campaign, of course! You have the alien players on Earth with limited alien gizmos and a secret but powerful alien enemy, which was the whole point of this adventure. The players are free to begin crime-fighting (or to try to rebuild society in a post-nuclear holocaust environment), while the saboteur will most certainly begin committing nefarious deeds.

In my campaign, the players sank the destroyer, hijacked a Russian helicopter, vectored the Russian search teams to the wrong location, landed on Little Diomede Island (Alaska), and immediately declared themselves to the world media. The truth about the crash of the *CSV New Hope* reduced the nuclear tensions between the U.S. and Russia, but began the competition for alien technology, with the West having the alien survivors and the Russians having the corpses, the flotsam, and whatever wreckage they are able to dredge up from the deep... But after a few weeks of fighting crime, a mystery plague began sweeping the Earth, turning humans into demonic creatures – with the players themselves possibly the carriers of the disease! (Yup, that saboteur was secretly working for the Sipathians. And yes, I got the demon plague idea from the Palladium RPG Book II: Old Ones, pages 171-172.)

But that may be the topic of another article.

Russian MiG-29M Fighter Aircraft

Type: Fighter.
Speed Class: 30, fossil fuel jet engine with afterburner.
S.D.C.: 500

Armor (Cockpit): A.R. 12, S.D.C. 250.
Armor (Engine): A.R. 12, S.D.C. 200.
Armor (Fuel Compartment): A.R. 10, S.D.C. 200, self-sealing fuel tanks.
Armor (Vehicle): A.R. 8, S.D.C. 300.
Weapons: (1) Automatic Cannon: See Heroes Unlimited, page 141. The gun is in a fixed mount, facing forward. It has 100 rounds of ammunition.

(2) Medium-Range Missiles: Light fragmentation warheads. See Heroes Unlimited, page 82. These can be radar-guided air-to-air missiles or air-to-surface missiles.

(4) Short-Range Missiles: Light fragmentation warheads. See Heroes Unlimited, page 82. These are infrared-guided air-to-air missiles. The missiles' IR guidance system can detect fires (like jet exhaust or camp fires) but not body heat.

Crew: 1

Notes: The Russian MiG-29Ms are multi-role fighters, designed to engage both ground and aerial targets. They normally fly in groups of three. They maintain contact with their ground controller at all times and follow the ground controller's orders to the letter. The pilots get nervous and indecisive (-4 to initiative) if that link is jammed.

The MiG-29 series are nimble aircraft and have a +2 to dodge.
Sensors: Forward-facing radar (44 mile/70 km range), IR search and track.
ECM/ECCM: Radar detector, decoy flares and chaff.

Russian Ka-27PL
Anti-Submarine Helicopter

Type: Helicopter.
Speed Class: 15
S.D.C.: 450
Armor (Cockpit): A.R. 12, S.D.C. 250.
Armor (Engine): A.R. 12, S.D.C. 200.
Armor (Fuel Compartment): A.R. 10, S.D.C. 200, self-sealing fuel tanks.
Armor (Vehicle): A.R. 8, S.D.C. 300.
Weapons: (1) Torpedo: Range: 10 miles (16 km); Damage: 3D6x100; Capacity: One single-rail hard point each; Rate of Fire: One; Length: 16 feet (4.9 m); Weight: 2,200 pounds (990 kg); Speed Class: 5 (underwater only). They are sonar-guided.
Crew: 4 (pilot, co-pilot, and 2 sonar operators).
Notes: This Russian helicopter is designed to engage naval targets. Its pilots maintain contact with their ground controller at all times and follow the ground controller's orders to the letter. The pilots get a bit nervous (-2 to initiative) if that link is jammed. This type of helicopter normally flies in loose pairs, with one using its sonar, the other engaging the enemy or deploying buoys. The crew members are all first level, with the pilots having Pilot: Helicopter 45%, Weapon Systems: 50%, and Navigation: 50%; the sonar operator has Surveillance Systems: 40%.

This helicopter can deploy sonar buoys, which float on the surface of the water but drop a passive sonar device to a set depth to listen for underwater activity. Any underwater noise above a certain threshold is automatically radioed in to the aircraft that dropped the buoy, along with the bearing to the source of the noise. A grid pattern of deployed sonar buoys can usually pinpoint all but the quietest of underwater vessels. Treat a sonar buoy as an unintelligent robot with Surveillance Systems: 30%.

This helicopter can also hover at low altitude (165 feet/50 m or less) to lower an active/passive dipping sonar. Passive sonar can get a bearing on underwater noise; active sonar can get a bearing and range on underwater objects, quiet or not. Add +25% to Surveillance Systems checks when using an active sonar to locate an underwater target.
Sensors: Forward-facing radar, 36 deployable sonar buoys, dipping sonar, and magnetic anomaly.
ECM/ECCM: Radar detector.

Russian *Sovremenny*-Class
Guided Missile Destroyer

Type: Naval Warship (Destroyer).
Speed Class: 2
S.D.C.: 8,000
Armor (Crew Compartment): A.R. 14, S.D.C. 600.
Armor (Fuel Compartment): A.R. 10, S.D.C. 400, self-sealing fuel tanks.
Armor (Naval Gun Turret): A.R. 12, S.D.C. 350.
Armor (Anti-Aircraft Gun Turrets): A.R. 10, S.D.C. 300.
Armor (Main Hull): A.R. 14, S.D.C. 3,500.
Weapons: (8) Moskit Anti-Ship Missiles: Range: 6 miles (10 km) minimum, 75 miles (120 km) maximum; Damage: 3D6x100; Capacity: four quadruple box mounts, no reloads; Rate of Fire: Singly or in salvos of up to eight missiles simultaneously; Length: 16 feet (5 m); Weight: 8,800 pounds (3,960 kg); Speed Class: 31. They are radar-guided and mounted in two banks of four missiles each. Reloading requires dockyard facilities.

(4) 130 mm (5.1 inch) Naval Guns: Range: 6 miles (9.6 km); Damage: 2D4x100; Capacity: 400 rounds per gun; Rate of Fire: Semi-automatic; Length: 13 feet (4 m); Weight: 4,400 pounds (1,980 kg). The ship's guns are radar-directed, but fire unguided projectiles. The guns are mounted two per turret, with one gun turret forward, one aft.

(4) 30 mm (1.2 inch) Anti-Aircraft Automatic Cannons: See Heroes Unlimited, page 141. These Gatling guns are mounted singly in light turrets. They have 3,000 rounds of ammunition each.

(48) Anti-Aircraft Missiles: See Heroes Unlimited, page 141. The missiles are radar-guided, have light fragmentation warheads, and are mounted in two banks of 24 missiles. Up to three missiles may be launched simultaneously. No reloads are carried.

(4) 533 mm (21 inch) Torpedo Tubes: Range: 10 miles (16 km); Damage: 3D6x100; Capacity: 32 torpedoes total; Rate of Fire: Up to four torpedoes may be launched simultaneously; Length: 16 feet (4.9 m); Weight: 2,200 pounds (990 kg); Speed Class: 5 (underwater only). They are sonar-guided. Reloading is manual but with mechanical assistance, and requires one full melee round per tube.

(2) RBU-1000 Anti-Submarine, Rocket-Launched Depth Charge Dispenser: Range: 328 feet (100 m) minimum, 3,280 feet (1,000 m) maximum; Damage: 5D6x10 per depth charge; Capacity: 60 rockets in storage bay; Rate of Fire: Automatic, bursts of up to six rockets; Length: 71 feet (21.6 m); Weight: 6,380 pounds (2,871 kg). The depth charges are set via sonar data and can engage targets up to 1,476 feet (450 m) under water. Reloading is automatic and takes two melee rounds per rocket.

(1) Ka-27 Anti-Submarine Helicopter (see above).
Crew: 21 officers, 329 enlisted.

Notes: This Russian guided missile destroyer is designed to engage surface and subsurface naval targets. Forty members of its crew have access to Kalashnikov rifles (typically AKM or AK-74). The rest are normally unarmed; the ship is their weapon. The crew members (officers and enlisted) are typically first to third level with four actions per melee, 15 S.D.C., and 14-21 Hit Points each; the fourth-level captain is an amateur boxer with 35 S.D.C., 26 Hit Points, and five attacks per melee. Russian naval training is not as rigorous as its Western counterpart: Russian enlisted sailors have only the basic military program (with General Athletics and Swimming in place of Running and Climbing) and one other skill program with an education bonus of +5%; Russian naval officers have the equivalent of Western military education (i.e., three skill programs at +10%; see Heroes Unlimited, page 45).

This ship has two motor launches, which it can use to send armed sailors to board vessels that have been halted and are not resisting. Each motor launch has a speed class of 2, no armor, 450 S.D.C., and can hold 20 personnel.

Sensors: Radar, sonar, and binoculars.

ECM/ECCM: Radar detector, decoy flares and chaff.

Russian *Arktika*-Class Nuclear-Powered Icebreaker

Type: Icebreaker Ship.

Speed Class: 2

S.D.C.: 8,000

Armor (Crew Compartment): A.R. 12, S.D.C. 500.

Armor (Engine Compartment): A.R. 10, S.D.C. 400, two atomic fission reactors.

Armor (Vehicle): A.R. 16, S.D.C. 7,000.

Weapons: This vessel is unarmed.

Crew: 13 officers, 125 enlisted.

Notes: This Russian icebreaker is designed to open a passage in the sea ice for other Russian vessels. It has a reinforced hull designed to ram sea ice as well as seawater pumps to increase the ship's weight to crush any ice floe on which it may "beach" itself. The crew members (officers and enlisted) are civilians, typically first to second level, with one action per melee, 15 S.D.C., and 14-17 Hit Points each. The third-level captain has 15 S.D.C., 21 Hit Points, and one attack per melee. They are unarmed but specialized sailors with the equivalent of technical school training. They will do their best to avoid combat, but if forced to fight, the strong-hulled ship is quite capable of ramming a surface target.

This ship has two Ka-32S helicopters, which are similar to the Ka-27PLs, except that each can carry 16 persons, has no armament or sonar buoys, and is equipped with a winch and cable. They are used for maritime utility transport and search and rescue.

Sensors: Navigation radar and binoculars.

ECM/ECCM: None.

Strange Things in the Bootheel

A Short Story by J.V. Adams

Sunday, October 25, 2009, 10:16 PM

Have you ever become aware that you're in the middle of something? That's what I suddenly realized this morning. There's something going on, and I don't understand it. I live in Poplar Bluff, Missouri. I'm single – no romantic entanglements for me, thank you very much. I drive a cab in town. Mostly, I drive in the afternoons and evenings, which gives me an opportunity to meet lots of different types of people.

I like people, and I think that the things that make us different make us special, and while I don't treat people differently, I don't see any harm in acknowledging differences. I started getting a repeat fare every so often this month. Funny little guy – he had real pale skin, and white hair. He didn't talk much, and always seemed just a little bit disoriented.

Anyway, it was tonight when I picked him up that something clicked. It's funny that I thought of it tonight; as this was the shortest ride he's been on. I picked him up at the lobby of Mercy Hospital tonight, and he wanted me to take him just a few blocks to the East Side. It wasn't too bad outside tonight, and the fare certainly wasn't very much. I think I'd have walked if I were him. Anyway, I dropped him off across the river from the Downtown district. That's why we call it the East Side – on the west side of the Black River, it's Downtown – business and commercial. On the East Side, it's more industrial and low-end residential.

It dawned on me that I was always dropping him off in about the same area, but never exactly the same place. It was always within about a three or four block area on the East Side. However, it seemed like I was picking him up from all over town every few days. I mentioned that this was a much shorter trip for him than his last ride. He didn't really respond one way or another. I then said, "Funny how I'm always dropping you off around here, but never picking you up from here." Again, no real response. Well, when we got there, he got out and paid. I drove away, and then it hit me. The last couple of days there had been reports of people missing from various parts of town. I may be wrong, but it seems like I've picked this guy up from the same parts of town as where those people disappeared from several times.

I'm going to bed for now, but I'll try and find out more tomorrow.

Monday, October 26, 2009, 4:12 PM

Well, I went back and double-checked the newspaper articles. There were three missing persons reported in the last few days. Today's paper had their names and some details.

The first was Bill Brooks, a construction worker. He went missing back on the 4th and was last seen at Snyder's IGA.

Grady Lincoln, an old farmer and retired MU Extension professor, was last seen on Wednesday the 7th after attending a wildlife management planning meeting at the TCRC.

And then, Renee Van Male, a secretary, was just reported missing yesterday. She was last seen on the 10th... right before she went shopping at J.C. Penny's.

And I'm not certain, since it's been 2-3 weeks ago, but I really think that I was in each of those areas around those times. I routinely pass through the parking lots of most of the grocery stores and retail areas in town. It seems like there's always someone who needs a cab ride home from the store.

The article went on, however, and disclosed that two more reports had come in this morning. The identities haven't been disclosed yet, but it's really strange. This is a fairly small town of around 30,000 people. This is a lot of people missing, especially since nothing like this has ever happened before.

Tuesday, October 27, 2009, 5:49 PM

More information was released today. The identities of the two persons reported missing yesterday were confirmed today. One was a prominent public figure!

Mr. Lee Sides, Poplar Bluff City Planner, hasn't been seen since the end of a meeting at the 1st Baptist Church on October 13th.

Eric Guererre, a PBHS student was supposed to have spent the night with a friend after the football game on the 16th.

Also today, Col. Ezekiel Washington (Ret.) and Julie Wheeler, a Dexter, MO High School student, were also reported missing to the media and confirmed.

Col. Washington was last seen on the 19th, and Ms. Wheeler was supposed to have been visiting relatives in town – down on Ditch Road, and never showed up. Her car was found abandoned in a parking lot not far from her Aunt's house.

I definitely remember picking my strange customer up from the football game, because I almost had an accident in the parking lot on the way there. The stupid cheerleaders bolted out from behind a bus right in front of me. When they realized what they had done, most of them quickly ran out of the way, but one rude girl flipped me off as she ran off. You don't quickly forget that. Such a sweet looking young thing, yet so ugly inside. The 16th was the most recent home game. Last Friday was an away game.

I'm also pretty sure I remember picking this guy up from the County Mart's parking lot about a week ago. That's not far from Ditch Road.

Wednesday, October 28, 2009, 7:36 AM

I had trouble sleeping last night. I'm almost too scared to go to work this evening.

Wednesday, October 28, 2009, 10:28 PM

After I wrote my entry this morning, I went back to bed and successfully fell asleep. Eventually, I woke up, groggy.

Even though I was reluctant to go to work, it seemed like it was going to be an uneventful night. Nothing but normal all night long. I was really feeling relieved and was about to call it a night when I turned from 8th Street onto Pine and there he was! He was standing on the corner under the streetlight; waving me over. I almost kept driving, but curiosity got the better of me.

When he was in, and gave me the address – same general area – this time, it was the corner of Walnut and C Street. I asked him, "Is there anything special going on in that area, man?" He just met my gaze in my rear-view mirror. Silence can be uncomfortable. After a couple of minutes, I tried again. "I never pick you up from over in that part of town, even though I drive through it all day long. You find me all over town though, and I take you there all the time." And then it slipped out – "All those people who keep going missing. Seems like more than a coincidence."

Again, a very uncomfortable silence, during which the back of my neck started to feel very hot as I feared his response. Eventually, we reached his destination. As he got out, his eyes found mine again.

"I remember no such thing, my son."

I pulled away, but stopped the car around the corner, out of sight. A desperate sense of purpose came over me. I got out and quickly walked back, staying to the shadows. I thought I had lost him, but right as I was about to give up, I caught sight of him entering an industrial building. One of those deals with only a few windows and mostly a lot of corrugated metal over aluminum studs for walls. Well, there was a stack of pallets near a window that let me get up high enough to look in.

There was some kind of large vehicle – a ship of some kind – in the middle of the floor. I don't know what it was made out of. It didn't look like metal and it didn't look like fiberglass or plastic either. It looked... both unbelievably solid, and sort of not there at the same time. It was an elongated oval in shape, and it had really smooth lines. I didn't see any noticeable seams, except for the real obvious ones where they had part of the ship removed for the work they were doing.

There were a lot of parts laid out on tables, on pallets and some on tarps on the floor. None of it looked like anything I've ever seen before. It did look like whatever it was, it was mostly done. Now you'd think that this would win the prize for the strangest thing I saw, but no. Turns out that I've been mistaken this whole time. There were a bunch of these guys. Damn if they didn't all look just exactly alike! It made me think at once of an old *Twilight Zone* episode I saw where all these little blond kids all looked the same. Except these weren't kids. They were all pretty small, now that I think about it. All definitely on the petite side. But they all had the same pale, pale skin and white hair. With them all looking the same, and moving about while they worked on the ship, it was hard to count how many of them there were. I think that there were at least six or seven of them.

That's still not the strangest thing I saw. I wasn't the only thing skulking around outside their building. While I was crouched there outside a window, I heard a sound from down at the other side of the same wall, near the bay door that would open to a loading dock of sorts. I got off of the stack of pallets... more like fell off, because as I started to climb down, the world sort of rolled on me. What my eyes saw made so little sense that I think the rest of my senses took a little vacation. All I remember was that it was large and black and had more sharp things coming out of it than something alive should have. It was scratching at that big garage door like a dog trying to get in from the rain. It wasn't barking — more like a roar combined with a scream. Three of these little white guys came around the corner, and I swear — pointed their hands at this dark, toothy thing and started blasting it. No guns or anything... just their hands. It looked like white light shot from their hands and hit the thing. It only lasted a few seconds.

That black thing didn't stand a chance. Two of them went back inside immediately after the shooting was over. One stayed and stood over the remains. A minute or so later, it seemed to begin to melt and in a very short while, there was nothing left except a bad smell in the air – kind of like rotten meat. Satisfied that his work was done, the last guy turned to go back inside too. It was then that I tried to get up. His head snapped towards me, and I didn't wait to find out anything else. I took off at a dead run, my heart pounding and my breath ragged. I didn't stop until I got to my cab, and took off like a drag racer. A few blocks later, I risked looking in my mirror, and I saw nothing. I was definitely done for the evening. I stopped by the IGA and got me something to drink away my fears. That's what I'll be doing next.

Good night!

Friday, October 30, 2009, 9:56 AM

The latest news is out. There have been two more people missing. Dr. Lydia Zhou disappeared on Sunday the 25 from Mercy Hospital. Mercy Hospital is located in Downtown. Look back up to my first post and tell me that's a coincidence! Then, also reported missing – this time on the 28th, Wednesday night — was Monsignor Michael Riggio. He disappeared after a meeting at Sacred Heart Catholic Church Wednesday night. Guess where Sacred Heart is: on 8th Street, about a block from Pine! I remember my mystery passenger on Wednesday night called me "my son" as he got out.

Somehow, I think that my passenger – or I guess, passengers – used to be these missing people. Why they mostly get in my cab, I have no idea. I hope they don't need a driver for their ship!

Saturday, October 31, 2009, 10:30 PM

Did you ever have a time when you couldn't tell if you were dreaming or not? I was still in bed. It was sometime this morning, I guess, as there was daylight coming in. I think it was daylight. I went from being asleep to being aware of a lot of light in the room. So much light... it was more than daylight. I couldn't move. Eventually, I got my eyes open just a little bit. It was so bright that I couldn't see hardly anything. I was aware of several people or things in my room all of a sudden. I don't know if I heard the voice out loud, or somehow, it felt like it was just in my head... I know that doesn't make any sense. Either I heard it or I didn't hear it, but I still understood it – inside my head. Maybe. Work with me on this.

I heard, "We nearly considered you for this mission, my son. But yours is another destiny. Search for friends and family in need. You must provide succor to them, for there is a darkness to be overcome. You can aid in this. Your heart and skills can lend to the upcoming battle."

Then, the blinding white light grew even stronger. I passed out again. When I woke back up, I felt really rested. Then I checked the time on my phone and realized that I had slept for hours. I got up, and I got into the car and drove over to the East Side to that building I had been at on Wednesday night. Past little swarms of kids in costumes, with parents walking behind them drinking coffee against the cold and taking pictures. Maybe it was the rest, maybe it was seeing something completely normal like small-town Halloween stuff, or maybe it was something else, but the fear was gone.

The building was a mess. It looked like the roof had been destroyed and completely caved in. The walls looked fine, except for some wicked scratches in the loading dock door. Looking real close at the paint on the wall, I could also see a difference in places... like part of it had been faded by exposure to sunlight over a period of years... except it was localized to right around where those scratches were, and only part of it, as if something had been in the way of some of the light. Oh, and no ship inside. It was gone.

There was a cab parked about a block away. Almost in the exact same place I had parked the other night. The driver's door was still open. The keys were still in the ignition, but the engine was dead and wouldn't turn over.

"Friends and family in need," they said? The only family I've got in the whole world is my little sister, Caprice. She's going to college up in central Missouri. I haven't heard from her in a while, though. Maybe it's been a couple of years. I guess I can look her up.

Oh... the license posted in the cab was for a Beverly Clark. It's probably too early, and no one will believe my story, but I'll guess I'll go and file a missing persons report now.